Broken Hoops and Plains People

A Catalogue of Ethnic Resources in the Humanities:
Nebraska and Surrounding Areas

Writers

Galen Buller, Indian Chapter
Ralph Grajeda, Chicano Chapter
Lillian Anthony-Welch, Black Chapter
Joseph G. Svoboda, Czech Chapter
Roger L. Welsch, German-Russian Chapter
Paul A. Olson, Scandinavian Chapter
Betty Levitov, Jewish and Italian Chapters
James McShane and Nadine Murphy, Irish Chapter
Corine Simon, Dutch Chapter
Domingo H. Cabacungan, Japanese Chapter

Photographer

Roger Rejda

Nebraska Curriculum Development Center

1976

The research in this book, as well as the printing of the first thousand copies of it, has been subsidized in part by the Nebraska Bicentennial Commission (Don Searcy, Chairman) and by the University of Nebraska Foundation in connection with the University of Nebraska systems office Bicentennial Committee. The opinions expressed in this book are those of the authors and no endorsement of them by the Nebraska Bicentennial Commission, the University of Nebraska Foundation, or the Systems Bicentennial Committee is implied.

This book was printed by the University of Nebraska Printing and Duplicating Service. Requests for this book should be addressed to the Nebraska Curriculum Development Center, 338 Andrews Hall, University of Nebraska, Lincoln, Nebraska 68588.

DESCRIPTIONS OF AUTHORS

The authors of the various chapters in this book are as follows:

—**Galen Buller**, with the assistance of **Karen Buller**; Mr. Buller works in English and anthropology at UN-L and is doing advanced work on Comanche literature. His wife, Karen Buller, has a Comanche background, has been counsellor of Indian students at UN-L, and is presently completing advanced work in psychology and Indian culture.

—**Ralph Grajeda** teaches modern foreign language and English at UN-L, has completed advanced research on Chicano literature and myth, and assisted in organizing some Chicano Cultural Awareness Centers in Nebraska.

—**Lillian Anthony-Welch** is the director of black studies at UN-O and has done work on oral history in Omaha and elsewhere.

—**Joseph G. Svoboda** is University of Nebraska archivist at Love Memorial Library and is in charge of the Czech oral history project there. Having been raised in Czechoslovakia, he represents one of the most recent waves of Czech immigrants.

—**Roger Welsch** teaches anthropology (folklore) and English at UN-L and is internationally known as a folklorist. His last major project has been in Germany and the U.S. for the Smithsonian Institute.

—**Paul Olson** teaches English at UN-L. He has done work on Plains Indian literature, myth, and medieval English literature, including Scandinavian backgrounds.

—**Betty Levitov** is a staff member of the Study Commission on Undergraduate Education and the Education of Teachers, a former Peace Corps teacher trainer and a student of literature and linguistics.

—The Irish chapter is by **James McShane**, who teaches

Irish and English literature at UN-L, and by **Nadine Murphy**, a student there.

 —The Dutch chapter is by **Corine Simon**, an emigrant from Holland, who teaches Dutch in adult education courses.

 —The Japanese chapter is by **Domingo Cabacungan**, a graduate student in sociology at UN-L from the Phillippine Islands.

 —The photographer for the book is **Roger Rejda**, a Nebraskan of Czech descent who has had several professional exhibits at the Sheldon Art Gallery, the Nebraska Student Union, and in other galleries.

 —Historical photos, unless otherwise identified, are the courtesy of the **Nebraska State Historical Society**, Lincoln, Nebraska.

TABLE OF CONTENTS

GENERAL ACKNOWLEDGMENT

The authors wish to thank the University of Nebraska Foundation and the Bicentennial Commission for their support. Thanks also to Jeanne Bishop, Jack Brodie, Karen Hanshew, Don Pieper, Jan Pieper, Arlen Reimnitz and Rich Rolfes for their editorial assistance.

PREFACE

Each editor prepared his/her own essay/catalogue. As we had less than six months from the time of the transferring of the money to the time that we had to go to press (and much less time for research), we have undoubtedly made mistakes and omitted important data. Please assist each author by calling attention to items which ought to be included in later editions.

The approach of each essay varies according to the group concerned and to the central principles which each editor saw as significant in bringing his group together: for Indians, the circle aesthetics seemed central; for Chicanos, the mestizo heritage; for blacks, the Malcolm X nation-building tradition; for Czechs, the fight for independence and free thought; for Scandinavians, the effects of the community-building philosophers; and for German-Russians, the quest for land. Each author also wrote her/his essay and catalogue from the perspective of his/her discipline: Roger Welsch as a folklorist stresses family folklore; Ralph Grajeda as a modern language scholar, bilingual tradition; Joseph Svoboda as an archivist and research specialist, the community artefacts, libraries, and collections; Galen Buller as an anthropologist-literary scholar, Indian aesthetics; Paul Olson as a "history of ideas" scholar, the history of Scandinavian reformist ideas; and Lillian Anthony-Welch as a black studies specialist, black cultural history. The essays on the less numerous ethnic groups were all commissioned and overseen by Betty Levitov, who did this almost without a budget and did an incredibly diligent and ambitious job without adequate support. It is because of her work that the less visible groups in this area are represented at all.

The differences among the various ways of writing essays

probably reflect differences among the ethnic groups as well as among the writers. Obviously one can learn from each essay how to study other groups (e.g., Welsch's folklore "family history" approach may be useful to black people or Swedes as well as to Germans from Russia). Each editor was responsible for his own copy, and each editor was asked to speak in her/his own voice, as a flesh and blood member of his/her own ethnic group, as an advocate and not as a disinterested researcher. I oversaw the general organization of the book and its progress to the press. Given the shortness of time, I have had very cooperative co-workers and I thank them. The historical photographs are mostly from the Historical Society Museum. The photographs of contemporary Czech, Swedish, Chicano, and Indian people and places were mostly done by Roger Rejda, master photographer, as were some of the photographs of sketches of earlier people and places. As this book goes out, I put it "under correction"—as Chaucer would say—knowing that it is as imperfect as its authors and as incomplete as the time in which it was written.

—Paul A. Olson

INTRODUCTION

The purpose of this book is to present a catalogue of resources from the past. The resources are resources in the humanities, which the people of the state of Nebraska and surrounding areas have, or have had, and which they may wish to use in building future communities for themselves. The concentration of the book is on six ethnic groups having a very visible place in the past of the state, and having relatively separate artistic traditions and communities or neighborhoods: Indians, Chicanos, black Americans, Germans (specifically German-Russians), Czechs, and Scandinavians. In the case of the Germans, we chose to emphasize German-Russians as having a unique history, community sense, and culture which had remained distinctive in Germany, in Russia, and in this area. Similar kinds of accounts could possibly have been written of Germans who came to this area directly from a single province of Germany (say Bavaria), and dominated the settlement of a town. The complexity and richness of the German tradition required that we concentrate on one strand of it.

Conversely, in the case of the three Scandinavian countries, the intellectual, artistic and social currents which swept them in the second half of the 19th century are so similar as to allow for treatment in a single chapter.

In addition, we have dealt with several groups having perhaps a less dramatic place in the history of the state or having a smaller population base: the Jews, the Irish, the Italians, and the Japanese. We have undoubtedly left out important groups for lack of time and poverty of funding; we would suggest that the next publication of this sort concentrate on World War II emigrants from the Baltic States, along with the Greeks, the Chinese, the Polish, and the Vietnamese enclaves there are by that time.

I.

The conventional interpretation of history in this state and nationally has been that the nation is a "melting pot" in which "the best of each ethnic tradition is fused with the best of other ethnic traditions, so that out of the totality will emerge something finer, more noble and complete than the culture of any one group." As a matter of fact, that has not happened. Save for such very superficial things as cooking, we have not as groups learned from each other. When groups "gave up something"—their language, their religion, their system for raising families and organizing themselves into groups, their architecture, crafts, or expressive culture—they did so generally because they were under strong pressures to do so from the forces which dominated the educational and economic system ("the eastern bankers" to use an old Populist phrase). These forces sought to standardize behavior through the public schools so as to make people rootless, moveable pegs in an assembly line industrial system; similar forces seeking standardization wanted to centralize power and build a nation capable of aggressive military action. Unfortunately, Nebraska was one of the most repressive states in the nation in its attack on foreign language-speaking citizens during World War I, and its ignominious place in that history is forever enshrined on the wrong side in the name of the case that permanently determined that foreign language-speaking people had *some* rights *(Meyer v. State of Nebraska)*. Equally ignominiously, the state and nation in this section of the country apparently required some persuading in the courts that an Indian "is a human being in the full meaning of the law" (the Standing Bear case), or that blacks are not objects to be auctioned off (cf. the black chapter below). Even now, our children are taught to regard, as models, Virginia plantation holders who held slaves and regarded full liberty as primarily a white male prize. They are taught to admire an Andrew Jackson who personally saw to the extermination of 30,000 Indians, a Robert E. Lee who fought for slavery, and a Teddy Roosevelt who fought for imperialism. As a child, I was taught by my school that "there was a Star Spangled Banner waving some-where (i.e., in heaven)" and that "God's great heroes" would get to go there, including Custer.

As a nation we have not "melted" in the sense that we have learned from one another what is best in the other's tradi-tion. Too often, we have wiped out—or nearly wiped out—traditions that could have been valuable to us in the future, in the name of immediate prosperity, a narrow conception of patriotism and might, or the centralization of power.

There is another side to America and to this section of the country from the "westward, the curse of empire" side, a side defiantly anti-imperial, respectful of the small group, of the dispersal of power and of the differences developed as a conse-quence of different histories, roots, or senses of proper scale. It respects the different requirements of differing spiritual and material environments. This side now needs some nurturing, but it is America too, Nebraska too. The "small group" vision of where we should go is symbolized by the now forgotten governor of Nebraska who vetoed a bill praising the veterans of the Spanish-American War for their work on the grounds that men should not be praised for fighting in an unjust or imperial-istic war, however much one might regret their personal sacri-fices. The vision is also symbolized in William Jennings Bryan who, as a pacifist, resigned as Secretary of State in Wilson's cabinet rather than cover for what he thought to be Wilson's deliberate cover-ups about the Lusitania episode and his design to get us into World War I on England's side. The "heroes" of this traditon are not so well known. They are people like Menno Simons for the German-Russians, Tomáš G. Masaryk for the Czechs, Crazy Horse for the Native Americans, Malcolm X for the blacks, the men of the Mexican Revolution and the grape boycott for the Chicanos, James Stuart Parnell for the Irish, and N.F.S. Grundtvig for the Scandinavians. All of them are *in* Nebraska's past and hopefully in its future: stubborn, willful men attached to poverty, to their own villages, and willing to do anything within their conception of their right to keep their people from oppression and to keep their people's dream (in Black Elk's phrase) "from dying in the bloody mud and being buried in the blizzard." I should like my children to know of such men.

II.

The melting pot vision never did work. The "melting pot" we have in common is a common aversion for the different, the slimy repertoire of Bohunk and Polack jokes, nigger jokes, greaser jokes, and other ethnic slurs whereby we cut down all differences to stupidity as we hide our insecurity in the presence of difference by asking hatred to pose as comedy.

The melting pot probably did not work for the reason that Black Elk gives: a culture is a hoop. Every part in a coherent culture connects with every other part and with the land and sky around. A culture—an authority system, an expressive system, a way of giving and receiving gifts, of telling right and wrong, a way of raising children and cultivating the soil—is not a TV dinner which can be packaged anywhere and used anywhere, the plastic unwrapped, salt and pepper added, and consumed. Each culture worthy of the name makes some sacrifice for the greatness it achieves, and the greatness cannot be achieved without the sacrifice. Nor can one feature of the culture—even cooking—be transferred to another cultural environment unhurt any more than a good-sized cottonwood can be transplanted. A 97-year-old Swedish lady in an old folks' home told me: "They tried to make ostkaka [a Swedish pioneer custard] here, but it was no more ostkaka than it was waxed paper. When we made ostkaka, you had to have eggs, lots of them, someone to stir it. . . ." And then she recited a catalogue of the circumstances unique to the pioneer farm which could not be simulated in an old people's home and which were requisite to the proper making of ostkaka. This book is written in celebration of such a woman, of those peoples and cultures which did not melt and of their visions: the tragic, the factious, the fighters of centralized oppression at every level and in every age. These people more than the professional patriots keep alive the notion that centralized authority is capable, as the Declaration of Independence remarks, of "a long train of abuses and usurpations" and can be designed to "reduce the people under absolute despotism."

Many Nebraska rebels such as Crazy Horse and Malcolm X keep alive the notion that it is the people's right, their duty, to throw off the government—unjust government—to provide new means for their future security; that idea had plenty of sanction two hundred years ago. When Jefferson said in 1787, "God forbid we should go even twenty years without a rebellion," he was uttering a call for continuous resistance to oppression which was echoed in Paine, and many other men who worked at creating a new era in the period 1770-1830.

As this book demonstrates, we have had rebels enough; yet, we have had little effective revolt. From Crazy Horse through the Populists through Norris and Bryan and the rebels of the thirties and the sixties, we have had leaders willing to say, "My people are hurting; they are being controlled by an illegitimate authority; they will stand for no more." But the people in that same period in this section of the country appear to have tolerated grievances analogous to those which prompted the founders to act against George in the Declaration of Independence; they have stood hitched for the fatiguing of their representatives into acquiesence (for instance, the Indian Tribal councils); they have accepted restrictions on the nationalization of foreigners (laws restricting immigration by third world people); it has been claimed that they have accepted "swarms of new officers" in the modern military and bureaucracies, and have tolerated a military which appears to be above the law (in the CIA) and arbitrary changes in the laws of neighboring provinces (e.g., introduction of client "arbitrary" regimes in South and Central America). Beyond all of this, many of us have stood hitched for an abrogation of our customary practices by government schools or popular authority, which the English colonists, with their appeal to the customary practice of the English nation, did not stand hitched for when they confronted analogous abrogations of their group system.

It may not be too much to say that the spirit of the 1770's and 80's, insofar as it is kept alive at all in this country, is now often kept alive as much by men conceptualized as "enemies of the people" as it is by those proposed as the country's leaders and heroes.

III.

If the melting pot is not the metaphor through which we can search out our common humanity in this western plains area, what is? What are the common experiences which we have had? This book suggests some:

—Most of us came as poor people, and many of us have forgotten the common yoke of poverty which we once bore.

—Most of us were at one time or another stoop laborers in the fields, either in the old country or here, and have learned to speak the word "farmer" or "cotton picker" with derision.

—Most of us lived in earth or grass and earth houses when we came (Pawnee, Omaha, Czech, Scandinavian, Irish, Chicano, black).

—Most of us lived on land which was, against all treaty, stolen from the Indian tribes of the territory, and wrenched our prosperity from their impoverishment.

—Many of us came to avoid standing armies and compulsory military service (the German-Russian Mennonites, the Scandinavians, the early Chicanos, etc.)

—Many of us tried to keep our language until 1918, our separate culture-based schools, our informal educational processes.

—Many of us, rightly or wrongly, now keep to separate towns or neighborhoods occupied primarily or exclusively by persons sharing a common religion, ethnicity, or historical tradition.

—Most of us began here, or came with some special vision of what the good life is or could be, and that is, or was, reason for our group's staying together.

For many of us that vision involved material things, but for many it *also* involved a picture of a radically freer, more egalitarian, more natural and more cooperative small-group social order; particularly was this the case for the Indian reform movements, the Scandinavian cooperative leaders, the German-Russian Mennonite groups, in many cases the free-thinking Czechs, the black homesteaders, and the Irish of O'Connor. This vision was soon lost in many groups.

It is possible to see the civilization of this section of the country as a product of two currents which sparked the resident plains culture pattern to new efforts: one coming from the Southwest and South, a current which produced the influence of the Aztecan civilizations on Pawnee and Winnebago civilizations, the Spanish exploration of this area, and the heavy and continued Chicano immigration now and since the Mexican Revolution, a current of belief mystical and communal in its force. The other current comes from the East, from the American and French Revolutions as they gave rise to raised aspirations and to some degree disappointed these aspirations in Middle Europe. Almost every European group which came here came in the midst of revolutionary struggle in the country of origin. The settlers who came often came because they had learned enough of what social change was like to want it, to want to construct model communities; they had experienced enough frustration of their hopes to be uncertain whether change was possible in their own countries. Thus, the Czechs, Scandinavians, and Chicanos each began to come as liberal-revolutionary work began to take hold in their countries and was aborted before it took hold for good; hence their work in the arts was often romantic-nationalistic, impressionistic, or rebellious against the established order.

The Germans from Russia escaped, for good or evil, many of the effects of the Enlightenment-19th century revolutionary spirit; they have perhaps practiced a different political game because of that; the people of the Indian nation have tried to preserve their tribal and collective entities in the face of western individualistic notions for over a century. And black people who came direct from slavery to Nebraska came to build whole black communities; later black "nation-building" was a primary agenda for black Nebraskans who were influenced by a succession of thinkers running from Booker T. Washington through Garvey to Malcolm X. That is, black conceptions of "liberty" were Exodus-like—conceptions of liberty for the black nation and not primarily conceptions demanding "freedom of enterprise" for the individualistic, aspiring black entrepreneur.

Indeed, it appears to me that, by the time the "liberal revolution" came to most of the European source countries from which immigrants from those lands came to Nebraska, the individualism of the 18th century revolutions had been softened so as to include an emphasis on cooperation, on the importance of the village, on collective folk customs. The barons of industry in the nation who fed opinions to Nebraska (for instance, Hearst in the 1930's) and their brothers in Nebraska pushed the older ethic of unbridled individualism because they had everything to gain from it; that ethic is not the main ideology of the idealistic among those who gathered strength from the West (the Mexican civilization, the Pawnee, the Winnebago) or those who gathered it from Middle European reform movements.

IV.

Now we have come to an end of an era, one in which Hamilton has triumphed over Jefferson. Students of the course of growth and change in the United States government tell us that the imperial presidency is at its zenith, the centralization of power at its height, and forces analogous to what Jefferson called "the banks" are able to buy and sell governments abroad and segments of our government at home. Our armies, weapons, and support encourage "arbitrary authority" to wield its might in the Arab world, in South America, in Africa, and our industrial growth is at its height. But, fortunately for the Bicentennial, the American people, according to recent polls, do not in the majority believe that our present institutions—the presidency, the congress, big businesses, the churches—are really working. They want something else, perhaps something more like what Jefferson or Paine envisaged (and only half practiced). Watergate may have demonstrated that tyranny will be found out, but it was only by the skin of our teeth or, rather, by the accident of a taping system. As we look to our future we may be called upon, again, to build new community institutions. By one means or another, we may be asked to claim ownership of our tradition in the terms described by John Dickinson, one of the representatives at the First Continental Congress:

> . . . As long as the product of our labor and the rewards of our care can properly be called our own, so long will it be worth our while to be industrious and frugal. But if when we plant-sow-reap-gather-and-thresh, we find we plant-sow-reap-gather-and-thresh for others, whose pleasure is to be the sole limitation on how much they shall take, and how much they shall leave, why should we repeat the unfruitful toil? Horses and oxen are content with that portion of the fruits of their work which others assign to them, but men are not.

The fruit of our labor should be economic justice for each group. It should also be fulfillment of that vision of complete community in whose name that group came and the reparation of Native American groups for the price of their coming. But, you say, "That is idle. We cannot altogether reclaim our separate traditions." And you are right. The 1918 war, the fearsome poverty of the 1930's, the language acts, the coercion of the schools, have all done their damage and isolated us from our pasts. And, yet, we know that we are at the end of an era and must turn somewhere.

Expressive culture is, to my mind, a statement about what we are and what we want to be. Our imperial line is symbolized by the "art" and "culture" which we subsidize. Our architecture is either heavily colonnaded stuff in the pompous Roman tradition (sometimes called Greek revival, sometimes called

Corinthian, sometimes called Howard Johnson modern), or concrete and steel monolithic (e.g., the federal building in Lincoln), which has all the grace and purity of Mussolini-modern; and though we have other traditions to draw on (as some of our better modern architects have known, the tradition of Native American architecture, of the earth lodge, of the Scandinavian wood and brick builders), we do not often choose to do so. Our painting and sculpture are neither local nor gifts from one visionary to another; they are manufactured according to styles developed in New York, governed by an ideology which sees design as an end in itself, and promoted as mercilessly at the centers of artistic production as anything Madison Avenue does. Our children are taught the literature of a world many of them will never see and which they do not inherit rather than Menno Simons and Lakota sacred stories or Omaha poetry or Winnebago tales or Ibsen and Kierkegaard, Rölvaag and Malcolm X, or the Aztec epics, Gonzales' poems or Chavez' essays. Our composers are not often played and persons in middle life do not make much music for one another any more (cf. Howard Hanson's remarks, Scandinavian Chapter). All of this may be a symbol of a lack of confidence in ourselves and our traditions. (We have been called a cultural desert so often, pilloried as ignorant, unsophisticated, stupid and provincial. It is no surprise if some of the insults rub off. Whenever *Punch,* the British human magazine, wishes to make an American look particularly ignorant and slobbish, the American, whether "he" or "she," is located in Nebraska.) Yet our traditions do seem to mean something in other regions for men of no mean competence in assessing our world and our country. In my proposal to the Bicentennial Commission for the grant which made this book possible I wrote to the following general effect:

> The Midwest has commonly lacked a sense of regional culture and of the dignity of that culture comparable to that developed by the "Fugitive School" in the South in the 30's, 40's and 50's. Whereas southern elite culture has been characterized by the Fugitives rather too attractively as a successor to the Roman Augustan age with its country villas, no similar

glittering characterizations have been applied to plains culture. Perhaps midwestern culture requires less pretentious emblems. It may be characterized in terms of the interaction between the "circle," settled culture of Native Americans and the nomadic, "Exodus" culture of the immigrants. Black Elk saw the white men who came to the plains as dog-like monsters who came to plunder gold and break the sacred natural cycles of the Sioux, but the settlers who came frequently saw themselves as the children of Israel finding a new promised land. The history of Nebraska in the late 18th, 19th and early 20th century is then, in part, the history of Native American attempts to maintain their culture and of settlers' attempts to domesticate European or Central American or African patterns in the same environmental and political milieu. Each broke the other's vision in part but celebrated his own in the breaking.

The effect of this interaction among Native American traditional groups and incoming immigrant groups was the production of artistic and cultural forms of unusual brilliance in a number of ethnic groups, particularly prior to their coming under heavy assimilationist pressures. For example, the works of the 19th century Winnebago, Omaha, and Sioux mythmakers, poets, and writers are studied seriously throughout Europe, for their spiritual wisdom, particularly by students of Carl Jung and Claude Levi-Strauss, but they are pretty well ignored on their home territory. The British Society for the Survival of Mankind, related to the prestigious Club of Rome and sponsored by such notable thinkers as Sir Julian Huxley, has found in traditional Plains Indian cultures a model of a decentralized planning and close interaction with the environment which it believes will be useful to world planners in a period of limited growth and shortages of fossil fuels, but the same cultures are not studied by our planners. The first serious black film work was done in Lincoln, Nebraska (1915-early 1920's), and the works of many excellent black writers have their roots in the strong, black vision which dominates in Omaha's Garveyite tradition and in Omaha's Malcolm X— surely an Exodus tradition. One could refer to architectural and novelistic work which has grown out of the Scandinavian experience as Scandinavian people (e.g., Rölvaag or Eliel Saarinen) began to fear that they would lose hold of that

experience; the dominant metaphor of this tradition, at least
of Rölvaag's work, is again the Exodus. We have in this area
German folk art and architecture which go back centuries; the
Czech cultural forms celebrated by Willa Cather and by many
Nebraska small towns still (though the European roots have
been cut); Chicano ballet and music which echoes old Mexican traditions as well as the work of the Mexican Revolution.
Many groups have tried to carry "the gold of the Egyptians
with them" and put it to use in a new land. This tradition of
encounter between the visions of West and East in the intractable plains and the art forms and alternative visions of the
future which it evolved are also of interest internationally to
planners, students of policy and students of the humanities.

The purpose of this book is to help us to get clear about
what our resources are, what futures projected from our various
pasts might be, so that we can get on with the business of building decent communities despite the lapses during World War I
and after, despite some failures to live up to our original revolutionary promise or to the hope which brought many of our
predecessors here.

This is not a book to be left idle. I would argue that we
need to work in a different way if we are to build meaningfully
on our separate paths. A different emphasis would be given to
voluntary lodges, churches, coops, and neighborhood organizations if this book were attended to. Different buildings would
have to be built, different books studied, and different music
played. Perhaps different paintings might be done. Many manuscripts would have to be edited and many lives presently
unstudied would have to be studied again, or studied for the
first time. The old people, who lived before 1918, would have
to be given respect and consulted. This would not mean that we
would try to create a sentimental or fake Czechdom or Swe-
dendom or that we would all dress up as fake feathered Indians.
The quest for an antidote to empire might even involve some of
us learning from each other on terms different from those
provided by empire. In a time of scarce physical resources and
poverty of vision, it may be useful to attend to the words of

this area's greatest novelist and to apply them not only to the Europeans but also to those Indian and southwestern groups which she later came to understand and respect:

> . . . In Wilber, in the old days, behind the big, friendly brick saloon—it was not a "saloon," properly speaking, but a beer garden, where the farmers ate their lunch when they came to town—there was a pleasant little theater where the boys and girls were trained to give the masterpieces of Czech drama in the Czech language. "Americanization" has doubtless done away with all this. Our lawmakers have a rooted conviction that a boy can be a better American if he speaks only one language than if he speaks two. I could name a dozen Bohemian towns in Nebraska where one used to be able to go into a bakery and buy better pastry than is to be had anywhere except in the best pastry shops of Prague or Vienna. The American lard pie never corrupted the Czech. . . . Knut Hamsun, the Norwegian writer who was awarded the Nobel Prize for 1920, was a "hired hand" on a Dakota farm to the north of us. Colonies of European people, Slavonic, Germanic, Scandinavian, Latin, spread across our bronze prairies like the daubs of color on a painter's palette. They brought with them something that this neutral new world needed ever more than the immigrants needed land.
>
> Unfortunately, their American neighbors were seldom open-minded enough to understand the Europeans, or to profit by their older traditions. Our settlers from New England, cautious and convinced of their own superiority, kept themselves insulated as much as possible from foreign influences. The incomers from the South—from Missouri, Kentucky, the two Virginias—were provincial and utterly without curiosity. They were kind neighbors—lent a hand to help a Swede when he was sick or in trouble. But I am quite sure that Knut Hamsun might have worked a year for any one of our Southern farmers, and his employer would never have discovered that there was anything unusual about the Norwegian. . . .
>
> When I stop at one of the graveyards in my own county and see on the headstones the names of fine old men I used to know: "Eric Ericson, born Bergen, Norway . . . died

Nebraska," "Anton Pucelik, born Prague, Bohemia . . . died Nebraska," I have always the hope that something went into the ground with those pioneers that will one day come out again, something that will come out not only in sturdy traits of character, but in elasticity of mind, in an honest attitude toward the realities of life, in certain qualities of feeling and imagination. It is in that great cosmopolitan country known as the Middle West that we may hope to see the hard molds of American provincialism broken up, that we may hope to find young talent which will challenge the pale proprieties, the insincere, conventional optimism of our art and thought.

. . . There is even danger that that fine institution, the University of Nebraska, may become a gigantic trade school. The classics, the humanities, are having their dark hour. They are in eclipse. But the "classics" have a way of revenging themselves. One may venture to hope that the children, or the grandchildren, of a generation that goes to a university to select only the most utilitarian subjects in the course of study —among them, salesmanship and dressmaking—will revolt against all the heaped-up, machine-made materialism about them. They will go back to the old sources of culture and wisdom—not as a duty, but with burning desire.

In Nebraska, as in so many other states, we must face the fact that the splendid story of the pioneers is finished, and that no new story worthy to take its place has yet begun. The generation that subdued the wild land and broke up the virgin prairie is passing, but it is still there, a group of rugged figures in the background which inspire respect, compel admiration. With these old men and women the attainment of material prosperity was a moral victory, because it was wrung from hard conditions, was the result of a struggle that tested character. They can look out over those broad stretches of fertility and say: "We made this, with our backs and our hands." . . .

. . . The generation now in the driver's seat hates to make anything, wants to live and die in an automobile, scudding past those acres where the old men used to follow the long corn-rows up and down. They want to buy everything ready-made: clothes, food, education, music, pleasure. . . . Surely the materialism and showy extravagance of this hour are a passing phase! They will mean no more half a century from now than will the "hard times" of twenty-five years ago (Willa Cather, "The End of the First Cycle," *Roundup,* ed. Virginia Faulkner, pp. 4-8).

Unfortunately, a half century and more has passed since Cather wrote, and we wait.

—Paul A. Olson

Indians: The Beauty of the Unbroken Hoop

By Galen Buller

ACKNOWLEDGMENTS

I am indebted to the following Native American people for their help in assembling the information: Alfred and Pat Minard, Perry Wounded Shield, Johnny Painter, Nikki Solomon, Louis and Anita LaRose, Mrs. Elizabeth Stabler, John Truax, Jean Black Elk, and Arlynn Knudsen. I am also indebted to Patrisha Heckel for her work in compiling the catalogue and helping me with the essay. In addition, Patrice Watson, Elaine Jahner, and Karen Buller (my wife) helped with the bibliography and pictures. I would also like to thank the Nebraska State Historical Society for help with the pictures. This essay is dedicated to the memory of Rollin Phillips, who helped me to better understand Native American people.

Omaha earth lodges. The earth lodges built by the Omaha were built in terms of the circle conception of beauty and generally faced the east, the direction of the dawning of new life. John Turner of the Omaha group indicates that the last earth lodge was built at Macy in the early 20's and that the interior was made of joined posts and branches woven together in a basketweaving pattern. Sod was then layered on top and the dwelling did not leak. The earth lodges were used in winter and were located near Fontenelle Forest and later near Macy.

These pictures show two forms of accommodation of traditional Plains circle architecture to new materials. *Above,* Frank Lloyd Wright's Wingspread at Racine, Wisconsin, based on Plains Indian architecture (the four "wings" of the building point in the four sacred directions as in Sioux ceremonial building and design and the central living space is a rounded or eight-sided building with layered room structure centering in a family fireplace as in the earth lodges). *Below,* Horsehead Lodge, built by the Omaha Indians for their own use at social meetings and dances. It stood until 1970 about two miles north of the Omaha agency. Notice the adaptation of earth lodge designs to new materials.

Opposite Page: Fool Bull, healer and holy man, Brule Sioux people (born 1844, picture, 1900). Two feathers for two times counting Pawnee coup; bear claw necklace, quirt, and "swift" fur related to ceremonial powers. Shield pictures face of the sun behind which he saw the eternal world. *Above:* Richard Fool Bull (1800's to present), son of Fool Bull, one of the last survivors of the original Wounded Knee; herbal healer, leader in the Native American Church and master of the art of story telling and making and playing the traditional flute. (Photos by Kay Hinkley; copy by Dick Littleton.)

THE OLD

Above, a sweat lodge, part of the old ceremonial life of most Plains tribes used for purification purposes prior to the undertaking of one of the larger rituals. *Below.* Little Chief in the early 1920's, over 100 years old, a master of traditional lore. Much of his life he kept to the old ceremonies and kept alive, with others, a knowledge of the old ways after the reservation had been turned over to the Bureau of Indian Affairs and the white missionaries. (Photos, Journal-Star Printing Co.)

THE NEW

Above. The new religion: the Native American Church, came to Macy and Winnebago in the early 20th century and thrives with all night prayer services and a morning feast. The teepee worship place follows the circle conception of beauty, opens to the east, marks the four directions, and centers in a half moon fireplace-altar. *Below.* Mr. and Mrs. John Turner are accomplished story tellers concerning the Omaha heroes Rabbit, Orphan and Monkey. Turner, in his 80's, was raised by Little Chief. Mrs. Turner belongs to the La Flesche family. (Photos, Journal-Star Printing Co.)

Above. Omaha Indians camping at the Macy, Nebraska, Pow Wow, September 2-10, 1922. The Chief is holding an outdoor council, circulating the pipe as solemnly as in the councils of former days of wars and uprisings. Fifth from left is Little Chief, grandfather of John Turner. *Below.* Early 20th century Dakota wedding and dance. (Both photos courtesy of Nebraska State Historical Society.)

1970's Pow-Wow at UN-L. The dancer is Pete Moore, Pawnee tribe. (Courtesy of Journal-Star Printing Company.)

Beadwork continues to be made, worn and given as gifts despite the influx of Hong Kong junk. Notice the pattern of the circular beadwork, a little reminiscent of the Sun Dance lodge with the center and the branches going out from the center. The beadwork is by Ann Kelly, a Sioux woman living in Lincoln. The headband design includes triangles with a dot in the middle, sometimes used by the Sioux to symbolize the hill of vision.

Above. The beadwork on the loom uses a floral motif (it was designed for a little girl). This motif, formerly most common among the woodland tribes, is now used everywhere. *Below.* Alfred Menard, wearing a headband and necklace; he and his wife, Patty Whitebear Menard, were major collaborators in the writing of *Hanblecheya*, an opera based on the sacred traditions of the Sioux and Cheyenne people.

Much of the present fight for civil rights and for relative cultural autonomy is directed toward giving the children an opportunity to take their place in meaningful relation to their tradition and to do so with tools which will give them a chance to cope with the malice of racism and the destruction of sense of identity wrought by the last hundred years.

Indians: The Beauty of the Unbroken Hoop

By Galen Buller

Nebraska's Native Americans are the one ethnic group within the state that laments rather than rejoices at the celebration of America's Bicentennial. It is at the expense of this particular ethnic minority that the other groups of people found a kind of refuge in the pioneering days of Nebraska's earliest years. The Bicentennial might best be described as the memorial of a tragedy, anything but the celebration of freedom. Louis LaRose, tribal chairman of the Winnebago tribe, sums it up as well as any when he says, "There's really nothing to celebrate; if I was to do anything, it would have to be in the form of farce."

The Four Tribes and How They Came to this Area

The four major tribes now residing in Nebraska—the Omaha, the Winnebago, the Santee Sioux, and the Teton Sioux —are well established in the state, even though only two, the Omaha and the Teton Sioux, were already living in Nebraska at the time of America's birth. Anthropologists have suggested that in an earlier period the Omaha may have lived much farther east, perhaps as far east as the Atlantic seaboard. The Omaha origin myths suggest, as well, that they came from the east:

> In the real beginning *Wakonda* made the *Washazhe*— men, women, and children. After they were made he said

"Go!" So the people took all they had, carried their children, and started toward the setting sun. They traveled until they came to a great water. Seeing they could go no farther, they halted. Again *Wakonda* said "Go!" And once more they started, and wondered what would happen to them. As they were about to step into the water there appeared from under the water rocks. These projected just above the surface, and there were others barely covered with water. Upon these stones the people walked, stepping from stone to stone until they came to land. When they stood on dry land the wind blew, the water became violent and threw the rocks upon the land, and they became great cliffs. Therefore when men enter the sweat lodge they thank the stones for preserving their lives and ask for a continuation of their help that their lives may be prolonged. Here on the shore the people dwelt; but again *Wakonda* said "Go!" And again they started and traveled on until they came to a people whose appearance was like their own; but not knowing whether they were friends or foes, the people rushed at each other for combat. In the midst of the confusion *Wakonda* said, "Stand still!" The people obeyed. They questioned each other, found they spoke the same language, and became friends. . . .

The people traveled on and came to a lake. There the Omaha found a Sacred Tree and took it with them. The people (Ponca) went on and came to a river now called *Nishude* (the Missouri). They traveled along its banks until they came to a place where they could step over the water. From there they went across the land and came to a river now called *Nibthacka* (the Platte). This river they followed, and it led them back to the Missouri.[1]

The Teton Sioux (a rather loosely used term which includes primarily the Oglala and Brule Sioux in Nebraska) have always been a migrant tribe following the buffalo from the western parts of what is now Nebraska all the way up to the Canadian border. Like the Omaha, the Western Sioux peoples probably came from areas further east, but in recent history the Teton Sioux have ruled the western portion of the Great Plains.

According to the Sioux people, there was a time long ago when men and gods lived on this earth together. There were, however, few people at this time and they were called the *Pte* people—they lived underground. Some of the gods who were not allowed to be among the *Pte* people wanted to be with men and so they prepared a plan whereby they could trick man into coming from the underground world and into the earth. They knew that if man tasted meat and learned about tipis that he would never want to return to his underground home. "So *Anog-Ite* (an evil spirit) prepared some food and clothing and a wolf brought it to the cave which led to the underworld, where mankind lived. The wolf gave the clothing and food to *Tokahe,* the First One, and soon he set out with three other men to find where such good things came from. *Iktomi* (the trickster) and *Anog-Ite* made themselves appear very young and attractive, and told the men that they were really very old, but the food of earth had kept them very young looking. They went back to the underworld, and told of the wonderful things they had found. Many people did not believe them, but six men and their families went with *Tokahe* to the earth. Soon they became very tired, hungry, and thirsty. *Anog-ite* tried to comfort them, but they saw the horrible side of her face and were very much frightened. *Iktomi* laughed and made fun of them. *Tokahe* was very ashamed, but *Wazi* and *Wakanka* (the old man and the witch) appeared and led them to the land of the pines. They showed them how to hunt, to make clothing and tipis, and how to live well on earth. They were the first people on earth and their descendants are the Sioux.[2]

Anthropologists have various conflicting theories about where the Teton group may have come from, but common sources suggest that they at one time lived near what is now Pipestone, Minnesota, and that they probably migrated there from points even farther east.

Directly to the east of the area inhabited by the Teton Sioux live the Santee Sioux. Though they are closely related to their western neighbors in language, religion, and life styles, they are relative newcomers to their Nebraska home. In 1853 the Santee, then in Minnesota, gave up their freedom, and went to live on local reservations by signing the treaties of *Traverse des Sioux* and Mendota. This humiliation was tragic enough in itself, but the conditions on these reservations became continually worse and even though food was sent to the reservation, the Indian agents seemed never to get the food to the people. At a meeting called to discuss the terrible situation on the reservation, the lower Sioux (including the Santee) confronted Thomas J. Galbraith, the agent, and a group of traders. Little Crow, spokesman for the Sioux, supposedly said at that meeting, "We have no food, but here are these stores filled with food. We ask that you, the agent, make some arrangement by which we can get food from the stores, or else we may take our own away to keep ourselves from starving." To this, the trader's spokesman, Andrew J. Myrick retorted, "So far as I am concerned, if they are hungry, let them eat grass." The Indians remained silent, for a moment, and then let out a whoop and left, it is reported.[3] This incident, along with several others on the already volatile reservation, finally led up to what is called the Sioux Uprising of 1862. It is said that following one of the battles in the uprising, Myrick was found dead, his mouth filled with grass.[4]

The uprising was soon quelled, however, and the Minnesota pioneers would have their due. With the sanction of the courts, the trials proceeded quickly. When the trials were concluded, 303 Indians were judged guilty of murder and were sentenced to death. President Lincoln, who heard of the "kangaroo" court, reviewed the cases and pardoned all but (unfortunately) 40. According to one report, 38 men were eventually hung (for the crime of self-survival).

Richard Fool Bull, a Sioux medicine man, retells the story his grandfather told him about the uprising. Supposedly two young white women escaped and after the uprising they identified their supposed captors. He says:

> They had these two young women, and one night they escaped, got away where they can't find them, and they finally found their way to Mankato. . . . There is a stockade there, you know, and Soldiers, Cavalry, . . . [They] round up all the

the Indians in that area and brought them [to] stand in a circle. And they had these two girls identify them. If they point like that, then they can stand aside. And well history said 38, but my father said there were 36.[5]

To make a long story short, the Minnesota citizens were at most only partially satisfied by the executions. What they really wanted was extermination, and if they couldn't have that then they wanted the removal of the Santee people from the area they now called home; hence, the 1863 legislation entitled "An Act for the Removal of the Sisseton, Wahpaton, Medwakanton, and Wahpakoota Bands of Sioux or Dakota Indians, and for the Disposition of their Lands in Minnesota and Dakota" was passed.[6] This Act provided for the final stage of revenge in the minds of the Minnesota pioneers. It removed the Santee first to Crow Creek, North Dakota, and after enduring appalling conditions there for several years, they were finally moved to what is their home today—Niobrara, Nebraska.

The history of the Winnebago tribe, natives of Wisconsin, and now residing in northeastern Nebraska, is in many ways similar to that of the Santee Sioux. Many of the Winnebago still live in Wisconsin, the traditional home for as long as anyone can remember. A large group was removed from the area, however, in 1863 (those removed were primarily from areas near where the lower Sioux were living). Most of the Winnebago who were removed to the Crow Creek reservation quickly left for the Omaha reservation because the Winnebago, like the Santee who were living at Crow Creek, were starving. In 1865, an arrangement was made with the Omaha Indians, who agreed to give the Winnebago part of their reservation. The Omaha to this day remember this act of generosity. At any rate, with this agreement the people came down to their new home, adjacent to the Omaha reservation, in and around what is now Winnebago, Nebraska. Although a part of the Winnebago tribe still resides in Wisconsin, the people who now live in Nebraska have developed their own identity, a combination of traditional Winnebago mores and more recently created ways, a lifestyle developed in response to a life of hardship and mistreatment by the "White Pioneers."[7]

So, these are the four groups most widely represented in Nebraska today. The largest of these groups is probably the Teton Sioux, though it is hard to say just how many there are at any given time because of the migrant nature of tribal members (many move freely across the state line to both the Pine Ridge and Rosebud reservations in South Dakota) and because of the loose structure of the Western Sioux (there is no way to take an accurate census). Because of these reasons, this group perhaps offers both the most diversity and the most problems in description. Historically, this group is the one—perhaps more than any other—who formed a barrier to the pioneers' westward expansion. Many of the famous chiefs who we so often associate with the Northern Plains Indians come from this group. And it is to this group that writers like Mari Sandoz and John Neihardt paid homage in books like *Crazy Horse* and *Black Elk Speaks.*

Sioux Pictures of the Community of Man and Nature

The two largest tribes within this grouping who live in Nebraska are the Brule Sioux and the Oglala Sioux. Together, these two groups probably number about five thousand. Although the integration between the various tribes that together we call the Teton Sioux is loose, the members of a particular tribe are still quite closely united. The primary forces which have traditionally kept members together within a tribe still play an important role in that regard. These are the importance of the family life and the importance of religion as integrating forces.

Actually, in the Sioux world, these two traditionally were, and still are to a large extent, manifestations of the same thing. In pre-contact days everything that occurred in the Teton Sioux's life was in some way related to his religion. The social, political, philosophical, legal and even geographical structures of the tribe were dictated by, and extensions of, the religious life that permeated their lives.

Wakan Tanka is, according to traditional Sioux belief, the one and only God. Leo American Horse and Joseph Cress have put it this way:

> There was, and is and will be *Wakan Tanka*,
> The Great Mystery. He is one yet many. He
> is the Chief God, the Great Spirit, the Creator,
> and the Executive. He is the Gods both Superior
> and Associate and He is the Gods—Kindred, both
> the Subordinate and the Gods-like. He is the
> good and evil gods, the visible and invisible,
> the physical and immaterial, for He is all in one.
> The gods had no beginning and they will have no
> ending Some are before others; some are related
> as parent and child. Yet the gods have no mother
> or father, for anything that has birth will have
> death. Since the gods were created, not born,
> they will not die. Mankind cannot fully under-
> stand these things, for they are of the Great
> Mystery.[8]

His existence permeates all things. His manifestations are all around us in nature—the wind, the sun, the sky, the earth. These are the parts of *Wakan Tanka* that we can see and deal with in our everyday lives. The four directions take on god-like characteristics, as do many natural objects.

> There are superior gods: *Inyan*, the rock; *Maka*, the
> Earth; *Mahpiyato*, the sky; and *Wi*, the Sun. And the associate
> gods: *Hanwi*, the Moon; *Tate*, the Wind; *Woope*, the Beautiful
> one; and *Wakinyan*, the Winged. There are many more Gods-
> kindred and Gods-like including the buffalo, the bear, the four
> winds, the whirlwind, the Spirit of the ghost and others. And
> there are the evil spirits led by *Iya*, the chief of all evil, the
> giant, and *Iktomi*, the spider trickster.[9]

The symbolism found within the four directions is carried over into the daily lives of the people. For example, the door of the tipi may open to the East, the direction of birth, or creation, or

morning. And the honored people of the camp probably sat on
the west side of the campfire, the direction of the Thunder
Powers, agents of spiritual power and wisdom. The Sky is a
masculine power, the strength of spiritual wisdom, from which
comes the power of the sun. The Earth is a feminine power
("Mother Earth"), a fertile substance from which we get our
physical nourishment. These beliefs (and the recognition for the
need of ecological and social awareness that they promote) are
what has kept the people together as a cohesive group.

Closely connected with this—actually a part of the religious structure—is their understanding of the importance of
familial cohesiveness. But this identity that one tribal member
had for his relatives in reality went beyond the bonds of any
kind of formalized religion. Clan structure was based on family
ties. Therefore, a tribal member lived with his family, fought
with them against common enemies, helped hunt for food with
them, and, in short, depended on them for survival. True, this
was all within a religious framework, but in a sense it trans-
cended this framework, much as the mundane daily chores we
all must attend to for survival tend to obscure visions of a more
supreme entity from time to time. Today the traditional religion is weak, though family ties remain strong. That is not to
say, however, that the old religion is gone. Far from it. Although the Teton Sioux have, to some extent, adopted the
Catholic Church and the Native American Church, there is a
powerful and important movement among the people to continue or return to the more traditional forms of religion.

The *Yuwipi* (a healing ceremony) and *Inipi* (a purification
rite) are still performed among many members of the tribe.
Black Elk says:

> The rites of the *Inipi* are very *Wakan* and are used before
> any great undertaking for which we wish to make ourselves
> pure or for which we wish to gain strength; and in many
> winters past our men, and often the women, made *Inipi* even
> every day, and from this we received much of our power. Now
> that we have neglected these rites we have lost much of this
> power; it is not good, and I cry when I think of it. I pray

often that the Great Spirit will show to your young people
the importance of these rites.[10]

Lame Deer, a medicine man from Winner, S.D., adds:

> In speaking of sacred things I will tell you first about the
> *Inipi*—the sweat bath. I do this because we always purify our-
> selves in the sweat house before starting one of our ceremon-
> ies. Whether we celebrate the sun dance or a vision quest, the
> *Inipi* comes first. It could be said that the *Inipi* was our first
> rite, that all the other ceremonies came later.[11]

Other rites include:

> The rite of the *Onikare* (sweat lodge) [which] utilizes
> all the Powers of the universe: earth, and the things which
> grow from the earth, water, fire, and air. The water represents
> the Thunder-beings who come fearfully but bring goodness,
> for the steam which comes from the rocks, within which is the
> fire, is frightening, but it purifies us so that we may live as
> *Wakamtanda* wills, and He may even send to us a vision if we
> become very pure.[12]

Finally, there are the *Hanblecheyapi* (crying for a vision)
and *Wiwanyag Wachipi* (the Sun Dance). The Sun Dance (which
at one time was banned by the federal government and then
became a tourist attraction) is once again becoming a focal
point in the reorganization of the traditional religions. The Sun
Dance is perhaps the most widely known ritual of the *Lakota*
religion, and perhaps functions as a rallying point for tribal
rebuilding. Although it takes place in South Dakota, the Sun
Dance has a profound effect upon the lives of Nebraska Sioux
people because it is here that the people are reminded of the
fact that first they are members of their tribe, and that second-
arily they are "citizens" (if they care to be considered as such)
of the United States. Furthermore, the Sun Dance probably
best exhibits through ritual the meaning of the Sioux religion.
It's based on the premise that man must periodically be re-
united with *Wakan Tanka* and his fellow man. The sinew ropes
that tie the sun dancer to the center cottonwood tree (the tree

whose roots are in the earth, the physical, and whose branches touch the sky, the spiritual, and which is in the center, metaphysically, of the universe) represent the ties that man must make with his surroundings, both natural and supernatural. The dancer's circular pattern around the tree represents the power of the circle in his life.

The circle is an important symbol in the life not only of the Teton Sioux, but of many of the Plains Indians. Actually, it is more than a symbol; it is a pattern. Lame Deer says:

> To our way of thinking the Indians' symbol is the circle, the hoop. Nature wants things to be round. The bodies of human beings and animals have no corners. With us the circle stands for the togetherness of people who sit with one another around the campfire, relatives and friends united in peace while the pipe passes from hand to hand. The camp in which every tipi had its place was also a ring. The tipi was a ring in which people sat in a circle and all the families in the village were in turn circles within a larger circle, part of the larger hoop which was the seven campfires of the Sioux, representing one nation. The nation was only a part of the universe, in itself circular and made of the earth, which is round, of the sun, which is round, of the stars, which are round. The moon, the horizon, the rainbow—circles within circles within circles, with no beginning and no end.
>
> To us this is beautiful and fitting, symbol and reality at the same time, expressing the harmony of life and nature. Our circle is timeless, flowing; it is new life emerging from death— life winning out over death.[13]

He continues:

> To a white man symbols are just that: pleasant things to speculate about, to toy with in your mind. To us they are much, much more. Life to us is a symbol to be believed.[14]

The cycle of morning to midday to evening to night to morning is related consciously in the mind of the Plains Indian to the cycle of birth to middle age to old age to death, to regenesis and a new life. The four directions can be used to symbolize this. East, for instance, can represent birth, or morning, or spring. West, by contrast, can represent maturity, or evening, or fall. This is why the door to the tipi might face east—the direction of beginning.

The Santee Sioux share much of the tradition, life style and religion with the Teton Sioux. The language is almost identical. What distinguishes the Santee from their western relatives is the uniqueness of their previous geographical location—that is, Minnesota. There, the people found wild rice, water fowl and beaver, instead of the treeless plains, the Rocky Mountains, and buffalo. This is most obviously reflected in their religious ceremony with rituals such as the fish dance. Also, the Santee suffered a tribal breakdown earlier because of their earlier contact with the whites.

Today in Nebraska there are, of course, many fewer Santee than there are Teton Sioux. The Santees tend not to be migrant, but rather are largely centered on the Santee reservation near Niobrara, Nebraska, or in urban centers in the vicinity. They have always been a more stationary people, which is reflected in their willingness and ability to farm. But these differences between the Santee and the Teton are minor ones.[15] Their differences are important in that they give the Santee an identity separate from the Western Sioux, but functionally they are all Sioux, and they all share a language and a religion. Because the Santee met the whites at an earlier date, the stories and rituals have to some extent been lost. It seems important that what does still exist should be collected and transcribed as soon as possible. Tribal members, incidentally, are currently collecting much of this information with the help of a federal grant.

The Winnebago and Omaha: Pictures of Human Community and of the Growth of the Human Individual

Today, the Winnebago and the Omaha are neighbors. They live side by side. This doesn't mean that they have identical life styles, however. True, there are many similarities. For that matter, there are many similarities between both of these groups and the Sioux. Like the Sioux, both the Winnebago and the Omaha life styles were determined and controlled by the religious atmosphere. The four directions, the circle, the earth and sky powers, and the clan relationships were all important. The primary differences were not philosophical, nor were they ritualistic (although neither the Omaha nor the Winnebago had a Sun Dance). Rather the differences were in how the philosophy was expressed. As is the case with the Santee, many of the stories and traditional practices are gone. But many live on in the minds of the old men. Anthropologists in the thirties were sounding the death knell for both the Omaha and Winnebago tribes as never again existing in the traditional ways. Margaret Mead, for instance, suggested that the Omaha naming ceremony was dead in the thirties, but men like John Turner are still doing that very ceremony in private to this day. The ceremonies are not dead; the tribe has been able to maintain many of the traditional ceremonies in spite of the meddling of bureaucrats and the misperceptions of anthropologists.

Like the Sioux, both the Omaha and the Winnebago had many religious stories. Only now the characters are different. The trickster is no longer the spider of *Lakota* tales, but now is a monkey for the Omaha. And the Winnebago, long recognized by other tribes as having an almost Dionysian sense of humor, have an entire class of tricky characters including Bladder, the proud one; Hare, the divine sacrificer; Turtle, the lady's man and military man; and the Tricky One, the one who deals with an awareness of his biological nature. And the circle is still important, but the significance and symbols of the four directions is different. And so the differences continue. There are, all in all, probably more similarities than differences between all four of the tribes, but the significance is in what makes each of them unique—the differences.

For all of the tribes, religion was, and is, a deeply personal experience. The vision quest—a time of personal reflection in a solitary environment—is common to all the Plains tribes. But, as Black Elk says in *Black Elk Speaks,* an individual cannot keep all of his understanding to himself. There comes a time when it is the individual's responsibility to share his religious experiences with the tribe. The individual man must become part of the circle; he must share his talents and experiences with the other members of the community.[16] This is most commonly done through ceremonies, such as the Sun Dance. The Winnebago had four types of ceremonies, Paul Radin points out in his definitive study on the Winnebago religion, *The Winnebago Tribe*. These are:

> . . . the clan ceremonies, in which only members of the clan could participate; religious societies, for which only people who had obtained blessings from the same spirits were eligible; the Medicine Dance, in which only initiated individuals could take part; and a semipermanent organization like the *hokixere* dance (a celebration for success in war), in which only individuals who were returning from a war party and had counted coup could participate.[17]

Of course, within each of these types of ceremonies, there were many different fetes such as the war-bundle feasts (each clan had a different one), or the buffalo ceremony, or the fasts (and this list could go on and on).

Since the Winnebago came into the Plains area so late in history, they have a unique combination of traditions which combines their earlier experiences as a fishing and farming tribe with their later experiences as a kind of "buffalo culture." So far as their life in Nebraska is concerned, they are a tribe who have always lived on a reservation. This, too, makes them unique —their earliest traditions are in no way related to their Nebraska experiences. Although they have adopted Nebraska as their home, it really is a second home, one in many respects far different from that of their ancestors. In addition, they are the only tribe now living in Nebraska who, until recent history, maintained continuous contact with the Algonquin tribes of the northeastern part of the United States. Since the Algonquin culture is so radically different from most of the Sioux-influenced Plains culture, the Winnebago bring to Nebraska a wide diversity of clothing styles, hunting techniques, and living accommodations.[18]

The Omaha, by contrast, are the only reservation Indians in Nebraska who live where they live by choice. The Missouri River Valley is their home, and their religious life and general life styles reflect this. Like other Plains tribes, they were a buffalo culture. Although home was (and is) along the Missouri River (earlier around Bellevue and now around Macy, Nebr.), the young men followed the buffalo herds throughout the northern Plains in search of the buffalo which was used for food, clothing, and shelter. In addition, they engaged in some farming. In the river valley, they raised some corn, squash, and other vegetables.

The Omaha tribal structure is made up of a variety of clans which, in turn, constitute two "half-tribes" designated the sky people and the earth people. Traditionally, the sky people were responsible for the spiritual fulfillment of the tribe, and the earth moiety was responsible for the physical necessities. This is a good example of the interdependence so often found within the tribes of this area. No person could live without the gifts the other members of the tribe had to offer. Often, the worst punishment that could be doled out to a tribal member was to ostracize him from the tribe, thus forcing him to seek out both his physical and spiritual nourishment on his own.

The Omaha religious structures permeate all aspects of their tribal life. These concepts, which are both universal and relational, account for the structure of tribal organization, ceremonial rites, tribal government and social life.

Duality is central to an understanding of Omaha religion. The visible universe and its maintenance are hinged upon dual images. Alice Fletcher and Francis LaFlesche elaborate, saying:

> An invisible and continuous life was believed to permeate all things, seen and unseen. This life manifests itself in two ways: first—by causing to move—all motion, all acts of mind or body are because of this invisible life; second, by causing permanency of structure and form as in the rock, the physical features of the landscape, mountains, plains, streams,

rivers, lakes, the animals and man. . . . Through this mysteri-
ous life and power all things are related to one another and to
man, the seen to the unseen, the dead to the living, a fragment
of anything to its entirety.[19]

Hence, the perpetuation of any one object or being is dependent upon its relationship with all other objects or beings.
These relationships are prescribed and regulated according to
the ethical and regular functions of natural phenomena. Nature
is seen as having male and female components; the sky is masculine, the earth is feminine. The continuance of life and maintenance of natural order depended, and to some degree still
depends, upon the union of these forces.

Although such duality is not unique to the Omaha, it functions significantly in the development of present activities. If
traditionally two divisions constituted the tribe—the earth
people and the sky people (and if these groups were further sub-
divided into what were known as clans, each of which "had its
designation, its rites, its place, its tabu and its personal homes,
although these distinctive marks were subordinate to the two
grand divisions"[20]), the distinction is to a degree still kept
alive. Traditionally the sky people were given the responsibility
of providing spiritual nourishment for the tribe while the earth
people were designated to provide the physical nourishment and
some of these old distinctions still carry meaning in common
social activities. Now many activities—even down to cutting
cake at birthday parties—require collaboration from members of
clans from two halves of the circle.

In old days, all tribal activities expressed this division into
male and female counterparts. Marriages, for instance, were exo-
gamous—typically, unions would occur between a member of
the sky people and one of the earth people. During buffalo
hunts, which occasioned great ceremonial rites, the camping arrangements reflected the tribal order based on this division. As
was true with many other tribes, the camping form was circular
with an opening to the east. The Omaha practiced this arrangement only during ceremonies; at *all* other times, the opening
faced the direction in which the tribe intended to travel. But at
all times within this encampment one would find that the

sky people constituted the northern half—the earth people composing the southern half. It has been suggested that this arrangement served other functions such as the provision of safety,
but in view of the religious orientation granted all else, it is
reasonable to consider this a reflection of their cosmic order.

All ceremonial rites, like the tribal organization and tribal
form, were premised on the belief that man stood in relationship to the supernatural powers and their decreed order. Certain
rites could be performed only by members of the gens whose
animal designations were associated with that rite. These
ceremonial functions presented in dramatic form the ideas
which promoted cohesiveness amongst tribal members and
bound them to one another for the purpose of mutual survival.
The rites through which each tribal member passed are carefully detailed by Fletcher and LaFlesche and include: the introduction of the child to the cosmos, introduction of the child to
the tribe, consecration of the boy to thunder, and the introduction of the person to individual life and to the supernatural.
These represent a calculated progression from a child's birth and
nonentity to the child's continued growth and placement
within the tribal structure. Fletcher and LaFlesche summarize
this process as follows:

> The entrance into manhood required a voluntary effort
> by which, through the rite of fasting and prayer, the man came
> into direct and personal relations with the supernatural and
> realized within himself the forceful power of the union of the
> seen and the unseen.[21]

Political unity in the Omaha tribe was stifled for years by
several factors. Environmental influences dictated that the tribe
range over a wide area of the Plains in search of buffalo. This
prevented them from becoming fully sedentary—and although
they did engage in some farming, their other efforts to get food
scattered segments of the tribe, at times resulting in their
complete disappearance. The numerous religious rites which
were within the strict keeping of certain groups also hindered
political unity. But at some point such political unity became

essential to the maintenance of tribal unity. And thus, according to the Sacred Legend, tribal government was initiated. Certain gens within each main division were selected to contain a subdivision which would provide one member to the governing council. These families were presented with a pipe as a credential. This governing council was composed of hereditary chiefs of which there were two orders. The elements of interdependence and duality are again evident in the organization of the governing body. The two sacred tribal pipes were the primary credentials of this central authority "both for the act of its creation and for the exercise of its functions. The ornamentation of the pipes, the semicircle arrangement in the council meetings, and the prerequisite of unanimous agreement among council members all stemmed from the Omaha beliefs regarding the manner in which the supernatural powers would have them operate." According to Fletcher and LaFlesche, "the duties of the Council of Seven besides that of maintaining peace and order within the tribe were making peace with other tribes, securing allies, determining the time of the annual buffalo hunt, and confirming the man who was to act as leader, on whom rested the responsibility of that important movement." [22]

Art as the Expression of a Vision of the World Radically Different From the White Vision

Since the life styles of the four tribes are so much alike, it should come as no surprise that the art forms of the tribes are also similar. Actually, the life styles of these people spawned the art forms. In other words, the old Indian stories, for instance, were more than pure entertainment. Since there was no writing, important historical and religious events had to be handed down from generation to generation by word of mouth. These were formed into interesting stories so that they could be more easily remembered. Also, stories were told as lessons in morality, manners, and skills. The stories, actually, record or form a concrete way of looking at the world in terms of medicine, psychology, architecture or any other field. They bring to life a philosophy that otherwise functions only in abstract terms. They unite the spiritual and supernatural worlds with the physical, allowing those who hear and understand to make functional an all-encompassing philosophy. As time went by, certain members of the tribe seemed to have a natural flair for telling these stories and so they became, by tradition, the story tellers. They developed what began as a pragmatic exercise into an art form, which has been passed down and still exists among Indian people today.

The symbolic structure used by the story tellers is the same one that is used by the religionists. As a matter of fact, this basic structure is used by all members of the tribe. The symbolism found in the stories is the same that is found in the traditional architecture, such as in the traditional arrangement of the tents in campgrounds, or for that matter, as in the Pow-Wow grounds at Macy, Nebraska, today. By the same token, this same structure which forms the stories and the architecture also formulates a basis for developing a world view and a theory about the evolution of nature and scores of other philosophical and psychological beliefs.

The development of ornamental clothes making is another example of an art form which evolved from traditional life styles. Originally, the only thing the old Indian woman had to work with was the buffalo hide. She had to learn how to best work with the hide to make warm and comfortable clothing. Some of these women became especially skilled at doing this. And then, of course, the desire for some decoration led to the art of beadwork, perhaps the most popular of the arts still existing among the Indian people.

Beadwork design is a beautiful example of the ability of the Plains Indians to convert the religious color symbolism and design into artwork. The designs incorporated into bead work can be interpreted into social and/or religious stories by using the colors as messages and the designs themselves as narrative symbols. It provides an excellent example of the marriage of fine art for the sake of beauty and functional art as a religious or social statement.

The dance was originally a socio-religious expression. The Pow-Wows which are so popular today among the Plains Indians evolved out of the war and victory dances which preceded or followed the hunts or skirmishes that these tribes lived with from day to day. These dances provided spiritual support for these hardships as well as psychological uplifting and a way to deal with the grief and suffering that the warriors often had to encounter. Today these dances are sometimes held as contests.[23] They have become a fine art for the dancers themselves and they provide the spectators with a social forum to get together and socialize or renew old acquaintances. These Pow-Wows express and emphasize the feeling for community which is an integral part of the Indian life-style and which is reflected in all the predominant art forms.

This symbolic structure—with its feeling for community—appears in a wide variety of Nebraska Indian life. It appears in the stories, dances, beadwork, architecture, tent arrangement in campgrounds, and at social events. In essence, it represents very different value systems from those of western technological society in terms of round vs. square ways of handling land and buildings, communal life styles vs. individualism, ecological awareness vs. the worship of technocratic progress, and giving vs. taking. These values are rehearsed in the stories, rituals, and art forms and are essential and basic to traditional Indian belief. It is to these beliefs that Indian people must look in any efforts to rebuild tribal awareness. This traditional structure currently formulates a basis for reviving new national feeling and political nation building on the Sioux reservations. Revival of interest in *Inipi* and *Yuwipi* among the Sioux, in the Medicine Lodge among the Winnebago, and in traditional ritual among the Omaha has been central to an awareness among these people of the strength of their tribes as nations in themselves.

What Native American Visions Can Tell
About How to Survive and Live Well

What does this mean? Essentially, it suggests that Indian

people who are interested in nation building along lines of traditional value are offering alternative life styles to a white culture
caught up in a technocratic web formed around the Gross
National Product and labor exploitation. The authors of *Blueprint for Survival,* who use as a basis for their analysis and
criticism of western social systems tribal societies such as the
various American Indian groups, suggest that "natural" social
systems are those which grow out of an eco-system. They
suggest that such societies point the way for the survival of
mankind in a time of pollution, shortage of fossil fuels, and
overpopulation. Only when a society puts itself "in tune" with
its natural surroundings can it function as a community for the
joint benefit of all members within the society. They sum it up
when they say:

> If we believe the role of a cultural behavior like that of
> any other type of behavior is to ensure the stable relationship
> of a system (in this case a social one) with its environment,
> then we must recognize that the cultural behavior of the tradi-
> tional societies [best exemplified by Native American small
> group societies], which we derogatorily refer to as primitive,
> is more "valid" than our own.[24]

This is not to say that current visions of Indian nation
building are, or ought to be, romanticized or over-sentimenta-
lized. Nor does it imply that various tribes ought to organize
independent of one another. Rather, there is a recognition of
the fact that there are resources which are useful and which can
link twentieth century Indians with their pre-contact ancestors.
And this can very well be a collective vision. Historically, there
were the beginnings of a collective vision between the various
tribes—one example of which was the Messianic vision resulting
in the Ghost Dance—but this collective vision was broken by the
Gatling guns of Wounded Knee. This collective vision—this concept of nation building through a united effort of many tribes
or even of interested and responsible non-Indians—this realistic vision of the twentieth century world is not only possible
but forms the basis of many Indian movements of our time.

The best illustrations of the useful resources Indians (and whites) must learn to use in this changing world are in the fields of psychology, community development, and prisons and rehabilitation, just to name a few. In the field of psychology, for example, men like the Black Elks or the Crow Dogs have continued to use traditional views of the nature of man's inner self not only to treat the mental conditions of tribal members, but to build upon in developing ways of existing in a changing world. This traditional awareness of psychology has profoundly influenced the white world's way of looking at man's inner self as well. Carl Jung, for example, developed many of his theories as a result of looking at the Winnebago hero and trickster stories, and at Neihardt's *Black Elk Speaks.*

Jung, in his book *Man and His Symbols,* uses the Winnebago Trickster cycles as a basis for his own theory of the four stages in the evolution of human identity; the stages are identity as biological man, identity as ordinary man on the street, identity as hero, and identity as spiritual man, conscious of both his inner and outer nature. He says:

> . . . This concept [that the image of the hero evolves in a manner that reflects each stage of the evolution of the human personality] can be more easily understood if I present it in what amounts to a diagram. I take this example from the . . . Winnebago Indians, because it sets out quite clearly four distinct stages in the evolution of the hero. In these stories (which Dr. Paul Radin published in 1948 under the title *Hero Cycles of the Winnebago*) we can see the definite progression from the most primitive to the most sophisticated concept of the hero. This progression is characteristic of other hero cycles. Though the symbolic figures in them naturally have different names, their roles are similar, and we shall understand them better once we have grasped the point made by this example.
>
> Dr. Radin noted four distinct cycles in the evolution of the hero myth. He named them the *Trickster* cycle, the *Hare* cycle, the *Red Horn* cycle and the *Twin* cycle. . . .
>
> The Trickster cycle corresponds to the earliest and least developed period of life. Trickster is a figure whose physical appetites dominate his behavior; he has the mentality of an infant. . . .
>
> The next figure is Hare. He, like Trickster (whose animal traits

are often represented among American Indians by a coyote),
also first appears in animal form. He has not yet attained
human stature, but all the same he appears as the founder of
human culture—the Transformer. . . .

Red Horn, the third of this series of hero figures, is an
ambiguous person, said to be the youngest of 10 brothers. He
meets the requirements of an archetypal hero by passing such
tests as winning a race and by proving himself in battle. . . .
With Red Horn we have reached the world of man, through
an archaic world, in which the aid of superhuman powers or
tutelary gods is needed to ensure man's victory over the vile
forces that beset him. . . . The danger to man's happiness and
security now comes from man himself. . . .

This basic theme (which is repeated in the last cycle,
that of the Twins) raises, in effect, the vital question: How
long can human beings be successful without falling victims to
their own pride or, in mythological terms, to the jealousy of
the gods?

Though the twins are said to be the sons of the Sun,
they are essentially human and together constitute a single
person. . . . In these two children we see the two sides of man's
nature. One of them, Flesh, is acquiescent, mild, and without
initiative; the other, Stump, is dynamic and rebellious. . . .

I have given this description of the four types of hero at
some length because it provides a clear demonstration of the
pattern that occurs both in the historic myths and in the hero-
dreams of contemporary man.[25]

Jung uses this diagram not only as a basis in his analysis of other
cultures and their myths, but as a working concept which he
applies in his own psychotherapy. His influence has been widely
felt, not only in the field of psychology, but in other areas such
as literary criticism, where men like Northrup Frye and other
archetypal critics have based their interpretations of literature
on Jung's analysis of Winnebago Trickster cycles.

In community development, traditional views of geographical settings working as extensions of a socio-religious
philosophy have a lot to say about the communal value of
real estate; those who would rather develop for personal profit

than for community advancement would do well to study the Plains tribes land sense. Private ownership of tiny individualized lots is an extension of the philosophy of individualism so prevalent in western society. Studies have shown, however, that real estate developments which include no public space have a higher crime rate. Without public space, there can be no sense of community. Traditionally, the tipis were set up in a circle around a public area. Every member of the tribe was forced to communicate with other members simply because of their geographical setting. Frank Lloyd Wright studied Plains Indian concepts of spatial design before designing many of his later buildings, including one of his most famous, Wingspread. Many of his late works incorporate the idea of public space and circular design for the sake of communal awareness.

In the area of prison reforms and rehabilitation, there is plenty of work which needs to be done. Traditionally, tribal punishment always pointed towards rebuilding the community —with an emphasis on rehabilitation. There was no punishment, as we know it in American prisons, but rather, there was an integration of the wrong-doer back into the community. The punishment was not based around the concept of separation, but around the concept of reintegration. If, however, the offender persisted in his wrong-doing, then, in some cases, it became necessary to ostracize him. This was the ultimate in penalties (and rarely used) because the community was essential not only for spiritual aid, but for physical sustenance as well. It was difficult for one man to get food without the help of others.

The American penal systems have proven unsatisfactory with regards to Native American people. The return rate is high. Alternate methods have been successful, especially in cases where alcohol is related to the crime (which is the case most of the time). Criminologists working with Native Americans have found that the best forms of rehabilitation relate to a person's reintegration into the tribe. The best work in this field to date has been done by people working with the Native American Rights Fund, Boulder, Colorado. Rick Williams and others have developed the plans for a minimum security prison in Eagle Butte, South Dakota. Here, they hope to develop a penal system that functions in a traditional way to help Native Americans redevelop a sense of community.

It is perhaps in the literature and the arts that the traditional visions applied to modern day models of nation-building are best seen, however. Writers like Vine Deloria, Hyemeyohsts Storm, N. Scott Momaday, and Rueben Snake recognize this need to integrate past wisdom and experience into an assimilated and changing world. Books like Storm's *Seven Arrows* stress the need for a weak and misled white society to adopt the strengths of the Indian culture. Momaday's *House Made of Dawn* and James Welch's *Winter in the Blood* appeal to the Indian's sense of his past as a foundation for rebuilding a strong community. These writers, like the great narrators of the past, believe in the power of the word as a means not only of attacking white imperialism but of formulating a rallying point around which the disillusioned and powerless can regain an identity and plan a strategy.

Historically, the art forms as they existed in Nebraska were much the same—whether they were a product of the Sioux, Winnebago or Omaha. The stories, for instance, although different in content (and therefore significant), were all told in the same way. And the beadwork, clothing, or dancing may have looked a little different, but they all took the same form. Today, there continues to be little difference between the forms the art takes in these four tribes. This is because the four tribes continue to live parallel life-styles.

These parallel life styles help the members of Nebraska's Indian tribes to identify themselves as a unique and individual people. They recognize the need for cooperation in the continuous fight for sovereignty. Today, in spite of the continuous efforts of White America first to commit genocide and then to suppress Indian people in this country—in Nebraska as well as in other states—the four tribes have made, and are making, great strides. Of course years of mistreatment, years of concentration camps called reservations, have left their mark on the

Indian community, but incredibly, Indians who live in Nebraska have, in less than a hundred years of adversity and oppression, overcome many of their problems. Together, they have formed the Nebraska Indian Commission. Together, they work in cooperation through United Indians of Nebraska and Inter-Tribal Industries. However, the problems are still immense. They include: alcoholism and other health-related problems, unemployment problems (especially on the reservation) which are, in part, the result of the problems of an inadequate educational system, and the problems of inequality in the courts and correctional institutions. Even though these problems are difficult ones to solve, they are not insurmountable. Through cooperation, Indian people have found that some inroads can be made toward ultimate solutions. [The catalogue of resources which follows is exemplary of the talents and the degree of cooperation which exist between the tribes still living in Nebraska today.]

FOOTNOTES

1. Standing Buffalo, "The Omaha Creation Account," in *Literature of the American Indian*, ed. Thomas E. Sanders and Walter W. Peek (New York: Glencoe Press, 1973), pp. 45-46.

2. Leo American Horse and Joseph Cress (eds.), *Lakota Stories* (Pine Ridge, South Dakota: Red Cloud Indian School, Inc., 1970), p. iv.

3. Roy W. Meyer, *History of the Santee Sioux* (Lincoln: University of Nebraska Press, 1967), p. 114.

4. *Ibid.*

5. Taped in Lincoln, Nebraska, 1975, KUON-TV, by John Flower.

6. Meyer, *op. cit.*, p. 140.

7. For a description of the conditions the Winnebago people endured see J.O. Dorsey, *The Thegiha Language* (Washington, 1890), the Omaha letters section, *passim*.

8. American Horse, *op. cit.*, p. v.

9. *Ibid.*, pp. v-vi.

10. Black Elk, *The Sacred Pipe*, edited and recorded by Joseph Epes Brown (Baltimore: Penguin Books, Inc., 1971), p. 10.

11. John (Fire) Lame Deer and Richard Erdoes, *Lame Deer Seeker of Visions* (New York: Simon and Schuster, 1972), p. 174. Mr. Fire (Lame Deer) has visited Lincoln upon occasion to teach classes or consult with Indian students and friends; he lives in Winner, South Dakota.

12. Black Elk, *op. cit.*, p. 31.

13. Lame Deer and Erdoes, *op. cit.*, p. 112.

14. *Ibid.*, p. 118.

15. For further information, see Meyer, *op. cit.*

16. John G. Neihardt, *Black Elk Speaks* (Lincoln: University of Nebraska Press, 1961).

17. Paul Radin, *The Winnebago Tribe* (Lincoln: University of Nebraska Press, 1970), p. 269. [Originally published as *37th Annual Report of the Bureau of American Ethnology*, Smithsonian Institution, Washington, D.C., 1923. Bison Book is a reprint.]

18. *Ibid.*

19. Alice Fletcher and Francis LaFlesche, *The Omaha Tribe* (Lincoln: University of Nebraska Press, 1972), p. 134, 2 Volumes (all footnotes are from Volume 1). [Originally published as *27th Annual Report of the Bureau of American Ethnology*, Smithsonian Institution, Washington, D.C., 1905-06. Bison Book is a reprint.]

20. *Ibid.,* p. 135.

21. *Ibid.,* p. 133.

22. *Ibid.,* p. 209.

23. There are many social and ceremonial dances and hand games performed as entertainment or as benefits without the concept of a contest.

24. Edward Goldsmith, *et al., Blueprint for Survival* (Boston: Houghton Mifflin Company, 1972), p. 114.

25. Carl Jung, *Man and His Symbols* (New York: Dell Publishing Company, 1964), pp. 101-07. [Copyright 1964, Aldus Books, London— first Dell printing, 1968.]

CATALOGUE

HOW TO UNDERSTAND THE RESOURCES OF INDIAN GROUPS IN THIS REGION

Introduction

The influence of Native Americans has extended far beyond the boundaries of the North American continent. *Black Elk* was "discovered" in Zurich, Switzerland; the Winnebago trickster tales generated some of the theories which Carl Jung later refined in *Man and His Symbols;* and hundreds of other major ecological, architectural, and plant innovations depend on Indian perception. Yet in spite of the interest which Indian culture has generated in academic circles, the lives of very ordinary Indian individuals have not been documented without reliance upon prejudiced stereotypes. Robert Coles has perceptively remarked that people are more complicated, more varied, more interesting, have more resiliency and more survivability than one may think. "I listen to them. You listen to them. Again and again." . . . A child psychiatrist and prolific Pulitzer Prize winner, Coles' comment contains an attitude, which, founded in his inter-actions with many members of various ethnic populations, has served to dispel traditional stereotypic approaches.

Conventionally, the approach has been to view ethnic minorities as impoverished and consequently label them "culturally disadvantaged." But with Coles' and other recent thinkers who know how to listen to members of a culture other than their own, we have been given a new perspective. If stereotypes can be abandoned, or acknowledged and set aside, society holds the potential to depolarize itself. As Coles says: "Shal-low labels lead to shallow programs." It is no longer necessary for minority populations to rely totally on government largesse when they possess the human resources to enter into a cooperative process of community build-ing based upon utilization of traditional history and values which serves to conjoin present and future.

A guarded attitude exists initially in most Indian communities towards outsiders. That is the case of most strong cultures. Indians with good reason have come to distrust snoopers; they have in the past been exploited as sources of information and often misrepresented while they reaped no immediate benefits from the research on them which was done. Indian peoples in the state of Nebraska and elsewhere are in full possession of their culture. It has perhaps become part of the deep structure of their lives and is therefore less visible to the casual observer. Many traditional elements continue to exert a strong influence upon the lives and actions of individuals and families, but for various reasons these elements themselves do not surface conversationally and are not immediately apparent unless one is born to the community or until one has spent many hours participating in it.

One example of this is the role which the Native American Church and the older and more traditionally structured religion continues to play. Within our Indian communities throughout the state, there are numerous individuals who could, if willing, testify to miracles resulting from their participation in certain religious ceremonies within each church. But these experiences involve both very personal and very sacred revelations/ gifts from those who have great power; thus it should be easy to comprehend their reluctance to publicize such matters to strangers. Historically, the government once persecuted members of the Native American Church because of its use of the sacrament of peyote in religious ceremonies. The religion was denounced and characterized as a 'cult.' Hence the reticence on the part of individuals to identify themselves as members and discuss the nature of their ceremonies. Yet to assume that the ceremonies have vanished is false. If religion provides an example of one element of traditional culture which serves to destroy the most common stereotype that exists about Indian people—that their culture is dying—other aspects of life furnish equally powerful examples of the strength of the culture: raising children, story telling, land use, crafts, architecture and so forth. The Indian cultures are being modified to account for external pressures. One can lament the fact that indeed some details of these traditions cannot be fully remembered, but the basic structures persist. They ask to be understood and admired.

The purpose of this catalogue is twofold. First, it is written to suggest how individuals, Indian or non-Indian, can know what the 'culture' and 'view of life' of all of the Indian groups living in Nebraska is like. Second, it offers Indian persons, if contacted, a means of expressing their own opinions about their lives and suggesting ways in which others may learn from, or relate to, them. It is important to recognize the difference between cooperation and control. Indian people are asking for self-determination—meaning that they would prefer not to remain *merely* recipients of largesse, but that they be allowed to become active planners in their own communities. Ultimately this catalogue seeks to stimulate mutual cooperation between Indian and non-Indian communities by providing information which will increase understanding and appreciation between individuals. But these ideas must not be isolated and divorced from the neighborhoods from which they were abstracted. Stereotypes can only be destroyed through the interaction of individuals who are willing to glimpse a vision of the whole.

There are a number of inobtrusive ways in which a person can become familiar with the history of Native Americans—past and present. At this point, a few such examples will be briefly described. A bibliography has been included which, although not complete, is extensive in that it contains the most authoritative books written, some of which are popularized while others are quite academic.

The University of Nebraska in Lincoln offers several resource channels through which information can be acquired pertaining to Native Americans. Departments such as Anthropology, Political Science, Education, and English have courses which deal specifically with aspects of Indian culture from both a contemporary and historical perspective. A Native American Studies Program was initiated in 1974 and is offered as a major area of study. Specific information including course descriptions of the above-mentioned programs can be obtained by writing the University of Nebraska. Other colleges throughout the state which serve Indian students are also in the process of developing programs of study similar to those at UNL.

The Council of American Indian Students at UNL sponsors the Native American Days' celebration each spring at which time Indian speakers are scheduled to discuss various topics which are currently considered controversial and/or informative. This celebration culminates in a pow-wow spanning several days and draws participants from a multi-state area. The pow-wow includes dancing and singing contests and is an excellent way for Indian people from tribes outside this area or for non-Indian people to gain information about Indian ways.

The University also sponsors a tutoring program for Indian children in the Lincoln community known as TONIC, which is run by Suzy Prenger (Andrews Hall, University of Nebraska). This is one good means of involvement for individuals qualified to tutor to develop contacts, not only with Indian children, but with their families and the public schools which serve these Indian children. The subject of Indian education is presently one of great controversy and complexity. Urban Indian children face circumstances far different from the circumstances encountered by the Indian child living on the reservation. One division of TONIC travels to the Winnebago reservation weekly to tutor Indian children living there. A much different perspective on what Indians are doing to develop their own educational system can be gained by visiting Winnebago.

The League of Women Voters has developed an Indian Rights Committee which monitors state legislation dealing with Native Americans. This committee is actively cooperating with many special interest groups in the Indian communities in the state by compiling and disseminating information pertaining to current concerns. Karen Buller is presently chairperson of the committee and a registered lobbyist at the State Capitol and should be contacted for detailed information and explanations regarding bills presently being considered by the legislature which pertain to the welfare of Native Americans in Nebraska. It is also possible to obtain a list of Indian-owned and operated businesses from the League office.

The Lutheran Church National Indian Board, headed by Gene Crawford, the Interchurch Ministries of Nebraska, and the Junior League are other dominant culture or integrated organizations which have been constructive and cooperative in dealing with Indian folk. Although these above-mentioned groups can each provide insightful information regarding Indian communities, it should be emphasized that they must be looked upon as *secondary sources.*

The major vehicles for public cultural expression which now exist for Indian people in this state are the frequent gatherings (pow-wows, hand games, benefit dances, gourd dances), religious societies, urban Indian centers and arts and crafts associations. This catalogue does not profess to be exhaustive, as there may be some organizations which are not listed; there are many communities having a small Indian population but no incorporated services. However, the major population centers have been contacted for information and that information will be described in this catalogue.

Pow-wows, or major Indian celebrations, are a primary vehicle for drawing together many Indian people from differing tribes in a social context charged with excitement. Two very important aspects of Indian tradition underlie these celebrations: "giving away" and "feeding the people." A person gives away money, food, or clothing when something special happens in his or her own life. For instance, at a recent pow-wow, a three-year-old boy danced for the first time. This brought such joy to his family that in marking the occasion they presented each group of singers with a monetary token indicating their delight. It is said that a person should give away to those in need rather than giving only to friends and family.

"Feeding the people" is an act of reciprocity. To ask people to participate in a pow-wow means that the host will feed the people abundantly. A shared meal holds great significance and is a means of honoring those who have traveled a long distance to participate in the celebration.

Attending a pow-wow is an exhilarating, but oftimes confusing, experience for a non-Indian individual. To fully appreciate what is occurring, one must understand some of the major distinctions between dancing and singing styles as well as possess some knowledge regarding pow-wow etiquette and the structure of the celebration. Charlie Archambault or Ronald Theisz from Sinte Gleska Community College in Rosebud, South Dakota, can be contacted for an extensive description of some Indian celebrations and ceremonies, but in this catalogue only a few major elements of pow-wow activities will be explained.

A flag song begins most dances and ceremonials. Each tribe has its own flag song which is an analogue of our "Star Spangled Banner." Typically, the Native American flag is displayed, which consists of a staff with eagle feathers (although each tribe has its own flag with distinctions in the staff, features or symbolism). The United States' flag is also normally honored at this time. Everyone is expected to stand during this song and remain standing during the grand entry of dancers which follows. The grand entry has its origins in traditional parades, but has also been influenced by a similar entry typically seen at rodeos. An emcee is the central figure in a pow-wow for it is his responsibility to announce all events, set the pace, provide continuity, and enhance the festivities with jokes and anecdotes. The pow-wows include intertribal dances, war dances, veterans dances, honor songs, and contest dancing and singing.

The main categories of contest dancing are the men's traditional dance, men's fancy dance, women's traditional (or buckskin) dance and women's shawl dance. Nebraska is considered a border state and therefore the various tribes exhibit both Northern and Southern Great Plains styles of singing and dancing. This holds true for the outfits of the dancers from the various tribes as well. The features which distinguish the men's fancy dance (counterpart of the women's shawl dance) from the men's traditional dance (counterpart of the women's buckskin dance) are the electric colors which typify the fancy dance outfits, the intricacy of footwork involved in their dance steps, the accelerated and pulsating rhythm of their movements and the highly stylized gestural and postural cues which denote the tribal style. Traditional dancers in contrast wear more subdued colors and portions of the outfits of both men and women are made from natural materials, such as eagle or turkey feathers, bone, and buckskin. The Lakota Sioux dancers and singers (e.g. the Porcupine

Singers from Rosebud, South Dakota) characteristically reflect the northern styles. The singing, for example, is high-pitched. The Omaha people, on the other hand, frequently represent the southern style. Specific descriptive elements of these two broad style categories will be elaborated upon in other sections of the catalogue.

Hand games fall into a second category of social interaction which serves to ensure ongoing traditions. The hand game is played by members of two teams. A member of one team hides a shell or stone in his/her hand and a member of the opposing team guesses in which hand the object is concealed by pointing a feather in the direction indicative of his/her choice. These hand games, which are also accompanied by music, dancing, give-aways and big meals, are generally held during the winter months to raise money for the upcoming pow-wows which occur sporadically throughout the spring, summer and fall. For descriptions of the variations among the tribes in hand game usage, one can consult the Bureau of American Ethnology bulletins.

Benefit dances are given to honor certain individuals or to act as memorials. During the Vietnam War many Indian men, upon their return, were given benefit dances by their families and friends to celebrate their meritorious deeds. Among the Indian communities there often exists a reverence for the American flag, even though the individuals and communities may not be enthusiastic about participating in the panoramic Bicentennial activities which are underway. Again, the traditional values which do still function as part of the deep structure of Indian lives have given rise to modifications necessitated by assimilation into the American mainstream. In the past, the men of the Omaha, Winnebago and Lakota-speaking groups won prestige and respect by participating in war activities. One had to perform a great deed or count coup to become initiated into certain societies. These societies still exist in altered forms but it is now the United States for which these Indian men fight. They have entered "our war arenas" to win "their honors."

Gourd dances are another version of Indian "doings," but these gatherings are sponsored by the Tia-Piah Society to which a person must be initiated. Other tribes have Tia-Piah Societies, but the Omaha tribe was given the gift of the gourd dance in April of 1970 by Kiowa friends. A large celebration accompanied this gift. The Tia-Piah Society is primarily a veterans' organization, although other men can be initiated after being screened and voted upon by the members. Among the Omaha people, it is the Sheridan family, now residing in Macy, who officiate at such gatherings; Clyde Sheridan (Macy) or Frank Sheridan (Lincoln) can be contacted for additional information regarding the Tia-Piah Society. Perhaps the most beautiful account of the form and meaning of public portions of the Tia-Piah has been written by the great Kiowa novelist, Scott Momaday (*Natural History*, February, 1975).

The religious societies which exist today are, as was explained earlier, a very private aspect of Native American culture. A description of the most important elements of Indian religions, elements which permeate all aspects of Indian life, can be found in the preceding chapter. For detailed information it is best to talk with individuals who might be willing, after a period of time, to discuss the subject in depth. One such group of individuals, the Rosebud Medicine Men's Association, recently visited UNL to discuss their traditional beliefs and answer questions for interested persons; a healing ceremony was also performed in the traditional manner with one peace pipe being offered symbolically for the whole group which had assembled to witness the ceremony. This association of medicine men was organized to prevent other Indian individuals, claiming to be medicine men, from distorting the facts about the activities of real medicine men. Association members, including Stanley Redbird (interpreter), Abel Stone (assistant medicine man), and Joe Eagle Elk (a medicine man), are articulate and very willing to discuss their ways in order to correct any misrepresentations that have been perpetrated by others. It should be added that their willingness to discuss the ways of medicine men and their religious beliefs is rare. A fair amount of controversy exists among Indian people as to whether or not these things should be discussed and displayed amidst non-Indians. It is possible to contact this association through Sinte Gleska, a community college in Rosebud, South Dakota. Also available through Sinte Gleska is a collection of videotaped materials concerning other religious ceremonies such as the Sun Dance, which was filmed in its entirety. [Sinte Gleska has a staff of 64, 80 percent of which are Indian, and a student population of several hundred, 90 percent of which are Indian; similar colleges exist at Winnebago, Santee, Macy and at Pine Ridge (Oglala Community College). Five different sorts of associate of arts degrees are offered to students attending this college.]

Among the Omaha tribe, the last knowledgeable medicine man, Charlie Parker, died last year. John Turner, an over-80-year-old Omaha who was raised by Little Chief, who was over 100 in 1922, does the traditional naming ceremony and preserves much of the deep philosophic knowledge of the people. Members of the Stabler family are allowed to perform certain ceremonies and rites. Charlie Stabler is frequently called upon to offer prayers at some "doings" and his son Lorenzo has also been taught these ways. According to traditional social structure, each gens or family was given the jurisdiction over certain ceremonies and this is still true today. If ceremonies are not passed on to the children, they cease to exist. Religious societies and religious leaders also exist on the Santee and Winnebago reservations, as well as in the Panhandle, each functioning in different ways. A listing of some of the societies can be found under the list of organizations belonging to United Indians of Nebraska.

One of the few Indian corporations in the state of Nebraska which deals in buying, selling and manufacturing genuine Indian crafts is the Eaglefeather Crafts Co-op in Chadron, Nebraska, headed by John Truax, an economic development specialist. The members of the co-op are Lakota Sioux Indians from northwestern Nebraska and southwestern South Dakota. Crafts such as beadwork, moccasins, war bonnets, head dresses, tom-toms, etc. are produced by local craftsmen. Mr. Truax has been most helpful in providing names of crafts people in the Panhandle and should be consulted for personal contacts. Officers in this organization include Cecelia Bartlett (Chadron), Mark Monroe (Alliance), and Victoria White (Crawford).

A bill which was considered by the state legislature this year, but was not passed, would have protected Indian crafts people by providing strict definitions as to what constitutes authentic Indian art and crafts. It would have encouraged quality control by prohibiting the sale of artificially manufactured products and Hong Kong junk as authentic craftsmanship. The passage of this bill, if coupled with the development of an Indian crafts guild, would have allowed Indian people to receive fair prices for quality work. Another program which is now being considered for funding has been proposed by Jean Black Elk, who is associated with the Lincoln Indian Center. The program would provide classes for individuals interested in learning to produce traditional crafts. It would also encompass the creation of a supply store and sales outlet for those crafts produced—similar to the co-op run by Mr. Truax.

One of the most easily accessible means of acquiring information is through contact with any of the urban Indian centers. These centers provide a broad spectrum of services and specific programs designed to meet the special needs of the urban Indian. There is a great need to provide additional funding for programs that have been designed. Currently, funding is received from the federal government and private (mostly church) agencies. To date, funds have been used to develop such things as alcoholism programs, breakfast programs for grade school children, women's sewing clubs which produce traditional beadwork, ribbon shirts and shawls for use in pow-wows, etc. A list of these centers can be acquired by contacting United Indians of Nebraska in Omaha.

A wealth of work has been also done by Indian individuals in such areas as beadwork, ribbonwork, painting, drawing, woodcarving, traditional clothes design, language, storytelling, oral history and poetry or other forms of literature. Beadwork, ribbonwork and traditional clothes design are closely connected with the pow-wow and other celebrations and ceremonies mentioned earlier. Beadwork done in the Southern Great Plains style is more intricate in design and done in smaller blocks of patterning while beadwork done in the Northern Great Plains style can be identified by the brightly contrastive colors. The patterns are worked in larger spatial blocks and are more geometrical. Components of the traditional dance outfits for the Lakota tribe (northern style) include a hair roach made of porcupine or deer hair, two feathers, or one attached to the center of the roach, a breastplate of bone and a back bustle fashioned in a "U" or a circle and composed of natural feathers. The southern style "straight clothes" include leggings, bright ribbon shirts, bandoleers, fans and tail dancer sticks, a white handkerchief tied around the head and knotted in front, an otter trailer, yarn ties hanging from the belt to the knees and *no bustle*. The fancy dancers have two bustles—a back bustle and a neck bustle. A "Chief's outfit," consisting of a buckskin shirt, pants and war bonnet is worn only by old men or men of high status; though there are now no "chiefs," it is generally assumed that a man of 50 to 70 years of age who is influential can wear such an outfit.

Many middle-aged persons who were taught traditional arts by their parents are now beginning to gain skill in those areas and teach them to their children and friends. Although many names were collected during research on this catalogue, it would be impossible to include them all. In some cases, individuals who were contacted were very gracious in describing their work but asked not to be mentioned in this catalogue. Again, it is best to contact reservation tribal councils or urban Indian centers to compile a list of names. The following list has been compiled by tribes and indicates contacts or craftspeople possessing expertise in various areas:

Winnebago Resources

Beadwork, ribbonwork, painting, woodcarving, etc.

Tommy Walker, Rolland Rave, Emma DeCora, Allie Hunter, Helen Kelsey, Edna Snow, Agnes Whitebeaver, Viola LaPointe, Virginia

Free, Maggie Smith, Jim Frenchman, Marie Johnson, Delmar Free, Donna Vandall.

Language

Felix White, Sr., Harold Buchanan, Lucy and Pete Rave, Sam Tebo, Minnio Little Bear, Wilbur Sharpback, Johnny Painter, Allie Hunter, Mike Whitesnake.

Folkstory tellers

Felix White Sr., Art May (publishes folktale materials), Delmar Free, Harold Buchanan, Neola Walker, Mike Whitesnake. Many of the older versions of Winnebago stories were published by Paul Radin in his series of books on the Winnebago; however, many other stories and interpretations are not set down in books and give a perpetual freshness to the culture. A collection of "Foolish One" stories told by Felix White recently, and set down by Kathy Danker, awaits publication. [It should be noted that many men and women in Winnebago know the old stories, but are reluctant to tell them.]

Oral historians

Felix White Sr., Sam Tebo, Minnie Little Bear, Agnes Whitebeaver, Johnny Painter.

Poets

Richard Walker, Reuben Snake (Mr. Snake's poems have been fairly widely published in books and newspapers but need to be collected).

Singers of songs

Wilber Sharpback

Omaha Resources

Beadwork

Elizabeth Stabler, Carroll Stabler, Howard Wolfe, Carmie Stabler, Carol Parker, Jim Hamilton, Lillian Sheridan, Pansy Phillips,

Dorothy Jones, Robert Lasley, Pat Minard, Mrs. Oliver Saunsoci Sr., Enoch Robinson, Wade Miller.

Language

Elizabeth Stabler, Lillian and Clyde Sheridan, John and Suzette Turner. [Mrs. Stabler teaches an Omaha language class at the penitentiary; Mr. and Mrs. Sheridan teach a language class at the public school in Macy.]

Folkstory tellers and oral historians

John and Suzette Turner, Elizabeth and Charlie Stabler, Oliver Saunsoci Sr.

Poets

Frank Love, Enoch Robinson. A collection of traditional Omaha poems collected by Dorsey, La Flesch and others has been translated by Larry Evers and is awaiting publication by the Indian Intertribal Press (Macy and Winnebago).

Painters

Wade Miller

Flutemakers

Stabler family

Singers of songs

John and Suzette Turner

Teton Sioux Resources

Beadwork

Annie Douville, Victoria White, Susan White, Vincent Bad Heart Bull, Kenneth Red Owl, Bob Horse, Annie Keller, Pretty Boy, Charlie LaPlant.

Painters

> *Oscar Howe (Mr. Howe, who teaches at the University of South Dakota, is perhaps one of America's great painters. He came out of a Lakota Sioux tradition and paints in a mixed traditional cubistic style.)*

Language

> *Annie Keller, Joe American Horse, Perry Wounded Shield.*

Folkstory tellers

> *Fool's Bull, John Fire (Lame Deer).*

Poets

> *Elizabeth Cook (eastern Sioux), published in the **Prairie Schooner** and a variety of other journals; John Arbuckle (general Plains and Navajo), published in a variety of Indian and University of Nebraska publications.*

Flutemakers

> *Richard Fool's Bull, Rosebud.*

Santee Resources

Folkstory tellers and oral historians

> *Edna Peniska (Santee traditional stories have been taken down by Jean Neely from Edna Peniska. These are available from Intertribal Press [Macy and Winnebago]. Another version has been put together by Robert Frerichs [available from Paul Olson, 338 Andrews Hall, University of Nebraska-Lincoln]).*

Santee traditional culture sources

> *Victoria Hawk, Caroline LeRoy (Ponca), Paul Robertson, Albert Thomas, Walt Peniska.*

One of the problems of coming to know the Plains cultures, a problem which younger generations within those cultures have in coming to know their pasts, is that so little of the expressive culture of the Plains tribes is set down in a form which can be taken in by younger Indians and non-Indians using media conventionally used in schools and educational institutions. Though Omaha, Teton, and Winnebago musicians have been recorded, records are not easily available. Some records of Plains music are available from Indian House, Box 472, Taos, New Mexico; other useful records are listed in *Akwasasne Notes,* available through The Mohawk Nation, Rooseveltown, New York.

The opera, *Hanblecheya,* scheduled to tour in the fall, was written by Bill Wallis. The idea for this opera was conceived nearly three years ago and has finally taken shape. Al and Pat Menard, members from Sinte Gleska College, and other members of the Rosebud community have assisted in providing information for the libretto. Perry Wounded Shield has done extensive work on developing a Lakota version of the English libretto. This opera is aimed at providing an art form which encompasses the essence of the Lakota ceremony "crying for a vision" and will hopefully produce a deeper appreciation for the subtleties of Lakota culture. The libretto is accompanied by three essays dealing with the history of Lakota culture, Lakota music and Lakota literature. These materials will also provide the basis for numerous workshops in various public school systems. For more information, contact Bill Wallis at Centennial College at the University of Nebraska in Lincoln.

No decent collections of ancient *and* modern Teton Sioux or Santee or Omaha or Winnebago literature have been made, and their art and architecture have been treated piecemeal, either as an interesting 'archaism' or as part of modern art or architecture without reference to the specific cultural and historical tradition of craft from which it emerges. Indian art, architecture, music and poetry are commonly treated in absurdly ignorant ways by critics trained in the norms of the dominant culture; they are regarded as something which can be separated from the Indian sense of community, of the meaning of life, nature and culture which gave rise to the art of Plains people. No one thing can be separated from "everything else" in the world we are describing.

Three major Indian organizations which serve the state of Nebraska are as follows: United Indians of Nebraska, the Intertribal Development Corp., and the Nebraska State Indian Commission. UIN is a coalition of tribal, urban and rural Indian groups and organizations in Nebraska which strives to promote unity of action and increased channels of support for

Indian self-development programs and aspirations. It was first organized in 1973 and presently receives nearly all its funding from religious organizations. During its last three years of operation, UIN has grown and reorganized its guidelines. Originally it aided in dispensing church funds to Indian programs. On July 1, 1975, UIN became prime sponsor for the CETA program in the area of Indian employment opportunities. Currently, its membership is hoping to bring the organization to the point where it can generate, design, and administer its own programs which are viewed as beneficial to the Indian people of Nebraska. Jan Searcy, presently the executive director, works along with seven members of the executive board in making decisions. A list of UIN's membership organizations and addresses has been included below:

The Many Trails Club
204 South Potash
Alliance, Nebraska 69301

American Indian Council, Incorporated
303 South Potash, Box No. 61
Alliance, Nebraska 69301

American Indian Satellite
 Community College
801 East Benjamin Avenue
Norfolk, Nebraska 68701

Native American Spiritual & Cultural
 Awareness Group
P.O. Box 81248
Lincoln, Nebraska 68501

C.A.R.E., Incorporated
 (American Indian Half-Way House)
2412 Templeton Street
Omaha, Nebraska 68111

Indian Center Industries Association
 Incorporated
4436 Ames Avenue
Omaha, Nebraska 68111

Winnebago Alcohol Service Center, Inc.
Chee-Woy-Na-Zhee, Incorporated
P.O. Box 694
Winnebago, Nebraska 68071

The Native American Church,
 Omaha Tribal Chapter
R.R. 6, Florence Station
Omaha, Nebraska 68112

Indian-Chicano Health Clinic
2401 South 20th Street
Omaha, Nebraska 68108

The Indian Center, Incorporated
243 South 20th Street
Lincoln, Nebraska 68501

Native American Student Association
Chadron State College
Chadron, Nebraska 69337

Urban Indian Cultural Club, Inc.
1107 North 29th Street
Omaha, Nebraska 68131

Platte Valley Lakota Association
805 N Street
Gering, Nebraska 69341

Council of American Indian Students
University of Nebraska
Lincoln, Nebraska 68588

The Omaha Tribe of Nebraska
Macy, Nebraska 68039

The Santee Sioux Tribe of Nebraska
Niobrara, Nebraska 68760

The Winnebago Tribe of Nebraska
Winnebago, Nebraska 68071

American Indian Movement
Gordon, Nebraska 69343

The Flying Eagle Council
Box 186
Minatare, Nebraska 69356

Tia-Piah Society
2401 K Street
Lincoln, Nebraska 68508

Nebraska Indian Inter-Tribal
  Development Corporation
Box 328   1805 Avenue F
Winnebago, Nebraska 68071

Seven Council Indian Youth
  Organization

Scottsbluff, Nebraska 69361

Sheridan County Lakota Association, Inc.
P.O. Box 252
Gordon, Nebraska 69343

Eagle Feather Crafts, Inc.
P.O. Box 1047
Chadron, Nebraska 69337

Alliance United Lakotas, Inc.
216 Missouri
Alliance, Nebraska 69301

Sioux Indian Center, Inc.
4851 Redman Avenue
Omaha, Nebraska 68104

Nebraska American Indian League
Route 1
Box 33
York, Nebraska 68467

American Indians United
University of Nebraska at Omaha
c/o Ralph Preston, Minority Affairs
Administration Building
60th & Dodge Streets
Omaha, Nebraska 68132

The Nebraska Indian Inter-Tribal Development Corporation contracts with the state of Nebraska for economic development grants. Art May is the executive director of the Inter-Tribal Corp. and is assisted by Louis LaRose, who is the chairman of the board. At this time, Inter-Tribal Development Corp. is responsible for projects such as a small publishing outlet, a woodland improvement project, reservation economic development work, and reservation improvement projects. Either May or LaRose can be contacted for information (May is at Macy; LaRose at Winnebago).

The purpose of the Nebraska Indian Commission is to "enhance the cause of Indian rights and to develop solutions to problems common to all Nebraska Indians." Specifically, the Commission must oversee and coordinate programs within the Indian communities, maintain communication with the Governor's office regarding the situation in these communities, educate the public concerning Indian welfare, develop comprehensive programs which will involve Indian peoples in their communities. Fifteen members comprise the Commission, with nine members constituting a quorum. A soon-to-be-named director, or Carol Spica, the secretary, can be contacted in Lincoln (1343 M Street—402-471-2757) for information. Very recently, LB 174 was passed which sets up new guidelines relating to the Commission on Indian Affairs. This bill provides information concerning changes which are being undertaken in the Commission structure.

Finally, there is an extensive network of programs in each reservation area to provide health and educational services for Indian people. For information concerning specific questions one might have, it is possible to contact any of the following resource persons:

Winnebago

Education

> *Terry Walters—Director: Office of Educational Services*
> *John Vandall—Education Director*
> *Neola Walker—Director: Adult Education, tribal council member*
> *Louis LaRose—Satellite Community College, Director*
> *Art May—CETA Counselor, Inter-tribal Development Corporation*
> *Louis Malinowski—vocational and employment assistance, BIA*
> *Gene Kennedy—Truant Officer*
> *Jim Snow—Johnson-O'Malley*
> *Jack Brightman—Upward Bound Program*
> *Rick Thomas—Upward Bound Program*
> *Laura Whitewing—Upward Bound Program*
> *Dorothy Holstein—Title IV Director*
> *Roberta Hall—Winnebago Pubblic Schools*
> *Berry Ballard—Counselor, Winnebago Public Schools*
> *Mr. Peneski—Superintendent*
> *Tana Lowry—Office of Educational Services*
> *Felix White Sr.—teaches language and folklore courses*
> *Naomi Thomas—library*
> *Gordon Beaver—State Employment*

Health

> *Nikki Soloman-Community Health Representative*
> *Norman Free-Emergency Medical Technicians and Ambulance*
> *   Service*
> *Lydia Free-Community Health Nurse, R.N.*

Betty Scott-CHR; Indians Into Medicine
Dolph Baptiste-Administrator, hospital
Carmine Tyndall-Women, Infants, Children (WIC)-hospital
Monte Smith-Director of Alcoholic Services

Macy

Health and Education

Loretta Mickel-Superintendent
Alfred (Buddy) Gilpin-Tribal Agency Director
Winona Porter-Tribal Educational Services
Eddie Cline-Tribal Chairman
Wayne and Pauline Tyndall-CHR (education also)
Clifford Cayou
Louis Provost Sr.-Tribal Council
Louis Provost Jr.-ICAP

Santee

Health and Education

Jim James-Tribal planner
Diane LaPointe-Community Services
Roger Trudell-CETA Counselor
Albert Thomas
Clemmet Mackey-Norfolk (resource person on above subjects)
Bob Mackey-Lincoln (resource person)
David Davies-home-school coordinator

The services and specialized information in health and education provided by urban Indian centers would be too complex to list here and may be discovered by contacting the persons noted in the UIN list previously mentioned in this catalogue.

Histories and Museums

The Nebraska State Historical Society is a depository for the most substantive collections pertaining to Plains Indian culture and history in this area. Some of Nebraska's county historical societies also have small

collections, but many of the collections have at some point been transferred to the State Historical Society and Museum. There are several areas
which should be surveyed by any individual hoping to get information
regarding Indian history: the museum, the state library, the photograph
room, the archaeology department and the archives. The library possesses
an extensive catalogue of literature. For assistance in obtaining volumes
concerning certain subjects, consult Ann Reinert, the librarian. Wendall
Frantz, curator of the museums, can provide assistance in describing the
extent of the state's primary exhibits. The archives contain a catalogue of
federal records which include agency reports from many of the old forts
which participated actively in the Indian wars. The Fort Laramie, Fort
McPherson, Fort Robinson, Fort Randall, Fort Sidney, and Fort Niobrara
materials contain a considerable amount of information about Indian activities in this state. The archives also possess the United States Bureau of
Indian Affairs collection consisting of letters received and sent by the BIA.
"This collection relates to the United States Government's administration
of Indian affairs, to the relations of Indians with white traders, settlers,
soldiers, and to inter-tribal relations. The documents are important in
studies of Indian economy and culture as affected by white settlement,
of the history of various tribes and of regional and Nebraska history "
(Federal Records Catalogue).

Two other portions of archival materials to be looked at would be
the United States War Department collection, which consists of 83 rolls of
microfilm pertaining to military affairs in Nebraska, and the United States
Surveyor General reports of land purchases and treaty violations.

The photograph room has catalogued a massive amount of photographs of Indian individuals and their artifacts, etc. The main categories
include a miscellaneous collection, as well as collections of Cheyenne,
Dakota Sioux, Omaha, Pawnee, Oto, Ponca, and Winnebago photographs.
Private materials such as the Anderson, Rinehart, Ricker, Simons, Tanner,
and Jeambey collections should also be consulted. Several books which
contain many of the better photographs from the above-mentioned collections can be found in the photo room and are as follows: *Historic
Indian Portraits* by Bill and Verla Rieske, *The Sioux of the Rosebud* by
Henry W. Hamilton and Jean Tyree, and *Brule* by Paul Dyck.

Dick Jensen is in charge of the anthropology and artifacts division
at the Historical Society and is well versed on all the archaeological sites
which have been recorded and studied. These sites number approximately
1,527. Articles generated by the artifacts housed at the Historical Society
appear in the *Nebraska History* magazine. One should also consult the

Index Guide to the contents of the publications 1885-1956 and the magazine of the Nebraska State Historical Society 1918-1956.

Letters were sent to all Nebraska County Historical Societies and the following societies contacted us to say that their organization possessed some artifacts or archival materials: The Museum of the Fur Trade (Chadron), Saline County Historical Society (Dorchester), and the Fort Robinson Museum (Crawford). Obviously many of the Nebraska tribes or tribes formerly in Nebraska have many of their precious belongings, sacred articles, and oral histories scattered in collections in South Dakota and Oklahoma and in the Peabody Museum at Harvard. One would hope that the time would come when the people would own these things themselves and be able to use them in nation building.

Addendum

The following people at the Nebraska State Penitentiary are seriously exploring Indian traditions as artists: Dan Lincoln, Melvin White Magpie, Perry Wounded Shield, Robert Lassik, Marla Spears, Tom Knutson, Freddie Grant and Prentiss Grant. Poets are Tom Knutson and Freddie Grant.

II

Chicanos: The Mestizo Heritage

By Ralph F. Grajeda

ACKNOWLEDGMENTS

This essay could not have been written without the cooperation
and the help of many people throughout the state. To all of
them I am deeply grateful. To "the old ones," in particular, am
I indebted. With gracious hospitality they opened their homes
to me; they shared their coffee and their *pan dulce;* and they
patiently and generously spoke to me about their experiences
and their lives.

NOTA DE AGRADECIMIENTO

*Este ensayo no hubiera sido posible sin la cooperación y la
ayuda de muchísimas personas de todas partes del estado. Por
el apoyo que me prestaron, estoy agradecido. Con los ancianos,
en particular, me siento endeudado. Me abrieron sus puertas
con bandadosa hospitalidad; compartieron de su café y pan
dulce; y con bastante paciencia y generosidad me contaron de
sus experiencias y sus vidas.*

This three-room adobe house, located at 808 14th Avenue, Scottsbluff, is one of many similar houses built in the colonia during the 1920's by Mexican beet workers. It was constructed in 1924 by Senor Santos Castaneda with the help of six friends, and was the only one having a slanted roof.

The old ones furnished the author with much of the history in this essay.

Mexicans on a train being transported to Nebraska to work in the sugar beet fields during the 1920's. They are listening to a lecture in Spanish on hoeing and thinning beets. (Courtesy of the Nebraska State Historical Society, Lincoln.)

Upper. Union Pacific Railroad work crew. *Lower.* Early depot. Notice the tents by the tracks. Many of these tent communities became permanent sites of present-day Mexican colonias. (Courtesy of the Nebraska State Historical Society, Lincoln.)

Upper. Another of the old ones at her craft.

Lower. Mexican needle-crafted table mat woven out of Maguey plant fiber. (Courtesy of University of Nebraska State Museum. Photograph by Roger Rejda.)

Right. Light brown clay statue of Our Lady of Guadalupe, patron saint of Mexico. The Virgin of Guadalupe continues to be extremely important in the lives of Mexican Americans in the state. (Courtesy of University of Nebraska State Museum. Photograph by Roger Rejda.)

Above. Ancient fresco from Temple of Agriculture, Teotihuacan (200 B.C.-250 A.D.) shows people taking part in an offering ceremony to Tlaloc, God of Rain.

Below. Teotihuacan. The famous Temple of Quetzalcoatl, Pre-Columbian Mexican god and cultural hero. Serpent heads decorate the facade.

Facade of Lermas' Cafe in Lyman, Nebraska. The paintings were done by members of the family, and clearly show Pre-Columbian and modern Mexican influences.

Below. Members of The Mexican Culture Development Dance Group, Scottsbluff. (Courtesy of *Scottsbluff Star Herald.*)

Above, opposite page. Mosaic mural by the Mexican painter, Francisco Eppens Helguera, School of Medicine, University City, Mexico City. The triple-faced mask represents the ancestral heritage of the modern Mexican and Mexican American. The Spaniard as Father is shown on the right; the Mexican Indian as Mother is on the left; the full face is that of a Mexican mestizo, representing the Son.

Above. Sally Ybarra Dittmar, Director of The Mexican Culture Development Dance Group.

Below. Carmen Montanez Parks, Director of The Guadalupe Dancers.

Above. A member of The Guadalupe Dancers, waiting during rehearsal.

II

Chicanos: The Mestizo Heritage

By Ralph Grajeda

The first Europeans to set foot on the Great Plains were the Spanish soldiers under Francisco Vásquez de Coronado, who in April of 1541 marched eastward from the Rio Grande in search of the fabulous gold-rich kingdom of Quivira at almost the same time that Hernando de Soto was seeing the Mississippi for the first time.

One year earlier, in July of 1540, Coronado, with an army of 225 Spanish mounted men, 62 footmen,[1] and 1000 Indians, had been bitterly disappointed in his quest for the Seven Cities of Cíbola. Expecting to find the legendary Seven Cities of pure gold, he found instead poor Pueblo Indian villages of red stone and adobe (the present Zuñi, New Mexico). That during the same expedition the army discovered the Grand Canyon of the Colorado and the Continental Divide near present-day Grants, New Mexico, was meager compensation for the disappointment of finding mud where gold was expected. Through his contact with the Pueblo Indians, however, Coronado met a slave of the Pueblos whom he called "El Turco" (the Turk), "because he looked like one." El Turco, probably a Pawnee Indian, told Coronado about the existence of a fabulously rich kingdom to the east: Quivira. Quivira, he said, was his homeland. Beyond Quivira

> There was a river . . . two leagues wide, in which the fish were as big as the horses of the Spanish cavalry. On the river the

natives propelled large canoes, with figureheads of eagles made
of gold; twenty oarsmen to a side rowed with their sweeps in
oarlocks of gold; and the boats also carried sails. If a chief
went by boat, he would sit in state on the poop, sheltered by
awnings. Tatarrax, the gray-bearded king of the country, took
his afternoon siesta under a great tree hung with little gold
bells which lulled him by their music as they swung in the air.
He was so mighty that he went out to war borne in a litter,
and overcame his enemies merely by unleashing huge grey-
hounds that tore his foes to pieces. This king prayed before a
cross and the image of a lady, the goddess of heaven. The
palace doorways were hung with blankets. The lowliest servants there ate from plates of wrought metal, and the jugs and
bowls were of gold.[2]

Lured by El Turco's iridescent description of this new
Eldorado, Coronado headed east toward Quivira in late April,
1541. Because supplies were scarce and because of damage
suffered in a hailstorm, Coronado sent back all of his army but
30 mounted men (his "Chosen Thirty"), and six footmen, with
whom he pressed on, travelling through the Texas and Oklahoma panhandles, through southern Kansas and crossing the
Arkansas River in the vicinity of present-day Dodge City,
Kansas. Eighty miles to the northwest (present-day town of
Great Bend), Coronado found the first of the Quivira villages.
And, as with the Seven Cities of Cíbola, a far cry this Quivira
was from that fantastic kingdom which El Turco had described.
Coronado found no gold-domed capitals, no king Tatarrax, no
great river with giant fishes, but instead a table-flat, wind-
swept region with straw-thatched mud huts. From these primi-
tive huts he was greeted by tatooed and nearly naked Wichita
Indians.[3] Some of Coronado's disappointment can be seen in
his letter to the King of Spain, October 20, 1541. "It was the
Lord's pleasure," he wrote:

> that, after having journeyed across these deserts seventy-
> seven days, I arrived at the province they call Quivira. . . . Not
> only are [the houses] not of stone, but of straw . . . the people
> in them are as barbarous as all those whom I have seen and

passed before this. . . . I remained twenty-five days in this
province of Quivira, so as to see and explore the country and
also to find out whether there was anything beyond which
could be of service to Your Majesty, because the guides who
had brought me had given me an account of other provinces
beyond this. And what I am sure of is that there is not any
gold nor any other metal in all that country, and the other
things of which they had told me are nothing but little villages,
and in many of these they do not plant anything and do not
have any houses except of skins and sticks, and they wander
around with the cows. . . .[4]

Coronado had El Turco strangled for lying, and after
spending 25 days in Quivira, led his tired and disappointed
Chosen Thirty back to the main army at Tiguex on the Rio
Grande, and then finally back to Mexico City. A defeated and
heartsick man, Coronado had no way of knowing that, though
he had not found the riches he sought, his expedition—as a 19th
century historian wrote—"for extent in distance traveled, dura-
tion in time, extending from the spring of 1540 to the summer
of 1542, and the multiplicity of its cooperating branch explorations, it equaled, if it did not exceed, any land expedition that
has been undertaken in modern times."[5]

Some early Nebraska historians placed Quivira within the
boundaries of the present state. Others conjecture that
Coronado marched further north than present-day Great Bend,
to Junction City, to Manhattan, and even approaching the 40th
degree latitude (present-day boundary between Kansas and
Nebraska). Kansas tradition locates Quivira near Coronado
Heights, a recreation area near the Swedish settlement of Lindsborg, Kansas. Close to Lindsborg, in the Rice County Courthouse at Lyons, Kansas, is exhibited a carved representation of
Coronado's helmeted conquistadores and Catholic missionaries.
One display case contains an artifact of questionable historical
validity: "The Coronado Stone," measuring twenty inches long
and twelve inches wide, which a farmer claims to have found in
1941; the stone has inscribed in Spanish the date of August 3,
1541. At the courthouse are also displayed bits of metal, which

Smithsonian archaeologists contend could have been chainmail links belonging to members of the Coronado expedition. In 1965-1966, Smithsonian experts examined thirty Rice County sites and identified them as one time being Quiviran Basket Maker villages. According to these archeologists, the Quivirans raised corn, used clay pots, and had other similarities to the Pueblo culture of the Upper Rio Grande.[6]

Modern scholarship hence locates Coronado's Quivira somewhere in central Kansas. In Nebraska, however, the early traditional view of Quivira is maintained by the Knights of Ak-Sar-Ben in Omaha, who in the most elaborate social display of pomp and circumstance in the state, crown the "King and Queen of Quivira" during the fall of every year.

Except as a historical curiosity, the exact location of Quivira is of slight importance. The greater significance of Coronado's explorations is that for the first time it revealed the Central Plains to white men—an historical occurrence starting 17th and 18th century explorations by Spaniards and Frenchmen and consequent settlement by what Robert G. Simmons—former Chief Justice of the Nebraska State Supreme Court—has called "the first Americans [who came] in exploration of this area."[7] This group of settlers, as a Nebraska historian has written, were "a shrewder if not a juster race . . . who were able to discern the true and inexhaustible body of gold hidden in the dull-hued soil."[8] The further consequent significance of Coronado's explorations of the Plains, of course, spelled a tragic destiny for the people already inhabiting the region: the Great Plains Native Americans.

A painting done by Ben Carlton Mead, now owned by the Panhandle-Plains Historical Society, shows Coronado and his Chosen Thirty at Palo Duro Canyon of the Red River in the Texas Panhandle. There, Coronado sits atop a majestic-looking white horse in full plume and armor, visibly at ease with the power and authority which he represents. A banner waves grandly behind and above Coronado's helmet, and three armed Spanish soldiers stand to his front and right. Directly in front of Coronado's white horse kneels a Catholic missionary at a rock, with hands at prayer as he looks in the direction of a young, loin-clothed Indian who stands with outstretched arms looking out into the distance away from Coronado, away from the missionary and the soldiers. Coronado's gaze goes out over and beyond the Indian's head, as his left hand naturally grips the sword hanging at his waist—naturally, as if there were no other place for that hand.

There were later Spanish entrances into the Central Plains, but these were confined to countermoves during the 18th century against the French who were making encroachments into territory claimed for the Spanish Crown. Not until the first part of the 20th century did the Spanish-speaking people again enter the Central Plains. This time the principals were not Spaniards but Mexicans—not whites but *mestizos* (people of mixed Spanish and Indian blood); not *conquistadores* but *peones* (members of the dispossessed Mexican working class); not adventurers in search of fabulous treasures, but humble people desperate for jobs that would enable them to survive.

It is more than a curiosity of history that the two entrances into the Central Plains by the Spanish-speaking people were so strikingly dissimilar. After Coronado's penetration in 1541, the Spanish-speaking people did not appear in the region in great numbers until approximately 370 years later, during the first decade of the 20th century. If Coronado's expedition speaks loudly of 16th century Spanish power and authority, the succeeding re-entrance of Spanish-speaking people speaks equally as loud of deprivation, poverty, and want. That the original explorers of the Central Plains were Spanish *conquistadores,* and the later immigrants were Mexican *mestizos,* is—in its irony—further instructive, for the very conditions of the poor in Mexico—those conditions which to a large degree "pushed" these people to the north—can be traced to the conquest and later colonization of that country by the very same *conquistadores.*

20th Century Mexican Immigration to the Central Plains

The history of the Mexican in what is now the United

States of America is unique among the various peoples who
have immigrated to this country. In a sense it can be said that
the first Mexicans did not come to this country, but that this
country came to the Mexicans. The United States, through its
war with Mexico, extended its boundaries in 1848 to include a
territory almost the size of present-day Mexico, in which lived
approximately 100,000 Spanish-speaking people—most of them
in the five southwestern states: Texas, Arizona, New Mexico,
California, and Colorado.

The majority of Mexican Americans living today in the
Midwest, however, are descendants of parents and grandparents
who were part of two massive migration waves occurring since
1900: the first from 1900 to 1920, the second from 1920 to
1930. One scholar estimates that between 1900 and 1920, the
number of Mexicans immigrating to the United States equalled
one tenth of the total population of Mexico.[9]

Of the more than nine million Mexicans and Mexican
Americans in the United States, between 1.5 and 1.6 million
live in the ten midwestern states. In 1960, for example, there
were approximately 500,000 Mexicans and other Spanish-
speaking people in Chicago, 50,000 in Detroit, 10,000 in
Minneapolis-St. Paul, 10,000 in Lansing, 40,000 in East
Chicago, Indiana and 20,000 in Kansas City (Kansas and Missouri). According to the 1970 census figures, there are approximately 130,000 Mexican Americans residing in Nebraska and
its neighboring states (50,425 in Kansas, 34,320 in Missouri,
18,295 in Iowa, and 28,680 in Nebraska).[10] Of these numbers,
a substantial part (perhaps more than one half), are second or
third generation midwestern families. Some of these families
and individuals have settled in the area within the last twenty
years, but the majority arrived and settled during the first three
decades of this century. They have played a major role in the
economic development of the Plains states, particularly in the
agricultural, railroad, and meat-processing industries.

Very few Mexicans lived in the Central Plains states prior
to 1900. According to an early study of Mexican immigration
to the United States, there were only 71 Mexicans living in

Kansas in 1900, 27 Mexicans in Nebraska. By 1910 the Mexican immigrant population had increased enormously in Kansas to 9,429, and 3,611 in Nebraska.[11] This growth in population can be understood in light of far-reaching and complementary changes occurring in both Mexico and the United States. In one country these changes "pushed" people out; in the other, the changes "pulled" them in.

The Porfirio Díaz dictatorship in Mexico (a period of rule that lasted 31 years, 27 of them consecutively) did bring about peace, prosperity and opportunity, but only for a select few—and that at the expense of the peasants. Under the Díaz regime the 19th century agrarian reform movement to destroy the feudal pattern of Mexican landholding was in fact reversed. By 1910 more than 90 percent of the villages in heavily populated areas of the country and the central plateau had lost their land. The *hacienda* system was extended and institutionalized by the absorption of village lands and concessions of public domain to those few individuals within the privileged circle around the President. Debt peonage, supported by outrageously low wages of from 12 to 18 cents daily—usually paid in kind, token, or credit through the *"tienda de raya"* (hacienda store)—supported these huge land holdings.

At the end of the Díaz regime in 1910, probably less than 3 percent of the total rural population owned any land at all. There were 834 *hacendados* (land owners) and approximately nine million landless peasants living under a miserable debt peonage. Of the 834 *hacendados,* fifteen owned more than 100,000 acres each; the *hacienda* of San Blas in the state of Coahuila, for example, contained almost a million acres. Despite higher prices of basic necessities, the income of the peon in 1910 was about the same as a hundred years earlier. The conditions of life for the peon at an *hacienda* are described in the following passage:

> A typical large hacienda centered on the hacendado's mansion—composed frequently of an enormous dining room, numerous bedrooms and bathrooms, a study, a giant kitchen, a

luxuriously furnished living room, a billiards room. Ample lighting, hot and cold running water, and beautiful flower gardens were among its features. Nearby was a modestly furnished house for the general manager, smaller houses for employees of confidence, a general office-supply-equipment shed, a church, a jail, a "tienda de raya" (hacienda store) that sold basic necessities to the peon and kept him in perpetual debt peonage, and at a distance of a quarter or a half mile from the rest of the buildings, the huts of the peons. The huts were usually one-room shacks made of adobe, without windows, lamps, beds, or running water; the peon and his big family cooked, ate, and slept in one small, dirt-floored room. In addition, some haciendas provided a small shack to be used as a schoolroom and for the conduct of civic affairs. The contrast between mansion and hut—between the life of the hacendado and administrator on the one hand and the peon on the other—bore heavily on the peasant as he daily entered the fields before sunrise and returned at sunset. To the peon, justice meant the unquestioned word of hacendado, administrator, jailor, and priest. And if the overlord needed assistance in keeping his peons in line, he simply called upon Díaz's rural shock-troopers. The poverty-stricken peasant had no hope of a better tomorrow, no promise of somehow raising himself from his deplorable status.[12]

Rural areas were particularly affected. Health conditions were intolerable, with high incidence of enteritis, pneumonia, malaria, and venereal disease. Education in rural areas was practically non-existent: in 1895, 86 percent of the population was unable to read or write. By 1910, four out of every five persons were still illiterate.

The powerful event in Mexico which pushed people to the north was, of course, the Mexican Revolution, which during the period of 1910 to 1920 caused an extraordinary amount of suffering, upheavel and confusion. Causes of revolution are always multiple and complex. As these causes are distilled to the daily life conditions of common people, however, they reduce themselves to simple and pronounced suffering. Mexicans in Nebraska remember with pain the experiences of this period in Mexico prior to their immigration to the United States.

A resident of western Nebraska, who was twelve years old when the Revolution started in 1910, remembers the hunger suffered by his family and the rest of the people in his village. Appropriately enough, he says, "Pasó la guerra civíl sobre mí" (the civil war passed over me). "The war did not come very close because of the hunger in our village. Soldiers would pass, and pass, and pass through there, where we lived; but they would not remain." Asked whether the villagers sympathized with the government troops or with the revolutionaries, he answers:

> No, there, there were neither revolutionaries nor *federales*, only people dying of hunger. There was nothing to gather, nothing grew. Everything was in ruins. We would harvest a little bit of cane. We would eat it, and the earth was left bald. . . . Much hunger. . . . It came to a point where I ate raw alfalfa.

A lady, also from western Nebraska, remembers the arrival of the government soldiers to her village:

> I was recently married. When they arrived they would take the young men [as recruits to fight on the government side]. Yes, by force. They would take the boys. My in-laws were outside. They asked them if there were any young men; and they told them "No." I was about the same age as my in-laws' daughters. There were two of them. My father-in-law was afraid that the soldiers might commit some harm against us. They hid us in the cellar for nine days. For nine days! So much that the people had to suffer! Well, my mother-in-law would take us water and some tortillas at night. My mother-in-law made food for them. She was used to regrinding the corn, and making the tortillas nice and thin to eat. But they hollered and ordered so much that she made the tortillas fat for them, without regrinding the corn. Later on, she would say, "I made fat tortillas. And I served them with anger."

A man who is among the early immigrant arrivals in Scottsbluff says:

Yes, yes, how can I not remember the Revolution. I was sixteen when the war started. That is why we came over here. It was ugly. There were times then when even the food would lose its taste in one's mouth. Where we lived [in the state of Guanajuato] it was large, what they call "haciendas." Many people. Well, you know, all went hungry. Some, those who did not die, left. The hunger forced them out. And there were left only seven families. . . . No, well, we didn't leave. And then they sacked the hacienda, burned it and committed barbarities. You should have seen it. A horrible thing! The people, you would see them one day and they would leave during the night. In the morning they would no longer be there. Well, the hunger would make them go.

We were like share-croppers—half for the man who put up the land, and half for us who put up the seed and the labor. Afterwards, another man rented the hacienda—he was very rich. . . . This man said he would provide nothing but the land. [He told us] "you are going to provide the animals, the seed, and everything; and I am going to provide nothing. But I'm going to give you two parts, and I will get one." . . . When the government people would come, they would take everything. But when the revolutionaries came—"bandits," they called them. Well, I don't know, because when these people came they would take everything that belonged to the hacienda. Like with us, they did it by rows. [They would ask us] "How are you splitting the crops here?" [We answered] "Well, the owner gave us two parts and one is for him." Well, that part, the owner's, they took. They did it by rows. Every third row of corn, they took. And the owner didn't get anything—what was his share. But the government soldiers would arrive and get into the houses where they would search the trunks and turn everything upside-down. And you see, that was the government, the government that was still in. They would dig to see if they could find money. . . . Finally, I told my father that if we didn't leave that place we too were going to die. He didn't want to. But he did. That was in 1916. We sold the few animals we owned, and we all left for the United States.

Another long-time resident of Nebraska, a Tarascan Indian who fought in the Revolution for three years before coming to the United States, remembers one battle:

> Ugly! One attack that I saw, the bloodiest, was the one
> of the Eleven Towns. That is close to Zamora. It's eleven
> towns joined together; for example, this corner is Santo
> Tomás, the next is Ixtlán, Tonaco, Tanaquillo, and like that.
> Eleven towns. Eeeeh, there we started! At three in the morn-
> ing. At five in the afternoon the killing stopped. Blood ran
> there like water runs after it rains, as much blood of animals
> as of people.
>
> There were about 2,000 revolutionaries there, a general
> barracks, concentrated ready to attack our town, Cherán
> [Michoacan]. And when the coronel received the message to
> get out, instead of the government troops fighting back, he
> sent us to attack all those people in the barracks. We were
> volunteers; they called us "soldados sin cuartel" [irregulars].
> We weren't many, about 300—from Paracho, Arantepaqua,
> Cherán, and other places. For the people who were at the
> barracks, we were not many. Well we started. But we knew the
> terrain, see? The mountains and everything. We crossed and
> left the horses on the hill, and entered on foot. There was a
> plain like this one—a pretty plain. There is where those towns
> are. There, I was part of the advance troop. We started the
> shooting at the very door of the barracks. Yes. Some were
> gambling, others sleeping, others drunk, others singing—well,
> you know, like people do. When the shooting began, you
> know, we were so few. It seemed that we were many. People
> died there. . . . I did not see another battle so large or so ugly
> as that one. Well, I tell you, from three in the morning until
> five in the afternoon! So much blood! Ugly! That was in 1917.

The major attracting force that "pulled" the Mexican immigrant to the north was the economic development in the
southwestern part of the United States at this same time, and
its corresponding need for cheap labor. The latter part of the
19th century saw the dramatic growth of agriculture enterprises
and railroad construction in the Southwest. Demands of New
England cotton mills, New York garment manufacturers, and
the export market spurred cotton growing in Texas in this

period. The Reclamation Act of 1902 and the construction in 1904 of the St. Louis, Brownsville, and Mexican Railways encouraged ranchers in the lower Rio Grande Valley to make use of federal monies for the creation of huge irrigation projects to grow table vegetable crops that could be shipped to large metropolitan areas on the new railroads' refrigerator cars.[13]

Also in 1897 the U.S. Congress imposed a 75 percent tax on importation of foreign sugar, thus encouraging the development of the U.S. sugar beet industry. Hence, by 1906, sugar beet acreage in the U.S. had more than tripled from the 135,000 acres planted in 1900. By 1920 that acreage had increased to 872,000 acres, with the Great Plains region (which includes the North Platte Valley in Wyoming and western Nebraska) producing 64 percent of the total crop grown in the U.S. From 1923 to 1932 Nebraska ranked second in the U.S., behind Colorado, in annual sugar beet acreage (74,000 acres), and first in the nation in yield per acre (12.7 tons).[14] These developments made for an increased need for agricultural laborers at a time when the traditional sources of cheap labor in Asia and Europe were drying up. The Chinese Exclusion Act of 1882, and the Japanese immigration cut-off in 1907, forced the economic interests to look south for workers. Many Mexicans entered the U.S. at this time on their own initiative. Many more were actively recruited by Southwest farmers and other economic interests. Many Mexicans entered illegally, encouraged by economic interests, in violation of Congressionally imposed prohibitions.

The first of the Mexican railroad sections hands responded to railroad recruitors and crossed the border at El Paso in 1900. Living in boxcars, they began to establish small boxcar and tent communities that since then have become the community *barrios* throughout the Southwest and the Midwest. By 1906 several carloads of workers a week were moving into southern California, establishing colonies, and then reloading for movement to locations in Colorado, Wyoming, Utah, Idaho, Oregon, Kansas and Nebraska. In 1908, 16,000 Mexicans were recruited in El Paso alone for railroad work.

By 1910, 2,000 every month were crossing the border for railroad work.[15]

A large percentage of Mexicans and Mexican Americans living today in Nebraska came, in fact, as railroad workers for the Union Pacific and the Burlington, through Kansas City. Across the breadth of the state—Sidney, Scottsbluff, Ogallala, North Platte, Kearney, Grand Island, Lincoln and Omaha—one can still find Mexicans who at one time or another worked as railroad section hands. Others came to the slaughter and meatpacking houses in Omaha. According to the 1920 census figures, there were 682 Mexicans in Omaha—in 1923 about 1,000. They lived in South Omaha, congregated near the three packinghouses.[16]

Still others, particularly in the western part of the state, began to work in the sugar beet fields around 1914, more than a decade after original experimentation with the raising of sugar beets by the University of Nebraska in Hall County. In 1905 there were only 250 acres of sugar beets in the entire North Platte Valley. In 1908 the Great Western Sugar Company started raising beets in this part of the state, and in just two years the increase in acreage warranted the building of a factory; it was at this time that the Ames, Nebraska, factory was moved to Scottsbluff and enlarged.[17] Since then, Scotts Bluff County has been the top sugar-beet producing county in Nebraska.

Initially, German-Russians were used as laborers in the beet fields of Colorado and Nebraska. German-Russian families (from Grand Island, Lincoln, Omaha, and Hastings) were, in fact, transported into beet growing areas. Japanese immigrants were also used as beet field hands. These sources of labor, however, began to disappear as the German-Russians and Japanese began to move to other jobs or became farm owners and tenants. Also, 1907 saw the cut-off of Japanese immigration to the U.S.; and the outbreak of World War I in 1914 stopped the flow of German-Russian immigration.[18] The results of these occurrences were later reflected in the changed nationalities of laborers shipped in by the Great Western Sugar Company. The development of the sugar beet industry in the western part of the state—with its concomitant need for field labor—assuredly helps to explain the concentration of Mexican Americans in that area.

Many of these workers came originally to the North Platte Valley as railroad hands, then, for a variety of reasons, changed jobs as more and more field work became available. After 1920, many came unassisted as *betabeleros* (beet workers). Many more (particularly after 1916) were recruited to work in the fields by the Great Western Sugar Company. In 1915, the Great Western Sugar Company recruited and transported 500 workers into its Colorado, Wyoming, Montana, and Nebraska sugar beet territory. By 1920 this figure had jumped to more than 13,000. In 1926, for example, the Great Western provided transportation for 14,500 persons, employed 55 labor agents (20 full-time for three months, 35 part-time), and sent out advertising materials consisting of 8,000 booklets in Spanish, 1,000 cardboard posters, 2,000 hand bills, 5,000 calendars, and advertisements in fifteen newspapers.[19]

In Scottsbluff, a community has grown up near the Great Western Sugar refinery, on land formerly owned by the Great Western and later sold to individual families. To this day that area remains the Mexican American *barrio* in that city, bordered on the north by East Overland Drive, and on the south by South Beltline Road between 5th and 15th Avenues.

Few of these workers came to Nebraska directly from Mexico. The majority came through Kansas, others from Texas, from Wyoming, from Oklahoma, New Mexico and Arizona. The reason for that enormous Mexican immigrant population growth in Kansas—from 71 persons in 1900 to 9,429 in 1910—is because, as a Nebraskan explains, *"Kianses era como vereda para el mexicano"* (Kansas was like a passageway for the Mexican moving north). Kansas City probably served as a temporary stopover and as a distribution center for Mexican workers looking for jobs in the eastern and midwestern states. Various *corridos* (Mexican folk ballads) mention Kansas or Kansas City as destination points or as stopovers for the people's movement to the north. *"Los Reenganchados a Kianses"* tells of the train ride, the treatment of the Mexican, and his strong nationalism expressed through his reaction to "this thing called union":

LOS REENGANCHADOS A KIANSES	CONTRACTED TO KANSAS
Un día tres de septiembre Ay, ¡qué día tan señaldo! Que salimos de Laredo Para Kianses reenganchados.	One day the third of September Oh, what an unusual day! We left Laredo Signed up for Kansas.
Cuando salimos de Laredo Me encomendé al Santo Fuerte, Porque iba de contrabando Por ese lado del puente.	When we left Laredo I committed myself to the strong saint, Because I was travelling illegally On that side of the bridge.
Uno de mis compañeros Gritaba muy afando: "Ya nos vamos reenganchados A trabajar al contado."	One of my companions Shouted very excitedly: "Now we are going under contract To work for cash."
Corre, corre, maquinita, Por esa línea del Quiri Anda a llevar este enganche Al estado de Kianses City.	Run, run, little machine Along that Katy line. Carry this party of laborers To the state of Kansas City.
Salimos de San Antonio Con dirección a Laguna, Le pregunté al reenganchista Que si íbamos para Oklahoma.	We left San Antonio In the direction of Laguna; I asked the contractor If we were going through Oklahoma.
Respondió el reenganchista: "Calle, amigo, no suspire, Pararemos de Oklahoma Derechito a Kianses City."	The contractor replied: "Quiet, friend, don't even sigh, We shall pass through Oklahoma Right straight to Kansas City."
Ese tren a Kianses City Es un tren muy volador, Corre cien millas por horas Y no le dan todo el vapor.	That train to Kansas City Is a flying train, It travels 100 miles per hour And they don't give it all the steam.
Yo les digo a mis amigos: "El que no lo quiera creer, Que monte en el Santa Fe, A ver dónde está al amanecer."	I say to my friends: "Let him who doesn't want to believe it Get aboard the Sante Fe, Just to see where he will be by morning."

Al llegar a Kianses City   On arriving at Kansas City
Nos queríamos regresar,   We wanted to return,
Porque nos dieron el ancho   Because they gave us a raw deal
Con las veras de alinear.   With the aligning bars.

Decían los americanos   The Americans said
Con muchisímo valor: With a great deal of bravery:
"Júntense a los mexicanos   "Round up the Mexicans
Para meterlos en la unión."   So as to put them in the union."

Nosotros le respondimos: We replied to them:
"Lo que es la unión no entramos,   "We will not join this thing called union
Esta no es nuestra bandera.   This is not our flag
Porque somos mexicanos."   Because we are Mexicans."

Like many of their compatriots who immigrated to the
United States, the Mexicans who came to Nebraska did not
come with the intention of settling permanently. Unlike the
European immigrants, Mexicans did not come to the U.S. with
the idea of cutting off all connections with the old country and
building permanent communities. Nor did they come into an
altogether foreign environment. Mexicans from the bordering
states (for example, Sonora, Chihuahua, Coahuila, and Nuevo
Leon), as well as finding a climate similar to the one which they
left behind, also found—in South Texas—established communities of Mexican people. For the immigrants from the central
plateau region (Guanajuarto, Jalisco, and Michoacan), the
climate was different in the north, but the sense of dislocation
must have been lessened by the presence of those established
Mexican communities: a church that offered masses in Spanish,
Spanish-language newspapers, Mexican music and food. If
racial discrimination was intense, there existed the momentary
refuge offered by the *barrio*. For many, the racial prejudice
against them became intolerable and they returned to their
country scarred and disillusioned. Some did as they had
planned: they worked in the United States, saved their earnings
and returned to Mexico after the Revolution began to quiet.
Many, of course, remained in the U.S. as permanent residents.
And many, many others were forcefully deported back to
Mexico during the depression, after their cheap labor was no

longer needed. As a result of massive and indiscriminate raids conducted by American immigration authorities in Mexican communities throughout the U.S., more than 400,000 persons were deported back to Mexico during the early thirties; the year 1931, alone, showing 138,519 Mexicans who were forcefully repatriated.[20] The following *corrido* is sung by a Mexican who remained in his country while his compatriots flocked to the U.S. In its critical tone can be read the attitude of some Mexicans toward their fellow countrymen who immigrated to the north, only to be exploited by the "americanos," and then deported back to their country, poor and suffering:

LOS DEPORTADOS

Les cantaré un corrido
de todos los deportados,
que vienen hablando inglés
y vienen de desgraciados.

Los tiran en donde quiera
a puro mendigar,
da lástima verlos
que no traen ni para almorzar.

Marchan para el norte
con gran gusto y afán,
trabajan en el campo
como cualquier gañan.

Se van al algodón
y dan muy mala cala,
trabajan en el traque
o en el pico o la pala.

Pues eso y más merecen
esos pobres paisanos,
sabiendo que este suelo
es para los Mexicanos.

Se tumban el bigote,
y mascan su tabaco,
parecen la gran cosa y no
cargen ni . . . tlaco.

Se pelan a la boston
como burros tuzados,
se van a las segundas
y compran trajes usados.

THE DEPORTEES

I shall sing you a song
of all the deportees,
who come back speaking English
and in wretched shape.

They are dropped off just anywhere
and have to beg their way.
It's a pity to see them
with not even enough to eat.

They set out for the north
with high hopes and eagerness,
they work in the fields
like any field hand.

They go to pick cotton
and get on very badly;
they work on the track
or with shovel or with pick.

Well, they deserve that and more,
those poor countrymen,
for they knew that this land
is for the Mexicans.

They cut off their mustaches
and chew their tobacco;
they seem like a big success
and they don't have a cent.

They cut their hair close
like a clipped donkey;
they go to second-hand stores
and buy used clothes.

Los corren, los maltratan
los gringos desgraciados,
no tienen vergüenza
siempre allá estan pegados.

They're rejected, they're mistreated,
by those gringo wretches;
they have no shame,
they still want to be there.

Por eso yo me quedo
en mi patria querida,
México es mi país
y por él doy la vida.

That is why I remain
in my beloved country:
Mexico is my country
and for it I give my life.

"Defensa de Los Norteños" (Defense of the Emigrants to the North) explains the situation of the Mexican who left his country, not gladly nor easily, but out of necessity. The last stanza of this *corrido* expresses the common desire of the immigrant to one day return to his country.

DEFENSA DE LOS NORTEÑOS

DEFENSE OF THE EMIGRANTS

Lo que dicen de nosotros
casi todo es realidad;
mas salimos del terreno
por pura necesidad.

What they say about us
is nearly all the truth,
but we left the country
from sheer necessity.

Que muchos vienen facetos
yo también se los dijera;
por eso la prensa chica
tuvo donde echar tijera.

I myself could have told you
that many come back boasting;
that is why the local press
speaks harshly about them.

Pero la culpa la tienen
esos ingratos patrones
que no les dan a su gente
ni aun cuando porte chaqueta.

But those who are to blame
are those unkind employers,
who don't give their people
enough to buy a jacket.

No es porque hablo del país:
pero claro se los digo
que muchos trabajadores
enseñan hasta el ombligo.

I'm not criticizing the country,
but I certainly tell you
that many of the laborers
are naked to their navels.

El rico en buen automóvil,
buen caballo, buena silla,
y los pobrecitos peones
pelona la rabanilla.

The rich go in automobiles,
riding a good horse and a good saddle
while the poor peones
go about half naked.

Siempre el peón es agobiado,
tratándolo con fiereza,
donde le miran los pies
quieren verle la cabeza.

The peon is always burdened,
is treated with cruelty;
the rich would like to see his head
where they see his feet.

'Lo tratan como un esclavo
no como útil servidor
que derrama para el rico
hasta el ultimo sudor.

Yo no digo que en el Norte
se va uno a estar muy sentado,
ni aun cuando porte chaqueta
lo hacen a uno diputado.

Allí se va a trabajar
macizo, a lo Americano,
pero alcanza uno a ganar
más que cualesquier paisano.

Aquí se trabaja un año
sin comprarse una camisa;
el pobre siempre sufriendo,
y los ricos risa y risa.

Los cuarenta y el tostón
no salen de su tarifa,
no alcanza para comer;
siempre anda vacía la tripa.

Que lo digan mis paisanos,
si yo les estoy mintiendo,
porque no hay que preguntar
lo que claro estamos viendo.

Mucha gente así lo ha dicho:
dizque no somos patriotas
porque les vamos a servir
a los infames patotas.

Pero que se abran trabajos
y que paguen buen dinero,
y no queda un Mexicano
que se vaya al extranjero.

Ansia tenemos de volver
a nuestra patria idolatrada,
pero qué le hemos de hacer
si está la patria arruinada.

They treat him like a slave,
not like a useful servant,
who pours out for the rich
his last drop of sweat.

I don't say that in the north
one is going to be well off;
nor that because one wears a suit
is he elected to Congress.

One has to work there,
hard, in the American fashion,
but one succeeds in earning
more than any of our countrymen.

Here one works a year
without earning enough for a shirt;
the poor man suffers always
and the rich man laughs and laughs.

Paid forty or fifty cents,
never more than that,
he can't get enough to eat,
his stomach is always empty.

Let my countrymen say
if I am telling a lie,
for it's needless to ask about
what we can clearly see.

Many people have said
that we are not patriotic
because we go to serve
the accursed *patotas.* *

But let them give us jobs
and pay us decent wages;
not one Mexican then
will go to foreign lands.

We're anxious to return again
to our adored country;
but what can we do about it
if the country is ruined?

---

*Patotas: literally "big feet,"
i.e., Anglo-Americans.

In spite of their desire to eventually return to Mexico, however, many Mexican immigrants remained in the United States. They found permanent work and raised families; and as new roots began to take, their hopes and dreams of one day returning to Mexico gradually dimmed.

Mexican Cultural Nationalism

The communities which Mexicans and Mexican Americans established—in the Midwest and elsewhere—remained Mexican. In spite of living in the North and in spite of adjusting to the changed material conditions of their new lives, these immigrants continued to think and feel and express themselves as Mexicans. To this day one can find identifiably Mexican communities in Omaha, in Grand Island, in Scottsbluff, and the North Platte Valley. In other areas of the state—Lincoln, Kearney, North Platte and Sidney—one still finds specific manifestations of the Mexican culture.

In talking with elders throughout the state, one is immediately struck by the strong sense of identity which they have as Mexicans. Though they have lived in the United States for forty, fifty and sometimes even close to seventy years, they continue to regard themselves as *"hijos y hijas de la patria"* (sons and daughters of the fatherland). This remains a wholly emotional tie to Mexico, of course, because in making their lives in this country—whether or not they have become U.S. citizens—they have shouldered the responsibilities of citizenship in the United States: they have worked, paid taxes, obeyed the laws, participated in their communities, served in the First World War, and they have sent their sons and grandsons to three wars fought by this country. Still, they consider themselves Mexicans. As an 82-year-old man who has lived here since 1916 puts it: "No, no, I can't say to you that this is my country. It is a good country, yes, but it is not my fatherland. My fatherland is Mexico." Another man says, "I have never wanted to become a citizen of this country. No, why should I? I am already an American, I tell them. I was born in America. Mexico is in

America. I don't need that [U.S. citizenship]. All of my life I have considered Mexico my country."

It is understandable, then, that for persons of Mexican ancestry—particularly for the elders—the Bicentennial celebration lacks the significance that it has for others. One must remember that in 1776, during the time that the Continental Congress was approving the Declaration of Independence for the thirteen colonies, permanent and thriving settlements of Spanish-speaking people already existed in Santa Fe, Tucson, Albuquerque, San Antonio, San Diego, Monterrey, and in other parts of the Southwest. One must remember, too, that Mexico's War of Independence in 1810 occurred at a time when the present-day southwestern part of the United States was part of the Spanish holdings on this continent, and, therefore, that in 1821 when Mexico won its independence, the region became part of the Mexican national territory and its inhabitants automatically became Mexican citizens. That is, during the 34-year period between the adoption of the Declaration of Independence in the U.S. and the beginning of the war for independence in Mexico, the national and cultural situation of the Spanish-speaking people in the Southwest remained unchanged. Neither in 1776 nor in 1810 did they live within the boundaries of the United States. Hence, Miguel Hidalgo—for the role he played in Mexican independence—is honored in his country and in parts of the United States in the same way that George Washington is regarded in this country. Hidalgo was the "father of his country," at a time when Mexico included much of the territory that presently makes up the United States.

The Mexican American War, through which the U.S. appropriated the Southwest, continues to be regarded as an imperialistic war by Mexicans living here. Recollection of such occurrences do not, of course, promote feelings of patriotism for the U.S., nor do the memories of having been victims of exploitation and racial discrimination. A long-time resident of Nebraska, whose two sons fought in the Second World War, describes his entrance into the United States in 1916:

. . . I registered and they led me to a basement. There they told me to take off my hat and they poured gasoline over my head. Then they told us to bathe in hot water. That's what I got: all my hair fell out.

They did that with all the Mexicans. They would pass us through there, they would bathe us. And then our shoes, they would tell us to stick them into a can of gasoline—well they would become hard. They had all those buckets there so that we could stick our shoes into . . . well, I tell you, that they treat a person however they want, no? Like animals.

A little later on, while working for the railroad, the superintendent of the [railroad] line went where we were working. He told us that we had to present ourselves on such and such a day in Grants, New Mexico. I asked him, "Why?" [He answered] "You have to register yourselves." [I asked] "What for?" and he said that for the war [World War I]. I told him that I was not an American, but a Mexican. And he said we had to go. "Well, alright," I said, "because here you people govern. But I would rather not." No, my friend, they hit you hard here. They said, "Well, if you're not from this country, why don't you go back to Mexico? Or why did you come here anyway?" Oh, yes, yes, they get at you from all sides. I didn't fight in the war because it ended—November 11th. That's my birthday.

This same man, in speaking of how Mexicans were treated in Nebraska during the 30's and 40's, remembers that in 1934 an elected official stated over the radio that the Mexican people in that community were undesirables. Many of the Mexican elders in Nebraska have that kind of experience to recount. A woman, for example, tells about how during the Second World War, immigration authorities arrived at her house one day and belligerently questioned her status as a legal resident of this country, and threatened to deport her back to Mexico. "Send me back," she told the authorities, "I will go. But send my son back with me. Right now he is fighting in the war." Such experiences appear to be common among the Mexican people of this state. Knowing of the Mexican's history in the United States and in Nebraska, it is not surprising that (at least among the elders) their emotional allegiance is not to the United States but to Mexico. Such historical background explains perhaps, the Mexican-Americans' lack of enthusiasm for the Bicentennial celebration of the United States of America.

Many Mexican and Mexican-Americans maintain communication with Mexico. Vacation trips are periodically made to Mexico, as are journeys to visit relatives and friends. One man, since arriving in Nebraska in 1914, has made more than fifty trips to Mexico. Families and individuals throughout the state make annual trips to the interior of Mexico to visit relatives. The connection made to that country, if not simply national in the usual sense, is emotional and has as its base a shared culture not only with the inhabitants in Mexico but also with people of Mexican ancestry who live in the United States. The strong nationalism observed during the celebrations of "las fiestas patrias" (the Mexican national holidays) in Scottsbluff, Grand Island, Lincoln, and Omaha, has almost wholly cultural connotations. What is emotionally celebrated on September 16 (Mexican Independence Day) and May 5 (defeat of the French at Puebla) are not so much political or military victories as such, but rather the sense of being Mexican: and that sense is broadly based on a common culture, the recognition of which places one as a member of an ethnic/racial family.

The Spanish word for that family at its most immediate level is, of course, *familia:* father, mother, brothers, sisters and extending to include grandparents, uncles, aunts, cousins, nephews, nieces, as well as *padrinos* and *madrinas* (god-parents at baptisms, confirmations and weddings). In traditional Mexican culture the *familia* is of considerable importance. It is the immediate social body in which one identifies, and it is the unified whole towards which one owes ultimate loyalty and responsibility, even over friends. It has an importance over and above the individual; through the *familia* is preserved a unified living within a body larger than oneself. One belongs necessarily; and it is through that belonging that one identifies. Hence, as the person acts, his actions reflect on all members of the *familia*. He is responsible not only for (and to) himself

but for (and to) his *familia.* The recognition or shame that
result from his actions have waves of felt repercussion that go
beyond the immediate self. Most immediately, then, *familia,*
in traditional Mexican culture, always means community. The
young person growing up is taught to be—quite literally—his or
her brother's and sister's keeper. In Spanish, the parents' and
grandparents' admonition to the youth is constantly: *Cuida a
tu hermano* or *cuida a tu hermana.* That sense of responsibility
for brothers and sisters remains throughout one's lifetime,
and includes a responsibility toward parents as well. The very
idea of "Homes for the Aged" goes directly contrary to traditional Mexican cultural values. The elders *(los viejitos)* are not
to be isolated, but continuously involved within the family. If
grown sons and daughters with families have responsibilities
toward parents, those parents too have felt responsibilities
toward the grandchildren. Aunts and uncles assist in the raising
of their brothers' and sisters' children. *Padrinos* and *madrinas*
(godparents) are responsible for raising the *ahijados* (the god-
children) in the event of the parents' death.

Beginning from this most basic of social units, the recognition of *familia* extends outward to include one's particular community (*barrio* or *colonia*), and then out even further to include
others, wherever they might live, who belong to the cultural
family. In Spanish there are a number of words to denote the
cultural family, but the one most commonly used by Mexicans
and Mexican Americans of all ages and from all parts of
America, is the emotionally charged word, *RAZA*—a word that
can be translated literally to mean "race," but is usually understood to mean "the people."

Much of the sense of identity felt first within the immediate family is extended out to the greater cultural "family":
La Raza. One's sense of self, then, is as a member of a people.
Self-identification, rather than being individualistic (and often
confined to the present or recent past), is instead communal,
and based on a people's history going back to the Olmecas on
this continent more than a thousand years before Christ. This
historical sense (not just an awareness of the Mexican past, but

a certain respect for it as something viable and real) does in fact appear quite common among the Mexican elders. In most instances, these early Mexican arrivals to Nebraska had very little formal education—in one instance, only four months of schooling. Yet, they know about their indigenous ancestors, about Maximilian, Benito Juárez, General Zaragoza, Porfirio Díaz and Hidalgo. The cultural heroes are uniquely Mexican, beginning with Cuauhtémoc, the last Aztec Prince, and including Hidalgo, Benito Juárez, Francisco Madero, Francisco Villa and Emiliano Zapata. Much of this history they learned from their parents while in Mexico; much more they taught themselves *after* their arrival in the United States. This is a history of La Raza. It is, therefore, recognized and respected as their own history.

Feelings of responsibility and loyalty, first directed towards the immediate family, are extended out to the larger "family." The value of self-advancement for the individual, for example, is often qualified by the greater good for the people. And, in fact, one's membership in the "family" is often felt to be dependent on his work done in behalf of the group. Speaking with an elder in the state, for example, I was surprised at first to hear him say that Don Porfirio Díaz (President of Mexico, immediately prior to the Revolution) was not "a son of the fatherland," for I knew that Díaz was in fact born in Mexico, was a *mestizo* and had, early in his career, fought against the French intervention. He continued to talk about the concessions made to foreign investors in Mexico during the Díaz regime and said:

> With the power that he had, he did as he wished. He was not of Mexican blood. He was French, or something else— because he did more for foreigners than he did for his own people. Look, everything that he could get away with, he took out of Mexico. He went and made himself a palace of pure crystal in France. That palace still exists. And the poor in Mexico continue to suffer. Well, the old man finally died, and, I don't know how, but his wife secured permission to return the man's bones to Mexico. So we have all of the old man's

bones there. But now he can't do anything. He was a man who
did nothing for the nation. He didn't want to because he was
not a son of the fatherland. For sure, he was born in Mexico,
but the blood in him was not from there. Why did he build
that palace in France? Why did he do more for foreigners than
for Mexicans? Well, he was not from there—in his spirit, I say!

The preceding description of one important aspect of
traditional Mexican culture is, of course, a model description.
Rarely, perhaps, has the reality coincided exactly with the
model. Nevertheless, in Nebraska one can still find vestiges of
those feelings and attitudes, particularly among the Mexican
elders. Unfortunately, among many of the Mexican Americans
in the state, such vestiges of their cultural background are often
scant.

Mexican Cultural Presence in Nebraska

As with other ethnic groups, pressures on the Mexican
American to become "Americanized" have been intense and
consistent. Hence a real separation often exists between the
Mexican-American youths and the grandparents and great
grandparents who were immigrants from Mexico. Mexican culture, however—if diminished by assimilationist pressures, and if
modified by the experience in the Nebraska-U.S.A. environment—exists as a way of being for a substantial number of
Nebraska citizens to this day.

Spanish, for example, continues to be a living language in
this state. Across Nebraska, it is, in many instances, the *only*
language spoken by the elders. Among some first and second
generation Mexican American families, however, Spanish is no
longer spoken at home. Remembering their own language-
associated difficulties in the society and in school, some
Mexican American parents attempt to shield their children from
those experiences by speaking only English at home. In the
entire state, however, it is probably in the Panhandle area that
one encounters more Spanish being used as the language of
family and community affairs. The presence of a community of

Spanish-speaking persons in the state is acknowledged by the services and media entertainment directed exclusively to this audience.

In small communities like Morrill in western Nebraska, Mexican films are shown weekly during the summer. Spanish-speaking radio programs exist throughout the state: Señora Montelongo's program in Omaha, UNO's station KVNO; Pete DeLeon's programs on Kearney's KRNY and Hasting's KHAS, and his weekly television program from Kearney, channel 13; Fr. Valdez' program on KEYR in Terrytown; and Alejandro Trinidad's program on the UNL station, KRNU, Lincoln. Religious services in Spanish are regularly offered at All Souls Catholic Church in Bridgeport; at the First Baptist Church in Scottsbluff; at Templo Bethel, Assembly of God Church in Scottsbluff; occasionally at Saint Mary's Catholic Church located in Grand Island; at Saint Mary's Catholic Church in Lincoln; and also in Our Lady of Guadalupe Catholic Church in Omaha.

There exist some variants of the Spanish language which one can hear in the state among Mexican and Mexican American residents. Mainly, these variants can be identified not by residence location of the speakers, but by age, place of birth, occupation, and length of time spent in the United States. The most immediately striking contrast is between the Spanish of the elder immigrant and his offspring (including the grandchildren, many of whom are college-age youths). Quite naturally, one finds that first generation Mexican Americans speak less Spanish than their parents do, and in some instances, none at all. In addition, there exists a qualitative difference between the Spanish of the immigrant and that of Mexican Americans. Though the majority of the elders have had very little formal education, their command of Spanish is extremely flexible and makes use of a wide vocabulary, some of which is formal, but including also colloquialisms appropriate to the area in Mexico from which they emigrated. In pronounciation, their language is standard Mexican Spanish rather than the Castilian Spanish of Spain.

Standard Mexican Spanish is spoken by some first generation Mexican Americans in Nebraska, but in the majority of
instances the Spanish language which they use and which they
teach their children is one that makes heavy use of Hispanized
English words, known as *"pochismos."* This describes, in fact,
the Spanish of the *barrio*—an amalgam of both Spanish and
English, and in some instances a mixture of Spanish and English
slang. The following list shows just a few of such *pochismos* in
common use in Nebraska. These expressions are used most
often by the younger Mexican Americans but the elder Mexican
immigrants to the state are not completely free of them.

English	Pochismo	Spanish
truck	troka, or troque	camión
train	tren	ferrocarril
brake (for car)	breca	freno
car	carro	automóvil
newspaper ("paper")	papel	periódico
match	mecha	fosforo or cerillo
to park	parquear	estacionar

The use of Spanish, Pochismos, and English in one conversation—sometimes in a single sentence—is perhaps more common
in Texas and other parts of the Southwest, but in Nebraska
one can at times hear assertions like: *"No fui al party porque la
ley me paró and gave me a tiquete"* (I didn't go to the party
because I was stopped by a policeman and given a traffic
ticket").

Another form of Mexican culture still present in Nebraska
is the use of *dichos* (proverbs), those "sayings" which contain
the accumulated wisdom and humor of the folk and provide
the native speaker with a shorthand way of saying much with
few words. The *dicho,* being part of the language, is most often
used by the elders who are the "preservers" of the folk culture
in the face of Americanization pressures. If, for example, one
wishes to emphasize the differences among people and the right

of everyone to decide for himself, he says *cada cabeza es un mundo* ("each head comprises a world unto itself"); if one wishes to express the sense behind "the rich get richer and the poor get poorer," or "when it rains it pours," the Spanish-speaking will say *al perro más flaco se le cargan las pulgas* ("to the skinniest of dogs the fleas will flock"). There are hundreds of such dichos, shared in common with Mexicans and Mexican Americans living in other parts of the country.

The use in Nebraska of Mexican and Mexican-American Spanish marks but one of numerous manifestations of the culture as it is lived in this state to the present. Other manifestations include *corridos* (folk ballads), *canciones* (songs), *cuentos* (tales), and *versos* (poems). The majority of the *corridos* that one can hear in Nebraska are based on experiences of the Revolution (a large number of them about Pancho Villa or famous soldiers under him). Like the *corridos,* many of the songs are Mexican; some, however, have been written in the U.S. and show clearly the influence of the "American" environment. This music is heard at Mexican dances throughout the state wherever people of Mexican ancestry reside. Mexican music can also be heard on the radio (at least once a week in Omaha, Lincoln, the Grand Island-Kearney area and the Scottsbluff area), on the jukeboxes at places like La Tropicana Lounge and Howard's El Charro restaurant in Omaha; the Monterrey and Los Sanchez restaurants in Lincoln; La Casa de Gonzales restaurant in Grand Island; Lerma's Cafe in Lyman and other places in the state, as well as on records and tapes.

Most of the poems and folk stories that are recited and told by Mexican people in the state are of Mexican origin. Among the most often told of these stories is *"La Llorona"* (the Weeping Woman), a tale so ancient and so central to what the Mexican consciousness has been that some people believe that its origin goes back to "the time in Mexico before the Spaniards" (pre-1519). Various versions exist; each version, however, contains an essential, haunting quality. Some versions associate the Weeping Woman with Aztec goddesses; others associate her with Doña Marina, otherwise known in history as

"La Malinche," the Indian woman who, in working as interpreter for Hernán Cortez and in becoming his mistress, is charged with having betrayed her own people to the Spanish *conquistadores.* Among the Mexican people in Nebraska, however, most versions of *"La Llorona"* revolve around an unidentified Mexican mother who killed her children, cut them into pieces, which she in turn threw into a river. Her punishment is to wander the face of the earth eternally until she finds all the pieces of her children. On certain nights, so the story tells, one can hear the woman crying for her children as she wanders the earth looking for them. Children, in particular, are told that they must be very careful, for if they misbehave, *La Llorona* will come and take them. An 81-year-old man who arrived in Nebraska in 1914 swears that he once heard the Weeping Woman. "I heard her," he says. *"Hasta se me enchinó el cuero"* (I even felt a creepy chill). "I heard her . . . but anymore all of that is changed. The people don't believe anything nowadays."

The poems that are kept are usually all memorized, commemoration verses for use during the *fiestas patrias.* Some have specific authors (like Antonio Plazas); others are anonymous. The poems sing the praises of Mexican heroes and heroic occasions: General Zaragoza, the military leader who defeated the French armies at Puebla in 1862; Fr. Hidalgo, father of Mexican Independence; Francisco Madero, leader of the 1910 Revolution. An elder from the western part of the state can recite Mexican verses, from memory, for hours. Asked how he learned all those verses, he answered: *"Yo era gato de casa grande en méxico"* (I was a "cat of a large estate" in Mexico, i.e., a boyservant in the house of the *hacendado*). "And everybody who was a cat of a large estate had to learn how to talk like the bosses. I was like a servant of the rich. I was about twelve or thirteen years old and I ran errands for those people. They had books, many books, arranged nicely in glass-door cases. And one was always around them. So that is how I learned. But I was interested."

Among "things that are Mexican," certainly the food is best known. People who don't know the difference between a *sarape* and a *sombrero* have tasted a *taco* or an *enchilada.* To some degree, no doubt, this wide recognition has been brought on by the quick-food *taco* drive-in franchises that proliferate throughout Nebraska as they do most other states. In Nebraska, the authentic Mexican food restaurants exist, many times alongside the drive-ins, from one end of the state to the other. At the western extreme, just a few miles from the Wyoming border is Señora Lerma's Cafe and Restaurant, serving the best down-home *chile verde* in the state (and in its exterior design representing a lonely, but brilliant, manifestation of Aztec art in the Midwest). At the eastern extreme is Howard's El Charro Restaurant on South 24th Street in Omaha. *Chiles rellenos* (stuffed peppers) can be found at Espejo's El Charron on South 20th Street in Omaha; *empanadas* (small, individual meat or fruit pies) and *menudo* (tripe soup) can, on certain days, be found at El Monterrey in Lincoln, North 48th Street. In the dozen or so other Mexican restaurants throughout Nebraska the common *taco, enchilada,* rice and beans can be found.

Less well known, however, are those Mexican foods that are associated with traditional holidays and fiestas. *Tamales* (an Aztec Indian dish) and *menudo,* for example, are eaten anytime during the year. Traditionally, however, Christmas (December 24 and 25) is not complete without *tamales;* and the same is true for *menudo* and New Years Day. *Mole* is present at weddings. *Capirotada* (a Mexican bread pudding for which there are as many recipes as households in a *barrio*) is present during the Lenten period.

In Nebraska some of these holidays are still observed with the traditional foods, but, unfortunately, along with so much else that is Mexican, a gradual erosion of the traditions is taking place.

Life in the United States has also affected many of the Mexican religious customs and traditions practiced in the state. The result of pressures to adjust to American Catholicism is noticed by the absence of certain religious fiestas and observances. For example, December 12, the *fiesta* day of the Virgin of Guadalupe, the patron saint of Mexico, is rarely observed in the state anymore, in spite of this being one of the most significant of days for Mexican Catholics. There are other significant observances that have either changed or have been forgotten altogether, particularly those related to the Christmas holidays and to the Lenten period, during which, traditionally, specific church ceremonies harmonize with family activity, food, music, and sometimes dance. Some religious forms remain, however. *Patrinos* and *madrinas* (godfathers and godmothers), for example, are still part of Mexican American weddings, baptisms, confirmations, and sometimes First Holy Communions. Still part of the wedding ceremony in some Mexican American communities is the use of the double-loop rosary that is placed around the bride and groom symbolizing the union of two-making-one. And still observed is the serving of the traditional Mexican *mole* at the wedding feast preceding the Mexican wedding dance to which everybody in the community is invited. One of the most beautiful of Mexican religious traditions is *La Bendicion* (benediction), a custom that is close to being a "lost art" in this state. The benediction usually is given by an elder—usually but not always a grandparent or parent to son or daughter, or grandchildren as they begin a new undertaking: school graduation, wedding, long trip, entrance into the military, etc. Though common elements are found in all of these prayers, there is no single form that the Mexican benediction takes. Some are short, some are quite lengthy. Some have been memorized out of prayer books; others are original, having been at one time created by a member of a family and passed on to succeeding generations. As practiced, most benedictions are a combination of memorized prayers that have been personalized by additions, omissions, and changes. It is quite usual for the same benediction to remain in the family for generation after generation, the mother passing it on to the daughter, etc. The following benediction was given this writer by an 88-year-old woman from western Nebraska as I left her house beginning the journey back to Lincoln:

BENDICIÓN

Con esta agua bendita de
   Dios consagrada
Se hace esta bendición,
Sus pecados sean perdonados,
Y su alma sea sanada.

El Señor le bendiga y le
   conserve.
El Señor le manifieste su rostro,
Y ruege consagrante hacia usted
Y le de paz.

Con el velo del santísimo
   sacramento
Sea su cerpo envuelto.
Ni herido ni muerto
Ni preso ni cautivo
Ni, perseguido de ningun
   enimigo, sea venicido

La bendición de Dios Padre;
La bendición de Dios hijo:
La bendición de Dios espíritu
   santo,
Le alcance todo el tiempo de
   su vida
Hasta su feliz partida al
   mundo de la eternidad.

La bendición de Dios padre;
La bendición de Dios hijo;
La bendición de Dios espíritu
   santo le alcance
Todo el tiempo de su vida.

La Virgen Santísima de Guadalupe
Le llene de bendición,
Le cubra con su santisimo manto,
Y lo lleve por buen camino
Todo el tiempo de su vida
Hasta su feliz partida.

La santa fe del cielo
Baje y sobre su cuerpo se
   extienda.
De males y de peligros lo libre
La santa fe del cielo.

BENEDICTION

With this holy water, by God
   consecrated,
Is this benediction given,
   may your soul be saved.
May your sins be forgiven
And your spirit cleansed.

May the Lord bless you and
   keep you;
May the Lord show you his face,
May He shower his consecration
   upon you
And give you peace.

May your body be sheathed
In the veil of the holy sacrament
May you escape injury or death
May you be neither imprisoned
   nor captive,
Nor overcome by any pursuing enemy.

May the blessing of God the Father;
the blessing of God the Son;
The blessing of God the
   Holy Spirit,
Reach you all the days of your life,
Until your peaceful entrance to
   Life Eternal.

May the blessing of God the Father;
The blessing of God the Son;
The blessing of God the
   Holy Spirit,
Reach you all the days of your life.

May the Holy Virgin of Guadalupe
Fill you with her blessing,
And wrap you within her holy veil.
May she show you the right way
All the days of your life
Until your happy going.

May the holy faith of Heaven
Descend and protect you.
From evil and danger
May the holy faith of Heaven free you.

"Esta es la Bendición.   "This is my blessing to you,
Dios lo bendiga. María   May God bless you. May the
Santísima lo acompane."   Blessed Virgin Mary accompany you."

At the celebrations in Nebraska communities of what are
called *las fiestas patrias* (the National holidays), food, music,
dance, poetry, handcrafts, costume, religion and history come
together in what are the largest—if not the only—Mexican *fiestas*
involving the entire community. Certainly the day observing
Mexican Independence from Spain (September 16) is the most
prevalently celebrated in more communities in the state—from
the elaborate "Fiesta Del Valle" in Our Lady of Guadalupe
Catholic Church in Scottsbluff to the *fiesta* sponsored by the
Mexican American inmates at the Nebraska Penal Complex in
Lincoln. Since early in the 1920's, when men like Señor
Herónimo Perez and Señor Martín Quijas and others created
what was probably the first Mexican organization in the state,
the *Comisión Honorifica* (Honorary Commission) in Scottsbluff, September 16 has been celebrated. During the late 20's an
Honorary Commission was also organized in Omaha under the
direction of Señor Gregorio Aquilera and others, serving not
only the purpose of sponsoring these *fiestas patrias,* but serving
generally as a cooperative organization for mutual assistance
among Mexicans in the barrio.

The other national fiesta that is celebrated in Nebraska is
May 5, marking the defeat of the French at Puebla in 1862.
Though not as popular as Mexican Independence day, this
holiday, too, when observed in the state, brings together most
of what exists as "Mexican" in the state.

Mexican Culture Important to Nebraska Development

There is no doubt but that Mexican and Mexican American
culture exists as a living reality within the boundaries of this
state; nor that the people of this heritage have played an important role in the economic development of the region. If in the
past a large percentage of the Nebraska population has been

unaware of their presence, it is because so many of them have been kept in the fields; and because their cultural heritage —however real and present within their own barrios—has been not only ignored by the larger community, but also repressed. The aim of educational, religious, social service and governmental institutions has been to Americanize the Mexican immigrant, along with the rest of the foreigners in this country. Unfortunately, this policy—implemented in different ways by different institutions—achieved some success. In noting the gradual disappearance of Mexican cultural forms in the lives of second generation Mexican Americans, we can see some of the effects of the Americanization process. This is, indeed, a loss, for within the traditional Mexican and the Mexican American culture—as within the culture of other ethnic groups making up the Nebraska population—exist viable alternatives for the process of building communities which are more responsive to human needs.

An extremely encouraging result of the national Chicano Liberation Movement that began during the mid 1960's has been a reawakening—particularly on the part of Mexican-American youth—to the value of their cultural and ethnic past, and a determined identification with that part of themselves that they have been taught to negate. In Nebraska this new consciousness expresses itself through the proud usage of the word "Chicano" by the youth wishing to define himself without a hyphen. It expresses itself in the presence of teenage Chicanos doing traditional Mexican dances in Omaha, in Grand Island and Scottsbluff—an activity that a few years ago would have been shunned as being "sissy." It expresses itself through the 17-year-old university freshman who quietly tells her professor that she wants to learn Spanish as quickly as possible because she wants to talk with her grandmother who is 86 years old.

82   *Broken Hoops and Plains People*

FOOTNOTES

1. Herbert E. Bolton, *Coronado, Knight of Pueblos and Plains* (Albuquerque: University of New Mexico Press, 1949), p. 68.

2. Francisco López de Gómara, *Primera y segunda parte de la historia general de las Indias cõ todo el descrubrimiento, y cosas notables que han acaescido dende que se ganaron hasta el año de 1551; con la conquista de Mexico y de Nueva España*, p. 288. Cited by A. Grove Day in *Coronado's Quest: The Discovery of the Southwestern States* (Berkeley: University of California Press, 1964), p. 191.

3. Bolton, *op. cit.*, p. 291.

4. *The Journey of Coronado 1540-1542, from the City of Mexico to the Grand Canon of the Colorado and the Buffalo Plains of Texas, Kansas and Nebraska, as told by himself and his followers,* translated and edited by George Parker Winship (New York: Greenwood Press, 1922), pp. 217, 219-20.

5. J.H. Simpson, "Coronado's March," *Smithsonian Report* (1869), p. 324. Quoted in J. Sterling Morton, *Illustrated History of Nebraska,* Vol. I (Lincoln: Jacob North & Co., 1905), p. 48.

6. Marshall Sprague, *So Vast So Beautiful A Land: Louisiana and the Purchase* (Boston: Little, Brown and Co., 1947), p. 333.

7. *Scottsbluff and the North Platte Valley,* 2nd ed. Published under the auspices of Scottsbluff Golden Jubilee Celebration Committee. N.D. (Contained in Scottsbluff City Library.)

8. J. Sterling Morton, *Illustrated History of Nebraska,* Vol. I (Lincoln: Jacob North & Co., 1905), p. 48.

9. Carey McWilliams, *North From Mexico: The Spanish-Speaking Peoples of the United States* (New York: Greenwood Press, 1968), p. 163.

10. Source: Cabinet Committee on Opportunity for the Spanish-Speaking, based on 1970 U.S. census; and Mid-West Council de la Raza, Notre Dame, Indiana.

11. Manuel Gamio, *Mexican Immigration to the United States: A Study of Human Migration and Adjustment* (New York: Dover Publications, Inc., 1971), pp. 24-25. Originally published by the University of Chicago Press in 1930.

12. Frank R. Brandenburg, *The Making of Modern Mexico* (Englewood Cliffs, N.J.: Prentice-Hall, 1964), p. 39.

13. McWilliams, *op. cit.*, pp. 163, 168, 177, 180-83.

14. Esther S. Anderson, *The Sugar Beet Industry of Nebraska*

(Lincoln: Bulletin 9, Conservation Department of the Conservation and Survey Division, University of Nebraska, April, 1935), pp. 25-27.

15. McWilliams, *op. cit.,* pp. 167-69.

16. T. Earl Sullenger, "The Mexican Population of Omaha," *Journal of Applied Sociology,* VIII (May-June, 1924), 289.

17. Anderson, *op. cit.,* pp. 21-22, 25.

18. Paul S. Taylor, *Mexican Labor in the United States,* Vol. I (New York: Arno Press and The New York Times, 1970), pp. 103, 105.

19. Taylor, *Ibid.,* p. 133; Anderson, *op. cit.,* p. 90.

20. Abraham Hoffman, *Unwanted Mexican Americans in the Great Depression: Repatriation Pressures, 1929-1939* (Tucson: University of Arizona Press, 1974), pp. 174-75.

CATALOGUE

HOW TO LEARN MORE ABOUT CHICANOS IN NEBRASKA

Though I am aware that the following catalogue is not comprehensive, no organization, community activity or other cultural resource in Nebraska was omitted intentionally. What follows is the result of several months' travelling and talking with people throughout the state, but principally in Omaha, Lincoln, Grand Island and the Scottsbluff area. It is intended for readers who wish to find out about Mexicans, Mexican Americans or Chicanos in the state of Nebraska.

Churches Offering Services in Spanish

St. Mary's Catholic Church
14th & K Streets
Lincoln

Our Lady of Guadalupe Catholic
    Church
2310 O Street
Omaha

First Baptist Church
1610 5th Avenue
Scottsbluff

St. Mary's Catholic Church
Grand Island

All Souls Catholic Church
617 P Street
Bridgeport

Templo Bethel
    Assembly of God Church
East 8th Street
Scottsbluff

Our Lady of Guadalupe Catholic
    Church
1103 12th Avenue
Scottsbluff

Organizations and Community Centers

Chicano Awareness Center
4825 South 24th Street
Omaha

La Fiesta del Valle, Inc.
Our Lady of Guadalupe Catholic
    Church
1103 12th Avenue
Scottsbluff

La Raza Cultural Center
605 East 4th Street
Grand Island

American G.I. Forum:
National organization with
    chapters in Omaha, Lincoln,
    Grand Island, and Scottsbluff

Guadalupe Recreation Center
1200 9th Avenue
Scottsbluff

Chicano Association of United
Students for Action (La CAUSA)
University of Nebraska
Omaha

Aztlan (Chicano Student
    organization)
Nebraska Western College
Scottsbluff

Mexican American Student
Association (MASA)
University of Nebraska
Lincoln

Midwest Council de la Raza
Post Office Box 606
Notre Dame, Indiana 46556

> Source of information on the Chicanos living in the Midwest. Issues monthly newsletter, "Los Dessaraigados."

National Education Task Force
    de la Raza
Midwest Regional Office
Chicago State University
9500 at King Drive
Chicago, Illinois 60628

> Provides services and information to communities and schools in the Midwest area. Concerned broadly with educational matters as they relate to the Spanish-speaking.

The Latin Club
6th and Taft
Grand Island

Mexican Awareness Through
Association (MATA)
Nebraska Penal Complex
Lincoln

United Mexican American Students
    (UMAS)
Chadron State College
Chadron

The Mexican American Commission
State Capital Building
Lincoln (402) 471-2791

> Created in 1972 by state legislative action, its function is, broadly, to serve the needs of the Mexican American community in Nebraska. Maintains a full-time director and staff in Lincoln, and a full-time regional director and staff in its Scottsbluff regional office: 1516 1st Ave., phone: 635-0541. Seven commissioners, chosen by the governor, represent the Mexican American people from the following areas of the state: Omaha, Lincoln, Grand Island, North Platte, Alliance, Scottsbluff, and Henry. Periodic, and regular, meetings conducted in different areas of the state, open to the public.

Food

Howard's Charro Cafe
5219 South 24th Street
Omaha

El Charro Restaurant
5223 South 20th Street
Omaha

Peppi's Macayo
10737 Mockingbird Drive
Omaha

Carmona's Cafe
2727 Q Street
Omaha

Monterrey Restaurant
525 North 48th Street
Lincoln

The Taco Hut
249 North 11th Street
Lincoln

Los Sanchez
2 miles north of I-80 on Hwy. 77
Lincoln

Carmen & Ricardo's Burrito House
U.S. 30 & D
Cozad

La Casa de Gonzales
218 South Wheeler Avenue
Grand Island

El Charro Del Norte
1912 Central Avenue
Kearney

La Casita
1911 East 4th Street
North Platte

La Paloma
1121 East 1st Street
Ogallala

El Nopal Cafe
712 West 1st Street
Ogallala

The White Swan
510 East 9th Street
Scottsbluff

Virgils' Mexican American Food
21st & Illinois
Sidney

Sam's-Leon Mexican Supplies, Inc.
5014 South 20th Street
Omaha

Hightower Market
901 9th Avenue
Scottsbluff

Casa Las Americas
2316 N Street
Omaha
Proprietor: Señora Montelongo

Lerma's Cafe
Lyman

Sam's-Leon Mexican Supplies, Inc. in Omaha and Hightower Market in Scottsbluff sell foods, spices, and accessories essential for Mexican cooking but usually not found in the ordinary supermarket. For example: *mole* in pasta; *canela, chile caribe; ojas* (maiz leaves) for *tamales, molcajetes,* and *tortilleras* (device for pressing tortillas), made in Mexico. Casa Las Americas in Omaha sells hard-to-find canned and packaged Mexican food—*nopales* (cactus), chile, etc., Mexican and Mexican American records and 8 track tapes, weekly/monthly magazines and periodicals from Mexico, candles and other Mexican articles and artifacts.

Traditional Dance Groups

El Ballet Mestizo was organized in 1973. Presently it is comprised of two separate groups: 20 teenage youths directed by Manuel Montelongo Jr., and assisted by Julie Torres; and a younger group of dancers, 5 to 10 years old, taught by Sally Castañeda. Both groups are under the direct sponsorship of the Chicano Awareness Center, and perform regularly in the programs created by the Center, particularly for the celebration of Mexican national holidays. Like other Mexican folk-dance groups in the state, El Ballet Mestizo has the direct participation of parents, and performs regularly in its immediate community: for various church groups, for public school functions, for UNO activities, businessmen's clubs, Offut Airbase functions, and for community weddings and birthdays. The older dance group has also been video-taped by the University of Nebraska at Omaha, and those video tapes are available through the University.

La Raza Cultural Center Dance Group, directed by Yolanda Chavez, Grand Island, is approximately three years old, and includes 30 performers, ranging in age from 5 to 20 years old. Parents are involved in the sewing of costumes, with transportation for the dancers, and with fundraising activities. Its dances are traditional: the Raspa, the Negra, the Adelita (about the women's role in the Mexican Revolution of 1910), Los Viejitos, and Jesusita en Chihuahua. The group performs for the fiestas patrias and for the celebration day of Our Lady of Guadalupe, December 12, at St. Mary's Cathedral in Grand Island. As well as performing locally within the Grand Island area, the Cultural Center Dance Group has also presented its program at the Nebraska Penal Complex in Lincoln, at the Czech Days celebration at Clarkson, at the state G.I. Forum Convention in Lincoln, and has appeared on KOLN-TV, Channels 10 and 11.

The Guadalupe Dancers, directed by Carmen Montañnez Parks, Scottsbluff, is the oldest existing Mexican dance group in the state, organized around 1960 and named by the present director, Ms. Parks, in honor of Our Lady of Guadalupe. Like all of the other Mexican dance groups, The Guadalupe Dancers is an organization involving entire families of the community. Performers are children (three years and older), and youths. Costumes are designed and hand-sewn by the mothers. Fathers design and make props necessary for performances. Dances include such traditional folk material as El Jarabe Tapatio, La Bamba, Juan Colorado and Mis Huaraches. Established traditional dances, like the Jarabe, are performed as set pieces, having been learned from the elders through various generations. Some of the traditional dances have been changed. Other dances are improvised. New routines are added continually.

The group's major performance is during La Fiesta del Valle (September 16) in Scottsbluff, but it also performs extensively throughout the year—locally in the Scottsbluff area, as well as in Colorado, South Dakota, Iowa and as far as Raton, New Mexico. In 1972 The Guadalupe Dancers were featured in the NETV video-taping of La Fiesta del Valle.

Ms. Parks was born, raised, and married in Scottsbluff, and has been associated with the group from its beginnings. As far back as she can remember there has always been a September 16th fiesta in Scottsbluff. Regarding her sustained commitment to The Guadalupe Dancers, she says, "What we're trying to do is keep alive the Mexican traditions, so our children won't forget who our forefathers were and what they did."

The Mexican Cultural Development Group, directed by Sally Ybarra Dittmar, Scottsbluff, has as its main activity the performance of Mexican folk dances, though it is concerned with the more comprehensive task of studying, perpetuating and sharing Mexican and Mexican American culture in its various forms. The group was created in 1972 by the present director who was one of the original Guadalupe Dancers. It includes 65 performers (from approximately 30 families), ranging in age from three years old to adults and parents.

The entire family is involved in this cooperative effort. The youth perform, and assist with research of folk dances, costumes and music. As well as performing, parents make the costumes and props, provide transportation, baby-sit for other parents and, with the help of the youths, cook the Mexican food needed during fiestas.

Its repertoire comprises 32 dances and routines, mostly traditional material modified to some degree by the Mexican American experience; it includes the various forms of the Jarabe, Polkas, Valses, the Jota and some of the Indian Matachine dances.

With the Guadalupe Dancers, the Mexican Cultural Development

Group performs during the annual Fiesta del Valle. They perform extensively within the Scottsbluff area and other parts of the state, including
the University of Nebraska-Lincoln and Chadron State College, and in the
past have travelled to Wyoming for performances.

All of the group's support is local; most of it is self-generated.
Through performance honorariums, donations and fund raising activities,
the group is self-supporting. It also maintains a scholarship fund for its
members.

Though not a professional dancer herself, Ms. Ybarra Dittmar, the
director, has an extensive background as a performer. As a child, she was
taught the old Mexican dances by her father, a man who was a proud pure-
blooded Mexican Indian and a "Volador" dancer himself in Mexico. Ms.
Ybarra Dittmar feels very strongly about the value of Mexican cultural
forms. She says:

> We have a culture to go back to. A lot of other people
> in this country don't. They don't seem to have anything to go
> back to. I think they have the desire to find something, but
> they've lost it—their culture. During our performances, I've
> had people come up to me and say, "This is really beautiful,
> Sally, you can express your culture through dancing, which
> takes you back to your cultural background. But we really
> don't know which way to go." One girl came up to me after
> our group danced at Chadron, and said, "I'm a mess; I don't
> know which cultural background I'm going to follow, but I
> have to pick one." That sounded funny, but I guess it's true
> about a lot of people. They really don't know where they
> belong. This girl was serious. She wasn't joking. She was very
> emotional in saying that. She also told me that you can see
> the pride on the faces of our kids, and the effect it has on
> other people when we have something that says *we are defi-
> nitely Mexican* and this is what we're doing. This is a Mexican
> folk dance. This is a Mexican dinner. This is a Mexican fiesta.
> But many people can't say those things about their own cul-
> tural background. I know of other ethnic groups that defi-
> nitely have something to fall back on—like the Czechs—but
> many people don't have this. We do; and we must keep it.
>
> No, I don't think [Mexican culture] will be lost. I really
> don't, because it's really in us. And I truly believe that. You
> notice [that] when you work with other Chicanos—the kids,
> and their parents too—when you're close to other Chicanos.
> Once they get involved, it's right there—and it shows!

Theater

El Teatro Chicano, directed by Abelardo Hernandez at the Chicano Awareness Center, Omaha, is a community theater group created in 1973, and modeled after the Teatro Campesino (farmworkers' theater) which began with the César Chávez movement during the mid-sixties in California. Like the Teatro Campesino, El Teatro Chicano is bilingual and bicultural. It is specifically oriented toward articulating community cultural values, goals, and aspirations. One of its broad intentions is to enlarge the audience's awareness of social, political, and economic issues, through the use of farce, slap-stick and other forms of ethnic humor. Many of this group's productions are the plays of Luis Valdez' Teatro Campesino "Actos"—brief (15-40 minute) presentations on such themes as: the Chicano's self-defeat caused by total Americanization; the foolishness of Chicano struggling against Chicano; the innocence of the Anglo American; and the necessity for a unified community.

This teatro group is made up of high school and university-age Chicano youths. It performs in the eastern edge of the state, but mainly during the May 5th and September 16th celebrations sponsored by the Chicano Awareness Center in Omaha.

Music

Radio & TV Programs

Señora Montelongo's Mexican
  Music Program
KVNO
University of Nebraska-Omaha

Pete DeLeon's Mexican Music
  Programs
KRNY—Kearney
KHAS—Hastings

Fiesta Latina Program
KRNU
University of Nebraska-Lincoln

Father Valdez' Mexican Music
KEYR
Terrytown

Pete DeLeon's Weekly TV Program
Channel 13—Kearney

Orchestras

Los Charros
Omaha

Macias Brothers
Omaha

(Reynaldo) Cervantes y sus
Caballeros
Omaha

The Don Juans
Tropicana Lounge
Omaha

Space Odyssey
Omaha

Mariachi de Omaha
Omaha

Tequila Sunrise
Omaha

The New Revelation
Omaha

Roberto Arsiaga y su Conjunto
Lincoln

The Latins
North Platte

Los Pobres Bribones
Nebraska Penal Complex
Lincoln

The Joe Guerra Band
Kearney

The Tito Garcia Band
Scottsbluff

Los Salazars
Scottsbluff

The Tacho Moreno Conjunto
Scottsbluff

Artists and Craftsmen

The following is admittedly an incomplete list of Mexican and Mexican American artists and craftsmen. Among the obvious omissions here are all of those elders in Nebraska who do needlework, who sing and play the guitar, accordian or violin, or who seriously and for a long period of time have practiced some other art or craft. The list is intended merely to be suggestive. I suspect that a thorough survey of the state would produce a list of individuals that would be pages long.

Linda Pérez, Omaha—Fine Arts graduate from St. Mary's College, Omaha. Has worked at the Joslyn Art Museum in Omaha, taught art at the Chicano Awareness Center, and continues to do experimental painting based on Chicano themes.

Bonnie Trujillo, Omaha—Painting, weaving, dress-designing.

Don Juan Barrientos, Omaha—Handcrafting of violins and guitars.

Fernando Castillo, Omaha—Graduate of South High School in Omaha. Painting and poetry. Also edits "La Llamada."

José Sánchez, Lincoln—Painting.

Arturo Barajas, Nebraska Penal Complex, Lincoln—Poetry in Spanish and English.

Rick Roman, Grand Island—Painting.

Steve Avila, Grand Island—Painting.

Don José Ramirez, Grand Island—Musician: guitar and violin.

Mike Romero, Ogallala—Portrait painter.

The Lermas, Scottsbluff—Mural painting using pre-Columbian motifs.

Instruction

Ethnic Studies Institute, UNL. Formal university course work offered in Chicano history, ethnic heritage, literature, sociology and education.

Park Elementary School Bilingual Program, Lincoln. This was a formal Spanish-English bilingual program—the first in the state—funded by the federal government during 1974-75. Presently the program continues with local state support, with one full-time teacher devoted to the bilingual, bicultural program for students in first to sixth grades.

La Raza Cultural Center, Grand Island and the Chicano Awareness Center, Omaha in their programming offer instruction in beginning Spanish, and in traditional Mexican dance. In addition the Omaha center offers instruction in intermediate Spanish, in English as a second language, in art, and in music.

Newsletters

"The Mexican American Commission Newsletter"
Mexican American Commission
Lincoln

"La Llamada"
Chicano Awareness Center
Omaha

Libraries

La Raza Cultural Center, Grand Island—Contains, also, Mexican artifacts and film-strip series, "La Raza."

Chicano Awareness Center, Omaha—In addition to books, owns Mexican artifacts, pictures, comprehensive film-strip series on the cultural heritage of the Chicano and a copy of the film version of Rodolfo Gonzales' epic poem, *I Am Joaquin.*

Mexican American Commission, Lincoln—Books, and recordings of Mexican music.

Park Elementary School, Lincoln—Teaching aids, books, tapes, records, as well as some Mexican artifacts.

Love Library, UNL—Contains *The Journal of Mexican American History* (Box 13906, Santa Barbara, Calif.), Vol. I (Fall, 1970)-Vol. III (1973); *Aztlan: Chicano Journal of the Social Sciences and the Arts* (Chicano Cultural Center, UCLA), Vol. I, No. 1 (Spring, 1970)-present. *El Grito: A Journal of Contemporary Mexican American Thought*, Vol. I, No. 1 (Fall, 1967)-Year VII, Book 4 (June-August, 1974).

Films

The following three films can be obtained from the Bennett Martin Public Library, 14th and N Streets, Lincoln:

"Voices of La Raza," 1971, 54 minutes, color. Documentary produced by the Equal Employment Opportunity Commission. Anthony Quinn, travelling throughout the U.S., explores the problems of Chicanos in their efforts to combat job discrimination.

"The Mexican-American: Heritage and Destiny," 1971, 29 minutes, color. Dramatized identity crisis felt by character, Roberto, who in the course of the film is led to an appreciation of his cultural heritage. Ricardo Montalban narrates.

"Mexican Americans: The Invisible Minority," 1969, 38 minutes, color.

Documentary film showing social, cultural and economic problems faced by Chicanos.

The following three films can be rented from The University of California Extension Media Center, University of California, Berkeley, California 94720:

"Salt of the Earth," 1954, 90 minutes, rental $47. Important socially conscious drama directed by Herbert J. Biberman during the McCarthy period. Suppressed in U.S. until 1965. Chronicle of a strike by Chicano zinc miners in a company-owned town in New Mexico. Strike issues affecting working conditions for the men are enlarged to include more far-reaching issues affecting the entire living conditions of the people, including women's equality.

"El Teatro Campesino," 1971, 60 minutes, rental $21. History of the Luiz Valdez' folk theater which had its origin with the Cesar Chavez farmworkers' movement during the mid-sixties. El Teatro as guerilla theater—performs musical numbers, a satirical skit, and a puppet show.

"Yo Soy Chicano," 1972, 60 minutes, color, rental $35. History of the Chicano from the pre-Columbian period to present. Leaders interviewed include Dolores Huerta (United Farmworkers Organizing Committee); Reies Lopez Tijerina (Federal Alliance of Free States, New Mexico); Rodolfo "Corky" Gonzales (Crusade for Justice, Denver); and Jose Angel Gutierrez (La Raza Unida Party—Chicano political party, Texas). Directed by Jesus Trevino for National Educational Television, Spanish with English subtitles and narration.

Other Films

"I Am Joaquin," 1969, 20 minutes, color. Can be obtained from Chicano Awareness Center, Omaha, or Lincoln Public Schools, Lincoln. Dramatizes Rodolfo Gonzales' historical poem of the same title. Concerns Chicano identity based on rediscovery and acceptance of the past. Produced by El Teatro Campesino.

"Requiem 29: Racism and Police Repression Against Chicanos," 1971, 36 minutes, color, rental $35. Can be obtained from Tricontinental Film Center, P.O. Box 4430, Berkeley, California 94704—telephone: (415) 548-3204. Documentary of the historic Chicano Moratorium in August, 1970, Los Angeles. Anti-Vietnam War demonstration which resulted in death of journalist Ruben Salazar. "Requiem 29" was directed by David Garcia and was the first film about Chicanos made by a Chicano film-maker. It won a Bronze medal for Best Documentary—Atlanta International Film Festival, 1971.

"Viva la Causa: A Documentary Film on the Mexican Mural Movement in Chicago," rental $12. Can be obtained from Kartemquin Films, 1901 W. Wellington, Chicago, Illinois—telephone: (312) 472-4366. Documents influence of the 20th century Mexican Muralists on contemporary Chicano painters from Chicago. Chicano muralist explains the art work. Community members comment on what the murals mean to them.

El Calendario Chicano

There are a number of different Chicano calendars printed every year. The best, probably, is "El Calendario Chicano," published and distributed by the Southwest Network, a non-profit educational research and publication center. The calendar contains a history of the Chicano, related through over 400 significant events from Chicano history on the day and month they occurred. In addition, each month on the calendar is decorated with original art work by contemporary Chicano artists. The Calendario sells for $3, and can be ordered from:

> El Calendario Chicano
> Southwest Network
> 1020 B Street, Suite 8
> Hayward, California 94541

Fiestas

Celebrations of Mexican Independence Day:

> La Fiesta del Valle (September 15-16)
> Scottsbluff

> Chicano Inmate Organization (September 16)
> (Mexican Awareness Through Association)
> Nebraska Penal Complex

Chicano Awareness Center (September 15-16)
Omaha

Mexican American Students Association (September 16)
University of Nebraska-Lincoln

La Raza Cultural Center (September 16)
Grand Island

May 5 Celebration (Mexico's defeat of the French at Puebla):

Our Lady of Guadalupe Church
Scottsbluff

Chicano Awareness Center
Omaha

Chicano student organizations at Nebraska Western, UNL and UNO sponsor an annual fiesta, usually in the spring. Music, food, dance, films, speakers. Aztlan organization at Nebraska Western also sponsors an annual fiesta organized around a Chicano art show-competiton.

G.I. Forum Dances:

At least once a month, at different areas in the state, the four Nebraska chapters of the National American G.I. Forum organization (Omaha, Lincoln, Grand Island and Scottsbluff) sponsor Chicano social dances. Also sponsor an annual queen contest to represent the state at the annual national convention of the organization.

Chicano Basketball and Softball Tournaments:

These are held at different times in Omaha, Grand Island and North Platte, sponsored by local Chicano athletic associations or by other community groups. Most of the participating teams are from Nebraska, some also from Colorado and Kansas. These tournaments are the occasion of more than athletics. Usually the tournament is the main activity around which a fiesta is created—with food and the indispensible dance at the end of the tournament.

Collections of Art, Artifacts and Handcrafts

Though there are small, individual collections of needlework and handcrafts throughout the state, the only organized and substantial collection of Mexican and Chicano artifacts in Nebraska, to my knowledge, is at the University of Nebraska State Museum—Lincoln. Almost all of the items are Mexican (i.e., from Mexico); a large majority of them have been donated to the University by the Mexican government. Included in this collection are blankets, costumes, needlework, pottery, straw-work, ceramics and handcrafts. This collection is not on permanent display, but can nevertheless be seen by making arrangements with the museum.

Oral History

The Mexican elders in Nebraska—those early immigrants referred to in the essay—constitute a source of information and wisdom that has yet to be properly appreciated, and recorded for posterity. To date, no serious historical, social, or cultural study has been made of the Mexicans in Nebraska. Nor has there been any serious attempt at preservation of personal histories, outside of a few family histories, that I am aware of. In this regard, Nebraska is not significantly different from other midwestern states, since almost all historical studies of Chicanos begin with the experience in Mexico, and end with the experience of the Mexican immigrant and his children in the southwestern part of the United States.

Since most of the early Mexican immigrants to Nebraska came as railroad crew-hands or as sugar beet field workers, the records of the Great Western Sugar Company and of the Union Pacific and the Burlington Railroad are of some importance for writing the history of the Mexicans in this state. At least equally important to that historical study, however, are the life experiences of those early immigrants themselves—their personal histories: point of origin in Mexico or the Southwest; experiences in Mexico during the early 1900's; active participation in the Mexican Revolution; experiences crossing the Mexican-United States border; experiences with U.S. immigration authorities, labor contractors and employers; participation in World War I; association, if any, with the I.W.W.; experience as unwanted "foreigners" during the economic depression of the '30's.

As stated above, the Mexican elders in Nebraska constitute the base for Mexican culture and history in the state. Oral transmission of this culture and history to succeeding generations, however, appears to be weakening. From talking with college-age Chicanos, and with "the old ones"—their grandparents—I note with regret that there is a continuously widening gap between generations in the Chicano communities in this state. Because of those assimilationist pressures already mentioned, it becomes more and more difficult for children to talk with parents; and it becomes almost utterly impossible in some cases for the children to talk with grandparents. A disturbingly large number of the elders that I spoke with regretted the fact that since they themselves could speak very little English, and since their grandchildren could speak no Spanish whatsoever— there could be no communication between them.

The oldest person I spoke with during the interviews for this essay was 86 years old; the "youngest" was 74. All were born in Mexico; all arrived in Nebraska during the first quarter of the century. The conclusions are clear: in ten years (by 1986), there will be few if any Mexico-born Nebraskans who lived through the upheaval in Mexico that caused, in part, the massive immigration waves resulting in the presence of so many Mexican Americans in this state. In the past, personal and family histories have been preserved after the death of elders, and passed on to succeeding generations. It appears that such is not the case in the present period. It thus becomes crucial that, in some formal and methodical manner, those personal histories be recorded.

III

Black People:
The Nation-Building Vision

By Lillian Anthony-Welch

ACKNOWLEDGMENTS

There are people who inspire you and there are people who encourage you—Paul Olson is a person who does both. He provided the writer and the black community with a vehicle for self-expression—to him we in Nebraska shall always be indebted. The black chapter work was assisted by the following persons: Liz Hruska, Karen Adams, Susan D. Furlow, and Ann R. Ventry. In addition, many of the older people listed in the catalogue were interviewed for the chapter by students in the Black Studies Social Science 200 class. Ann Ventry was responsible for the graciousness of Louvenia Butler's sharing her life and wisdom with us. I would also like to thank the collective black community for their perseverance which made the writing even possible. Pictures came from Perspectives Afrikan Commercial Photography. The Nebraska State Historical Society assisted with some references.

Malcolm X speaking to Charles Washington, Omaha black community leader and promoter of black enterprises. Malcolm X was born in Omaha, has a museum dedicated to his memory there, and is the main symbol of the growing sense of the need for a separate black identity which emerged from the white race riot in 1919 and surrounding community events. Malcolm's tradition grows also out of the Garvey tradition of his father, the Reverend Earl Little, an Omaha preacher.

Above. Zethro Brooks, black homesteader presently living in Omaha, Nebraska, and a useful resource concerning the history of black homesteading.

Above. The receipt for Zethro Brooks homestead given in 1913 at Broken Bow.

Louvenia Butler, one of the oldest persons interviewed for the oral history background to this essay (see chapter for her interview). Ms. Butler has clear memories of tales of slave days and of returns to Africa ("home") told her by relatives who had been slaves. A 1904 study of black people in Lincoln contains several reflections of interviews with Lincolnites who had been slaves and also displays their interest in their African identity.

Black music in Omaha came in all kinds: *Upper*, Jimmy Jewel was the owner of the Musicland Dance Hall, and his mother sang in the world-famous Fisk Jubilee Singers *(below);* Charles Williamson, reflecting black prominence in the musical world, was president of the musicians' union *center).*

THE FISK JUBILEE SINGERS.

One of the continuing strengths of the black community in Nebraska has been the strength of black women. *Above,* the headquarters of the Nebraska Association of Colored Women's Clubs. *Below,* picture of 1944 leaders in the third annual meeting of Nebraska Association of Colored Women's Clubs.

Sometimes it is useful to recall the strengths of people who fought their way through the harsh and racist system which began after the Civil War and grew harsher as the 19th century rolled along and culminated in the 1915-30 and 1960 struggles. One such person was Robert Taylor, born in York, Nebraska, in the 19th century. He was a medical doctor and distinguished spokesman for his people. The portfolio which follows is such a recollection. *Above and below: Robert Taylor's medical certificates.*

Above. Robert Taylor's school at York and *below,* his 1905 high school certificate.

Above, Taylor as a high school student, and *below,* a basketball player at York.

Above. Taylor and a York athletic team.

Below. Taylor graduated from the University of Nebraska at Lincoln, was on its athletic teams, and made a name for himself at guard in football.

Taylor at Creighton where he received his M.D. degree in 1912. *Above,* the cadaver room; *below left,* the class portrait and *below right,* the degree parchment.

III

Black People: The Nation-Building Vision

It is all but impossible to know much about the African-American experience without considering the experience as a three-pronged experience: first, the African experience; secondly, the slave experience; and third, the African-American experience.

Africa is the oldest continent on earth so far as man is concerned. It is where man began. Until recently, Africa has been presented as the "dark continent." The question has to be asked: Why was Africa presented as the "dark continent?" If one visits European museums, for instance the Museum of Folk Art or Frobenius Institute in Frankfurt or the British Museum in London, one finds artifacts which are astonishing—countless and priceless artifacts from the continent of Africa which present evidences of a bright and illuminating civilization. There are carvings, clothing, mantels, jewelry, sculptures in gold, ivory and brass, all interlaced with precious stones and with the symbolic imagery representing the philosophy of life of the peoples who created the work. Of course, since Europeans possessed easy access to the continent of Africa, the technology to subdue, and the communication vehicles for interpreting the African civilizations through mass media, they were able to conceal the truth about African culture. By concealing the truth, Europeans were, in turn, in a position to elevate their own prestige—making themselves superior and others inferior. It is now known that learning and culture were significantly alive in Africa from the very earliest times and particularly from the 8th through the 16th and 17th centuries. Universities, governmental systems, and religious systems were thriving in Africa at the time when Europe was enshrouded in that period referred to as the 'Dark Ages'. Although the Atlantic slave trade and, later, colonialism were to bring a cultural eclipse to Africa, they did not erase the fact that there existed, at many different times and places on that continent, numerous highly developed cultures.

Until the twentieth century, most people also accepted the belief that the African-American had no past worth mentioning or that, in any case, the ancestors of Africans came from such widely scattered parts of Africa that none of their meager cultural inheritance could have survived. Melville J. Herskovits, in his book, *The Myth of the Negro Past,* addressed this issue and, in the course of that book and his other writings, did much to dispel the notion that African culture did not survive in the Western Hemisphere. So did other scholars, such as Paul Robeson, Drs. W.E. DuBois, Carter G. Woodson, Leo Wiener, Charles H. Wesley, and John Hope Franklin.

> The survival of varying degrees of African culture in America does not suggest that there has been only a limited adjustment of the Negro to the New World situation. To the contrary, it merely points up the fact that he came out of an experience that was sufficiently entrenched to make possible the persistence of some customs and traditions. . . . After all, perhaps the survival of Africanisms in the New World was as great as it was because of the refusal of the members of the dominant group in America to extend, without reservations, their own culture to the Negroes who they brought over.[1]

The Atlantic slave also contributed to the distorted image of Africa and its inhabitants. Africa was truly dissipated beginning in the fifteenth century, a dissipation which culminated in the absolute oppression and colonialism of the eighteenth and nineteenth centuries. As one writer indicates:

. . . the finest flower of African youth had been wiped out with bullets, swords and knives; by starvation and exposure to the elements; and by suicide and sheer fatigue during the long marches from the interland to the sea-coast. But these were only some of the means by which they died, since many died in the ships while crossing the Atlantic and Indian Oceans. The finest flower in any country's population consists essentially of its young ones in the prime of their youth and those middle-aged persons possessing the finest skills. These two groups are usually those with the greatest vested interests which they are prepared to defend to the bitter end whenever such interests are threatened. It is they who are also the healthiest and strongest in any society. Therefore, they are usually the ones who suffer most in cases of invasions and wars. Perhaps the best proof of this in Africa is the fact that 44 percent of Africa's population in 1971 was below the age of fifteen years, 60 percent of the population was under eighteen years of age in the same period. These figures show a huge generation gap which will take a long time to even out. It shows that at some time in the not too remote past, the sires of most Africans had been elderly men. Thanks to their virility even in old age, it went a long way in ensuring the continuation of the African race in the face of threatening extinctions.[2]

There is every reason to believe that significant features of African culture survived the night of slavery: the circle game, the folk tales of spider and his relatives, the religion of inspiration and possession, the arrangement of group dance, art, and games in circles, and the use of basic patterns developed through inspired improvisational schema—all are both African and African-American. Most of all, the children are treated alike in both cultures. There are four African proverbs which bear witness to the African appreciation of the "finest of flowers": the children.[3]

Proverb 1. "There is no wealth where there are no children." Among the African communities and the African-American communities, the children have always been regarded as persons of great value. The value expressed is based on the belief that true happiness includes the children. Children were of great help to the parents. Historically, it is important to note that the old and aged parents of the African people passed into the care of their children, and that this is true yet today in African-American rural communities of long standing which have not been uprooted by the recent out-migrations from the South or the ministrations of culturally insensitive 'social welfare.'

Proverb 2. "Children are the wisdom of the nation." This proverb recognizes that children are frank, trusting and friendly. It is, I think, a proverb which not only describes African children, but many, many children in African-American communities.

Proverb 3. "A child saw a war that destroyed a city." The significance here is that the children as they grow have experiences which provide knowledge and wisdom: thus, it is expected that they should show knowledge from experience. Often anthropologists and students of human behavior who look at black American communities such as Liebow, DuBois, Abrahams or Malcolm X, describe our children in ways that suggest that they are knowing beyond their years.

Proverb 4. "One who loves the children of his fellow will surely love his own children." It has been said that the truest test of love is to love sincerely that which is not one's own, whereas it is common and easy for a man to love and value things that are closely related to him or are actually his own. People who are unkind to children are often rebuked with this proverb. The degree to which African-Americans in their battle for the schools have fought not 'for their own' but for other people's children suggests that the sense of this proverb still has meaning.

If one takes a look at these proverbs, one can understand why women taken in slavery killed their babies and themselves. Even the children taken into slavery, who had a sense of being loved and endowed with wisdom, revolted against being captured, even if their actions meant death.

Of the many who chose to live, some chose to live in

perpetual hope of rebellion. An example of the wisdom and experience of the captured is Cinque, son of a Mendi chief of Sierra Leone, West Africa, who was captured in 1839 by Portuguese slave traders. He was taken on the ship *Amistad.* The ship had set sail for Havana, Cuba, to the Island of Principe with the slaves. Cinque plotted an escape with other slaves and subsequently took control of the ship. Lt. Gedney of the U.S. Navy then captured the ship and brought it under the jurisdiction of the Connecticut courts.

The Spanish minister demanded the return of Cinque's ship and the slaves. A Hartford, Connecticut judge rendered the first decision in the case, ruling that the ship, cargo and slaves should be surrendered to the judicial decision of the United States (the defense attorney was John Quincy Adams, who was 73 years old, in poor health and almost blind). In his second ruling, the judge ruled in behalf of the *Amistad.* The Africans should not be placed in custody of the President, but must be freed immediately! [4]

This fight for freedom, this appreciation of children of future generations' freedom, did not end with the *Amistad* story but has continued to the present day. The original committee which was formed to assist Cinque and the other Africans became the American Missionary Association which founded 500 schools which still exist today and include Dillard and Fisk Universities, Houston-Tillotson, LeMoyne, Talladega and Tougaloo Colleges, colleges now also supported through the United Negro College Fund drive which makes a major effort in Nebraska. The story also continues in the form of the Amistad Research Center and Race Relations Department at Fisk University.

Africans and the Settlement of the American Continent, Including the Plains

A growing body of research suggests that Africans were among the first permanent settlers of America. In fact, some scholars believe that it was an African explorer who made the

first voyage to the New World. One such example is cited by
Peter Martyr, who states that Balboa found Africans when he
landed in 1513. Supposedly these Africans were from Ethiopia.
Other evidences have been cited by Professor Leo Wiener of
Harvard who writes (in his *Africa and the Discovery of Amer-
ica*), that African-Americans may have come before the
Spaniards. Moreover, the Spanish explorer deLeon had Africans
with him in 1528. The African presence came very early.[5]

But the presence very quickly turned from a presence to
an oppression. The 16th century Spanish conquistadores very
soon learned to enslave the Boricuan Indians in the West Indies.
And when Boricuans died, Africans were sought by the millions
to replace them.

African culture and heritage continued in the New World,
manifested differently, of course, but it is evident that even in
bondage the African continued to build communities. Skilled
laborers, who were builders of the new colonies, brought past
experience into their servitude. Builders who cleared the lands
contributed to the industrial revolution, for it was their univer-
sality and their heritage which prevented their creativity from
being stifled. Africans, in spite of their bondage, became some
of the great inventors of industrial machinery which revolution-
ized America—new shoe lasts, lubrication systems, steam boil-
ers, vacuum evaporating pans, etc.[6] As the revolutionary efforts
of the African-Americans began when they were first sold into
slavery, these fires also continue kindled in the hearts and minds
of all ebony people to the present days.

Yet this ebony person—so like the stone-like wood, hard
and with varied mixtures of beauty—black, brown, tan, white—
was not destroyed. Unfortunately there has been a great emphasis placed on the fact that the ebony person came to the New
World as a "slave." The image which the word "slave" conjures
up is that of a sub-human being, speaking no intelligible language, uttering gibberish or guttural animal-like sounds. This
sub-human was perceived as innately immoral, ugly, and unable
to think; he was seen as cursed with the curses of Ham and
Cain; and, therefore, all his acts had to be governed by a master

who would civilize and Christianize him and prepare him for freedom in the next world if not in this.[7]

The imagery which treats white men as superhuman and other races as dependent is almost as prevalent today as it was during the slave period. Originally black and white 'bondsmen' were treated pretty much alike. During the 16th and 17th centuries slaves were eligible to become free after five or more years of service; they could become free citizens, depending on the contractual arrangements. But later, freedmen became as much a threat as abolitionists in that they represented the possibility that black people could rule themselves. They represented an image of freedom which might inspire the slaves to rebel as they did in Haiti and elsewhere during the late 18th and early 19th century revolutionary period. The first person to die in the American Revolution was an African-American who was fighting for *his* freedom.[8] (The Daughters of the American Revolution still refuse to accept this fact; they claim that Crispus Attucks "was a rioter and trouble-maker.") At this point in time, Africans, Indians and Europeans were treated as indentured servants, and Africans were not necessarily singled out as different from any other indentured group. The inevitable question then is: What conditions created nineteenth and twentieth century racism toward people of color?

Although the Africans were listed and treated in the early 1600's as servants and their relationships with others were generally confined to their being in servitude, color was not yet a necessary reason for scorn. The early colonial population was made up of large numbers of white and black bondsmen who basically had the same economic and political status. At this time "color" was not an issue among the bondsmen or the lords and masters. It was in the middle seventeenth century (1600's), when the American economic system was being developed in its classical capitalistic form, in connection with European systems having a similar character, that red and black persons were dehumanized and treated as chattel. Heredity became the criteria which determined whether a person was a slave or free. In December, 1662, Virginia declared:

Whereas some doubts have arisen whether children got by an
Englishman upon a Negro woman shall be a slave or free, Be
it therefore enacted and declared by this present grand assembly that all children born in this country shall be held, bond
or free only according to the condition of the mother.[9]. . .

It is clear, then, that slavery, as it was institutionalized,
came to be based on race. The legitimization of slavery had its
beginnings in the Virginia legislature, where much of the Bicentennial History also begins, and the legitimizing process continued throughout the states from the 1660's through the
1850's and early '60's until finally the slaves became the property of the master, having no human rights or privileges, a denial
based solely on the pigmentation of their skins. Through these
acts, words, declarations and laws which were part of our
colonial history and which were followed by similar acts, words,
and laws at the time of the American Revolution, the first
colonists institutionalized human slavery in America and the
concept of the "Negro" as naturally, deservedly subservient and
enslaved emerged.

Once enslavement was legalized, the consequences were
devastating. Black people could not own property, retain possession of their earnings, or have any legal control over their
children. All legal rights were denied, the most important being
franchise, the essential instrument for correcting wrongs. With
these conditions, all blacks were deprived of educational opportunities that would provide the necessary ingredients for liberation. Against these overwhelming injustices, however, the
African-American campaigned forcefully, using persuasion,
rebellion and revolts to change them. Liberty was sought by
individuals for the collective good of African people by various
means. Robert Alexander Young, for example, authored a
piece called "The Ethiopian Manifesto" in 1829; in the same
year David Walker made "An Appeal to the Colored Citizens
of the World." Martin Delaney's critical analysis of African
people was published in 1855 under the very long title *The
Condition, Elevation, Emigration and Destiny of the Colored*

People of the United States. Frederick Douglass wrote his autobiography titled *My Bondage & My Freedom* in 1855 and campaigned for the liberation of black people all of his life. Organizations which reflected the same spirit were: the African Civilization Society, the African Baptist Society, African Emigration Association, the African Methodist Episcopal Church, African Methodist Episcopal Zion Church and The African Society. The struggle against servitude was carried on by individuals as well as organized groups.

It is worthy to note that the reference to the "self" was African; "Negro" had not appeared as a part of the black nomenclature. At the turn of the century, the National Association for Advancement of Colored People and the Urban League incorporated the term Negro. "The French are from France, the Irish are from Ireland, the English are from England, the Germans are from Germany, the Negro is from where? Is there a negroland? Only slaves and dogs are named by the masters, men name themselves."

The American Revolution and the Origins of Nebraska: A Black Perspective

Some years ago (1968) a Nebraska black leader, Senator (then Mr.) Ernest Chambers, called attention to the limited commitment to freedom which characterized the careers of the fathers of the revolution.[10] The conference was an education conference dedicated to considering professionalism and community control in education. Mr. Chambers mentioned Washington's slave holding and Jefferson's black mistress as signs of the "half revolution" which we had then. When Mr. Chambers spoke, some historians present treated him as getting the Jefferson history ludicrously wrong. Since then, historians have established that Jefferson's interest in his black mistress was almost surely the basis for his failure to stand up for what his conscience told him was right and his uneasy compromises with and rationalizations of slavery. The same sort of tired compromise went into the formation of Nebraska as a state (though it was supposed to be a free, non-slave holding territory and a free, post-Civil War state).

In 1866 Nebraska was attempting to receive statehood, and its constitution reflected the far reaching effect of the color malady even as the original national constitution did:

> The Nebraska constitution restricted the suffrage to *Free White Males.* This was not an oversight occasioned by the manner in which the constitution was rushed through the legislature: The House of Representatives had voted down a resolution to strike the restriction from the constitution by the resounding margin of thirty-six to two. Negro suffrage had been debated by historical legislatures all during the war, but it had never been more than an academic question in Nebraska, where there were few, if any potential Negro voters. Even so, the preponderance of sentiment against it in 1866 is surprising. . . .
>
> General John M. Thayer, who had acted as an intermediary between Congress and the territory, carried a certified copy of the Act to Washington, and on March 1, 1867, President Johnson reluctantly signed a proclamation admitting Nebraska as the thirty-seventh state.[11]

Though the state of Nebraska intended to be a state which confined suffrage to free, white males, it was not without its debts to African-Americans at the time of its founding. We all like folklore and legend, and it is even more enjoyable when we sometimes discover that a fabled hero's story is really true. Many have heard about the legendary York and his escapades; they were not just fantastic stories. York, a slave, servant, interpreter and mediator, was with the Lewis and Clark expedition and the 1804 accounts suggest that he was not the totally oppressed slave that many blacks had become by the turn of the century. Lerone Bennett, in his recent book *The Shaping of Black America,* writes:

> "It was the Negro," Cabeza de Vaca, the Spanish York who came to public attention as the guide of the Lewis and Clark expedition of 1803. Although he was a slave, York was

one of the most important men in the expedition. Olin D. Wheeler said, "His color, kinky hair, size, and prodigious strength were a revelation to the Indians and he was looked upon as a very god. He was the greatest kind of great 'medicine' and the tribes from the north of Missouri to the mouth of the Columbia took particular pains to propitiate his sable majesty. And he was so overwhelmed with feminine attention." York served as scout, interpreter, and "medicine man" and was generally the center of attention among the Indians. On one occasion William Clark noted that ". . . the three great Chiefs (of the Arikaras) and many others came to see us today . . . much astonished at my black servant, who did not lose the opportunity of (displaying) his powers of strength, etc., etc. . . ." The next day Clark noted: "Those Indians were much astonished at my Servent, they never saw a black man before; all flocked around him and examined him from top to toe. He carried on the joke and made himself more terrible than we wished him to do." It should not be thought, however, that York was a minstrel. At one meeting a chief ran his fingers across York's face to see if the black would rub off. York whipped out his knife and fixed the offender with his eyes. This incident became a part of the legend of the Nez Perce tribe whose chroniclers said the black man "make big eyes much white in eyes and look fierce at chief."

Along with his other duties, York served as interpreter. Charles McKenzie, of the North West Company, said that "a mulatto (York), who spoke bad French and worse English, served as interpreter to the Captains, so that a single word to be understood by the party required to pass from the Natives to the woman to the husband, from the husband to the mulatto, from the mulatto to the captains."

Although the evidence is not conclusive, there are some indications that York later cast his lot with the Indians. In 1832, a trapper said he met a black chief of the Crows who said he had accompanied Lewis and Clark on their expedition. The black chief, who is probably York, was "residing in the Crow village at the junction of Bighorn and Stinking rivers . . . had . . . four Indian wives and possessed much reputation and influence among the Crows."[12]

Because there is a York, Nebraska, some people have speculated about possible African-American backgrounds which may account for the naming of this town. Was it named after York, the African? Lillian B. Fitzpatrick has researched the name and tells us that York, Nebraska was named by "Mr. Wooley, who owned the land named for a resident family."[13]

After York and Lewis and Clark had completed their exploring work and further surveying was completed, first the hunters, trappers and herders came and then the settlers. Black settlement in Nebraska began with the pioneers and the wagon trails, and with them came injustice and racism. Though the wheel of fortune often turned for the whites seeking economic relief, the very opposite of economic relief often followed or preceded the black pioneer. Although the territorial census of November, 1854, listed only four slaves in Nebraska (in Richardson County) there was one or more slaves among the settlers in Niobrara County in 1855, and in 1857 one man in Otoe County is recorded as having five slaves. Later, in 1858, a bill was introduced to abolish slavery, but it was not enacted.[14]

Nebraska was not only a new territory for settlement for blacks, but often was used by slave owners to illegally transport slaves who had escaped by the underground railroad. The slave owners used wagons with false bottoms to bring the slaves back to Missouri. As late as 1860, Nebraska, New Mexico and Utah had only 24 black people in each territory; yet, this tiny group was barred from voting or from serving in the armed forces. Blacks were also being legislated against in Nebraska by personalities such as Governor Black, who in 1860 vetoed the territorial legislation to abolish slavery. The stories about slavery in Nebraska are neither so dramatic or brutal as those about the great plantations in the South recounted by Frederick Douglass or Frederick Law Olmstead in his *The Cotton Kingdom* but they do tell us one thing: that before the state was founded, African-American people could be bought and sold at sheriff-sponsored events and without sufficient express public concern for the human rights of the black men and women sold to stop a public sale:

Early in 1860, C.J. Holly of Nebraska City borrowed $300.00 from William H. Hall. He gave a mortgage on his two old household servants whose names were Hercules and Martha. When the debt came due, Mr. Hall foreclosed the mortgage. The slaves were sold as a result at a sheriff's sale in Nebraska City. Mr. Hall bid them in so as to recover the money he had loaned Mr. Hall, and he immediately after, took the slaves to Missouri. The sale of these slaves at public auction brought about great disapproval in Otoe County. That same summer, the assessor listed for taxation purposes a Negro girl about twelve years old, whom a Missourian had brought to Nebraska when he and his wife settled on a farm South of Nebraska City. The farmer made an unsuccessful protest against his taxation. This twelve-year-old girl was perhaps the last slave recorded in Nebraska territory.[15]

The Post-Civil War Days: Homesteading

After Nebraska had created a constitution which limited suffrage to free white males, after it had permitted, in its territory, the sale of black people at public auction, it is not surprising that the post-Civil War history was what it was. The post-Civil War period saw the growth of the Ku Klux Klan in the South and its gradual spread northward until it became a major force in Nebraska in the 1920's and appearances of occasional lynchings and killings of black people without intervention from the law (the best known of these were the Klan's attacks on the house of Malcolm X's father in Omaha recorded in the beginning of the *Autobiography of Malcolm X* [1925] and the 1919 race riot in Omaha in which one black man was shot over a thousand times by an angry white mob which had picked out an innocent man on whom to vent its fury). Black people were gradually placed in the worst possible employment situations in the post-Civil War period and denied any fundamental human rights in Nebraska—now not because the constitution denied them, but because state authority failed to act to protect black rights all too often. But African-American people after

the Civil War endeavored to participate in the same "land of
opportunity" push which brought people of European extraction to Nebraska to find land and a better life.[16]

The brief chronology included in the appendixes may be
helpful to the unfamiliar in noting the progressive migration of
blacks to Nebraska: Tom Brown, who participated in buffalo
hunts in the 1840's; Sally Bayne, who was the first black settler
in 1855; the black ex-slaves who came to Nebraska in the '60's
and '70's; Robert Anderson, a black ex-slave who became the
first black homesteader in 1870; Charles Meehan, who formed
the black colony at Overton, Nebraska (1885) and a second
colony in DeWitty in Cherry County (1907)—all of these
stories are important.

African-Americans who migrated and settled in Nebraska
did so as individuals, but some settled in African-American
colonies. Such was the case of William Walker and Charles
Meehan. Each family staked a claim near Overton, in Dawson
County. The homes of these early settler-pioneers were not too
different from the African-Americans' motherland, for many
of the homes in their motherland were made of sod-earth
homes. This community flourished and eventually there
were founded all of the necessary establishments needed: the
Post Office, a grocery store, a church, and a school—with African-Americans servicing all of these establishments. This colony
lasted for approximately 33 years. Some of this group went to
found a colony near Brownlee in Cherry County in 1905.
The last African-American to leave Brownlee went in about
1940.

A relative of a few of the early black pioneers provides
us with insight into the everyday lives of the black homesteaders. Mrs. Lue Day, granddaughter of the Charles Meehan
who moved to Overton, Nebraska, in 1885 and later moved
with a black community north and west of Brownlee, Nebraska
in the Kinkaid country in the "Sandhills," writes:

> Grandpa moved to Overton, Nebraska in 1885 and took
> up a homestead, but someone else had taken it before—then
> moved on without clearing the title in some way so that

Grandpa was not able to get title to the land, so he moved to Cherry County for he wanted to stay in Nebraska. I think I said he was white, and Grandma Meehan was colored. Color never made a difference to Grandpa. You were a person and a man and a lady. Of course, most of the people were of mixed parentage somewhere back in their lives, as a picture of old timers will show you.

George Brown [another black settler in the area] also came from North Buxton. He and his wife were both part Indian, and also Seventh-day Adventists. He really had two Sundays, for he also respected your Sunday. But if he had hay on the ground—not raked up at sundown Friday—or potatoes plowed up but not picked up, it stayed there till Monday morning. Even if the hay got rained on or the potatoes got frosted. He did not turn a lick of work on Saturday. He'd do just what was necessary on Sunday to wind up Friday's work. But if you had trouble on Saturday and asked him to help you, he would say, "The ox is in the ditch" and help you willingly. . . .

As to the taking up of homesteads in Cherry County, my grandfather, Charles H. Meehan was about the first. My mother, Rosetta, her brother Dennis, and a William Crawford and George Brown, drove through with three wagons from Overton to about twelve miles up the North Loup River from Brownlee to take up homesteads. My mom (Rosetta) drove one wagon, Uncle Den drove another, and Mr. Brown rode with Uncle Den. Mr. Crawford drove his own wagon, Charles Meehan and Crawford both had homesteads that bordered on the Loup River. Mr. Brown's set back aways—but only about one third a mile. They built sod houses—everyone did, as there was and still is no lumber available there by natural growth. Except cottonwood. Meehan planted one fourth mile of cottonwoods and they are still standing. He also planted a few evergreens, but never cut any of them. Crawford lived in a half dugout at first, open air style, till he got his home built.

There were only bullsnakes and garter snakes in the Sandhills, If you killed a bullsnake on Grandpa Meehan's place, you got told about it. He maintained they kept down rats and other rodents. Only if they were around the house could a bullsnake be killed. There were some people named

Stewart who lived straight south of us. On Big Creek we rented
hay land from them, and in the spring on the north side of the
creek below a big "blow-out" was a garter snake den. I remembered one day when Howard and Lena killed 86. The next day
I went with them and we killed 65.

It was over there on Big Creek that we kids broke the
driving horses to ride. After preliminary taming, Dad would let
us drive them on a four horse team going with the hayrack to
feed the range cattle and bring back a load of hay for use at
the barn. We'd drive the horses head on up to the stack so they
couldn't easily get away, and crawl across their backs till
gradually they tamed down so we could sit astride.

Everyone ate plenty of grouse, prairie chicken and rabbit. If you got fresh meat and weren't going straight home,
you pulled out the entrails and stuffed it with grass. Fresh
green grass. Refrigeration, or even ice boxes, was only at the
drug store for ice cream, and as I remember, ice cream could
only be bought in the summer. Of course, lots of people had
an ice cream freezer they used in winter for making home
made ice cream from a custard base. And potatoes and such
were stored in a deep hole in the ground covered with hay and
tarp if you had no cellar. I will remember having to eat frozen
potatoes to "remind you to stuff the hay back tightly in the
hole next time you get some potatoes out" (quote from my
parents). Every member of the family had to eat the frozen
potatoes so we all remembered. My parents stuck together
when it came to discipline with us kids. . . .

Uncle Den raised cane and had a mill where he ground
and cooked it and sold the sorghum in gallon pails for 40
cents. Aunt Ida's sister, Esther Shores, also taught school at
District 113. She was a pretty girl, but we kids teased her because she was scared to walk across the footbridge between us
and Grandpa Meehan's shed crawl. If I remember rightly, the
members of the school board put up and maintained the footbridge. It was a suspension type, put across at the most narrow
spot, therefore the deepest, and Esther lost more books, pen-
cils, etc. till the school kids would carry her things across.

When we homesteaded, Dad planted quite a few trees of
various kinds, including Black Hills spruce. We watered and
watered them, but in the '60's there were only six trees left. We

used to put hay in the roads for better traction. I remember Dad working on the county roads at that job.

Aside from [a] stolen saddle horse, I can remember once having anything stolen—that was after we moved the homestead. One night when Dad was away freighting and someone (there were two on horseback) put 67 chickens in sacks and rode off with them. They were beautiful big Buff Orpingtons— just fryer size—we heard them and old Shep tried to bark them away. Howard wanted to take the shotgun and go out, but Mom wouldn't let him. The hen house sat closer to the hill than the house and it wasn't till they rode off that we could see them.

The women wore riding skirts—great voluminous skirts that looked like long dresses but were really riding skirts— divided skirts much like the culottes of today, only there were yards and yards to each leg. And most of the women I remember who did ride horseback rode astride—a few rode side saddle—all were excellent riders. I don't suppose anyone forgot the time Mrs. Griffith and her two children were walking over the hills to a party at Curtis' and Mrs. Griffith picked up a pretty white scarf in the road, thinking someone else had lost it and she might return it. But the scarf was the broad white stripe down the back of a skunk.

Every fall a group of the men—sometimes a group of the ladies—would take two or three wagons and go up on the Snake River northwest of our settlement and pick wild plums, grapes and cherries to be made into jelly and jam. They'd go and stay three-four days to a week. Closer to home we picked chokecherries, ground cherries, plums, grapes—but they weren't so plentiful as on the Snake River. The Sandhills had good water and it was soft.

Dad did a lot of freighting for people. And always hauled the coal for the school. He freighted from Seneca with a four-horse team. Took two days to go and two days to come back about 40 miles. I remembered him saying how much easier pulling it was for the horses when we got a wide-tired wagon. And to keep the tires tight you just crossed the river and came back to get the wood good and wet. Dad broke a lot of mules and horses to drive when he was freighting.

Daddy Hannah "wasn't very well thought of by the Negro community." If you wanted a haircut you had to go to his home not to his shop. He had a large grove and his place [and ours] held a big picnic there every first Sunday in August. When we built a new house he used the old house to store cow chips for the heater and cookstove. That was standard fuel. Cow chips with dry hay to start them burning.

When I entered my first foot race at Brownlee, I won every 4th of July. My brother Howard won the boy's race and Uncle Bill Meehan the men's race. He'd go part way, then run backwards and still win. Dad was on the Sluggers baseball team, and they had a good team, and John Scott wouldn't play if you gave him a white mitt. B. Woodson would go to sleep playing the mandolin at a dance and never miss a note. Turner and Joe Price were both good on piano (both moved to St. Paul—Turner died in 1963), violin and guitar. And the quartet: Dad as boss, Boss Woodson, Harrison Steele, and I can't remember the fourth man. It was something one doesn't forget.

Dad and Mom sent to Lincoln Library for books, stating numbers and ages of us kids, and they'd send books galore. We had through the months the entire Britannica Encyclopedia and classics, autobiographies, poetry, including works by Paul Lawrence Dunbar [the great 19th century black American poet], some of which were written in a style we kids could not understand, for nobody talked like that that we've ever known. So Dad had to read and explain them to us. "Dialect" was learned from a book. When Dad made the "first reading" we didn't know what he was talking about. He had picked up some German from his college-educated brothers, but this wasn't German, neither was it the accent of Grandpa Meehan's native Ireland.

Don Hannah now owns most of the homesteads. . . . Then the Hannah home was sod like everyone else's but what a beautiful home ranch he has now. And I envy him, his wide valleys and the singing hills that holds so many happy memories for me. There wasn't much money, ever, but our folks did their best to give us the best they possibly could, and I feel we had a wonderful childhood.

No record of the Sandhills would be complete without

mentioning Bert and Ida Morgan. Beloved by all the kids especially and when Bert made the 24-mile trip down-river to Brownlee. He waved to [us] all along the way, the road was across the river from us, and when he came back he stopped at every house where there were children and filled our pockets and aprons with candy and gum and crackerjacks. Another neighborly thing that was practiced there, everybody asked did you need anything from town, and brought it back by your. house or left it at your gate. It was a good way of life. . . .
. . . One thing I wish I had from there: our branding irons. Yes, we had fun there, lots of fun. And if I were to go back to country living, it would be to ranch life. . . .[17]

Mrs. Day's letter presents a picture of black homestead life which parallels that presented by perhaps the first black novelist from this area, Oscar Micheaux, who homesteaded in South Dakota but published his novels through the Woodruff Press and Western Book in Lincoln [*The Conquest* (Lincoln: Woodruff Press, 1913); *The Forged Note* (Lincoln: Western Book Supply, 1951)]. Micheaux's theme in the first novel is the necessity that black people become self reliant, avoid intermarriage with the white community, and create a great black "immigrant" empire in the northwestern part of the United States in the still unoccupied territories. The second novel is a kind of portrait of the behavior of oppressed black people in the urban South, one which often turns its anger against the victim rather than the masters in the South's struggles. Finally, in *The Homesteader,* Micheaux turns back to how the black nation can free itself and explores the notion that individual African-Americans must serve as an "example" to the black people of America. He eschews broader notions which involve issues of power, settlement and community formation which appear in *The Conquest.* Micheaux, like Booker T. Washington, has a sense of black nationhood and the need for community building; he recognizes the need for civil and human rights, but like Washington, he is more inclined to push issues of building internal strength than confronting white oppression.[18]

Though the black communities near Brownlee and the other Nebraska "homesteading" communities survived until the '20's, they mostly died in the period just before and just after the First World War. No one has given an adequate account of what these communities were at their height or of what made them go under. Perhaps economic troubles, growing Klan influence, isolation from other blacks, crop failures, the intensification of northern racism, and the chauvinism of the World War I period all contributed. In any case, the destruction of the African-American rural communities in the '20's meant that, thereafter, black community building ideology was urban—a ghetto matter—in Omaha and, to a lesser degree, Lincoln. Usually when the Black person refers to his residence area as being in the ghetto, he or she speaks with affection. On the other hand, when "outsiders" (including some blacks who have moved out of the ghetto, the T.V. Jefferson caricature type) speak of the ghetto, they speak with disdain and/or fear. Would that all could respond to the heart beat of the ghetto which has been captured in music and song by Donny Hathaway in his "The Ghetto." "The Ghetto" is not a tour of desperation and deprivation, but an exploration of the happy elements, the elements of the street that we enjoy.

TALKING BOUT THE GHETTO

THE GHETTO	THE GHETTO	THE GHETTO
Stompin Feet	*Clappin Hans*	*Freedom Fighters*
THE GHETTO	THE GHETTO	THE GHETTO
Mama	*Daddy*	*Love*
THE GHETTO	THE GHETTO	THE GHETTO
Preachers	*Prostitutes*	*Pimps*
THE GHETTO	THE GHETTO	THE GHETTO
Barber Shops	*Beauty Parlors*	*Styles*
THE GHETTO	THE GHETTO	THE GHETTO
Pain	*Death*	*Life*
THE GHETTO	THE GHETTO	THE GHETTO
Fights	*Baby Crying*	*Children Playing*

THE GHETTO	THE GHETTO	THE GHETTO
Our Hope	*Energy*	*Creative*
THE GHETTO	THE GHETTO	THE GHETTO
Desegregation	*Education*	*Brothers & Sisters* [19]

The only words sung on the record are "The Ghetto," but listening to Donny Hathaway sing, one can piece together rhythmic sounds which are repeated phrases underneath the phrase "The Ghetto," which tell about the phases of life in the area. The joined words are representative of the collective people, living in a community wherever black people reside. But urban black life in Omaha has not always taken the form which it takes now, and black people were not always centralized in one area of town in Omaha.

In 1892, an article entitled "Omaha's Black Population" appeared in the *World-Herald*. It tells us something about how Omaha's black community looked to a white outsider almost thirty years before the 1919 race riot:

> There is certainly no race which has a better right to call itself American than that which, before this country became a republic, was brought here by the hundreds and which has grown to millions. . . .
>
> The Afro-American is a nation within a nation.
>
> In Omaha there are 6,000 of them. That does not seem to be a large number, and yet is is a fact that to the stranger the percentage of African-Americans upon the streets of this city appear to be large.
>
> But it is my opinion that the reason this seems to be the case is because so large a part of them are persons of independence, activity and a greater or less degree of importance, such as one naturally would not expect from a race which has labored under tremendous disadvantages.
>
> That these disadvantages did not disappear with the enfranchisement of the Negro anyone will admit. A senseless race prejudice, the direct and undeniable result of the institution of slavery, has held the Afro-American back as relentlessly as did the mandates of his former master. Prejudice hunts him

out and tracks him down with an instinct as keen as that of the bloodhound which used to track him through the midnight forest. . . . If it was the intention of the white man to break the spirit of the black man, then he may as well suffer the mortification of knowing that he has failed.

The black man is having a good time. He has learned to govern himself, which is difficult for any man to do, but particularly difficult for a man who has been allowed the exercise of no moral responsibility, but has been ruled with arrogance and tyranny.

After the systematic effort of this country for over 200 years to destroy this self-respect of the Afro-American, is it not a good deal to expect that in a quarter of a century that self-respect will reach par?

The honest and accurate knowledge of what the colored Americans are in this city is enough in itself to remove the last remnant of prejudice from the mind of any fair man or woman.

There are, then, as stated before, about 6,000. The children are in the public schools, the women are almost all in their homes, comparatively few of them being at any sort of work which take them away from home. The employments of the men are many. But they would have been yet more varied if it had not been that the doors of opportunity have so often been closed to the man with colored blood in his veins. Certain occupations have thus far been closed to such. It is doubtful, for example, if a colored merchant would succeed. There are none in Omaha.

The Rev. John A. Williams, pastor of St. Phillips' Protestant Episcopal Church, is a young man who has but recently taken up his ministerial duties. He is a man of strong opinions, and he stands very staunchly for the rights of his race. He has sent many communications to *World-Herald* upon this subject, particularly those in protest against the frequent lynchings of Negroes in the south.

Among the other ordained ministers who have now or have recently held pastorates in this city is the Rev. John R. Richardson.

The attorneys are Silas Robbins, Daniel Lapsley and Mr. Kelly. The practice of these attorneys is almost exclusively among men of their own race.

For many years Dr. W.H.C. Stephenson has alleviated the physical ills of his compatriots; and for a less length of time Dr. M.O. Ricketts has been here, and has won the reputation of the being a very careful physician as well as an exceedingly likeable young man.

The Progress is the journalistic organ of the Afro-Americans. It is a weekly paper, and it stands in every way for the progress of the Negro. L.L. Barnett is the editor, and his labors since 1889, when the paper was started, have been unceasing, and in the face of no inconsiderable difficulties. The circulation of the paper is 5,000. It is, as a general thing, earnest in its tone, and does not materially differ from any other weekly paper with an avowed object, except in one department, which is edited by some incognito, who signs himself "The Owl," presumably because he sees in the dark. The self assumed duties of this individual are unique in journalism. He reminds Sister J. that she cannot expect to keep one foot on the church choir and the other on the ballroom floor. He tells Brother R. that it is very well for him to shout at the prayer meeting on Wednesday nights, but asks him where he was last Friday at 11:30 in the evening. The position of public censor appears to be far from quiet, judging from the retorts "The Owl" makes, but he apparently never halts in the execution of what he considers his duty. *The Progress* is the only paper in the world, so far as I have seen, with a clean composing room. The floor of the average composing room is generally coated with mud and tobacco juice. It is never washed, though it is sometimes scraped. The wall reminds one of Lew Wallace's description of the walls of an Aztec house of worship. Cockroaches sprout gayly over everything and mice play about the feet of the proof readers as they sit jabbering off their interminable columns.

But the composing room of *The Progress* is clean as most people's sitting rooms, and on high stools sit two very agreeable and comely young women setting type. These are Miss Virgie Johnson and Miss Laura Barnett, and with the assistance of Mr. J.M. Darsey, who is one of the handsomest men, black or white, among the printers in this city, they set up the type for their paper.

. . . Of course, many men in the business are not so fortunate as to be their own employers. . . . A great many colored men in this city find employment as calciminers, plasterers, paper hangers, expressmen, porters, waiters, and servants. A number of the women are dressmakers, some do washing and ironing, nursing and many other forms of domestic work.

If one were to reply to the question, "In what part of the city do the colored people live?" he would probably reply, "the Third Ward." And perhaps more do live there than anywhere else. At the recent primary for the nomination of candidates for the city council, the officers of the primary were colored men, though the majority of the voters are white. But the truth is that the homes of the colored men are scattered all over the city. And many of the homes are of comfort and of beauty. One of the finest—probably the most expensive—is that of Mr. Singleton, at 22nd and Charles Streets. It is said to have beauty of architecture, to be finished hard woods, and to have the very latest modern improvements. If any one man were to be named as foremost in the republican element among the colored men, it would probably be Mr. Singleton.

It is roughly estimated that the property owned by Afro-Americans in this city would aggregate $700,000.

John Lewis is one of the richest, and said to be worth $50,000 in cash, not to mention much property. Thomas Cambell is thought to have $40,000 over and above his property. Mrs. Lizzie King has $60,000; A.O. Adams, $40,000. A large number own their homes and though, as is inevitable, some of these homes have mortgages upon them, yet far the greater number are unencumbered.

The patriarch of the community is Father Washington, who has watched the flight of 108 years and who has reminiscences about many illustrious persons who have been gathered to their fathers, and had monuments erected to their memories. . . .

It is the fashion of some people to say that, aside from the fact that the federal authority of our government was asserted in the Civil War, that the whole strife and agony was a waste. In short, they assert that the abolition of slavery was not worth the price paid for it.

Setting aside the abstract moral question of the degrading effects of slavery upon the race of enslavers; and the absence of liberty, which is the life of life, to the enslaved, there still remains the fact that a body of humans, now numbering about 11,000,000, have become factors in a free government. Whether they are factors for good or for evil is a question about which there is some disagreement.

The other day I drove out over the hills that lie just west of the city. The sunflower was in bloom there, and raised its royal head all along the roadside and in the midst of the fields. The plume of the golden rod waved in the sunlight, and the meadows were thick with that other golden flower, which apes the golden rod, but the name of which I do not know. The sky was bluer than anything else in the world except the crevasse or a glacier; and the wind that came rioting in from the plains was such a wind as blows only here in the west, where neither mountain nor lake disturbs the mellow warmth of its gay progress. I came across a little house set down in the midst of the sunflowers. A young wind-break of willows and cotton wood trembled, and shook, and glittered in sunlight and breeze. About on the grass clucked a group of barnyard fowls; they chattered importantly to each other in the shade of the barn or scratched up the dust of the road. The house was painted tastily, and at the windows the muslin curtains sucked in and out, and threatened to knock the pots of pink geraplums off the window sill. Someone was singing, and the voice was that of a Negro. No other voice has that unctuous swell, that trick of modulation, that capricious ebb and swell of sound.

A man came out with a little girl in his arms. She tried to pull his hat off. She showed her adorable teeth. Her little curly head bobbed up and down. The young man got her under his arm and held her there while she laughed and struggled. Then her mother came, looking out to see what the noise was, and she made the baby she had wave its tiny dark hand at them. I was so near I could see in the house. The pine floor was like snow. The chairs suggested comfort; the dishes were blue and white; two high chairs stood side by side and on the corner of the sewing machine was a copy of the *Century*. The children wore embroidery; mother was dainty in her dress and her face was round and sweet and full of content.

And someway over me there came a vision of the slave cabin; and the toil that stood for servitude. Lies and theft took the place of this truth and industry. Stealth displaced this candor. Fear usurped this self-respect. The whip of the slave driver was the spur to activity instead of the love of success. And the babies, with their merry faces changed into the sad victims of the slave market—they became a part of the traffic in human flesh, in human hearts!

And I wondered how in the name of all that freedom means anyone could be so dull, so selfish, so criminal as to say this liberty counts for nothing! . . .

In colleges and schools, in churches, in shops, fields, kitchens, offices, this great people is working out its emancipation from ignorance. They present no problem to this republic except that which was first made and is now sustained by the white race. . . .[20]

At the same time as the dream of freedom and nationhood in rural areas on the homesteads or in the western plains was fading for blacks in this area, the notion of black nationhood for African-Americans was receiving fresh focus for urban people in the Omaha area. The 1919 white race riots and massacre of a black man by a mob of 5,000 may have prompted this focusing of the sense of community. Marcus Garvey's ideology may also have contributed. Garvey has been seen as the father of the idea of black power, of Pan-Africanism, of the notion that black people had to form their own businesses, mutual organizations, political alliances with Africa, and their own self-image if they were to be free. He advocated an alliance between oppressed black people and all other races having a similar experience. The chief Garveyite in Omaha in the 1920's was Earl Little, the father of the child known to Omahans as Malcolm Little, or the man known to us as Malcolm X—perhaps the greatest of black fighters for freedom. Malcolm spoke for a new sense of community among black people and the oppressed people of the world generally. Malcolm frequently spoke of his father's attraction to Garvey, and more recent scholars see in that Garveyism the root of Malcolm's own belief:

> [In Omaha] my father, the Reverend Earl Little, was a Baptist minister, a dedicated organizer for Marcus Aurelius Garvey's United Negro Improvement Association. With the help of such disciples as my father, Garvey from New York City to Harlem was raising the banner. . . . I remember seeing the big shiny photographs of Marcus Garvey that were passed from hand to hand. My father had a big envelope of them that he always took to these meetings. [21]

Malcolm's father, for his troubles, found his house threatened in Omaha:

> When my mother was pregnant with me, she told me later, a party of hooded Ku Klux Klan riders galloped up to our home in Omaha, Nebraska, one night. Surrounding the house, brandishing their shotguns and rifles, they shouted for my father to come out. My mother went to the front door and opened it. Standing where they could see her pregnant condition, she told them that she was alone with her three small children, and that my father was away, preaching, in Milwaukee. The Klansmen shouted threats and warnings at her that we had better get out of town because "the good Christian white people" were not going to stand for my father's "spreading trouble" among the "good" Negroes of Omaha with the "back to Africa" preachings of Marcus Garvey. [22]

No definitive history of Garveyism and its descendants in Omaha has been written, but it is hard to believe that the present strong black leadership in the city does not owe its strengths to Garvey and to Earl Little and to Malcolm X.

Malcolm X was born in Omaha to Earl and Louise Little, May 19, 1925, at 3448 Pinkney Street. His father had migrated there from Georgia and his mother from the British West Indies. Malcolm, a one-time dope peddler, pimp, hustler, convict, who lacked a formal education, became a resounding prophet; speaking with wisdom from his experiences, rejecting the western values and speaking out without fear to all who would hear, he became a Muslim, becoming the man, Malcolm X. An example

of his fearless approach to life and to issues is a telegram he sent
to the American Nazi Party. In this telegram he stressed the
continued maintenance of black community identity while expressing also the terms which required black people to maintain
a separate identity and the terms which might eventually allow
for ethnic intermingling:

> We Afro-Americans feel receptive toward all peoples of
> goodwill. We are not opposed to multi-ethnic associations in
> any walk of life. In fact, we have had experiences which enable
> us to understand how unfortunate it is that human beings have
> been set apart or aside from each other because of characteris-
> tics known as "racial" characteristics.
>
> However, Afro-Americans did not create the prejudiced
> background and atmosphere in which we live. And we must
> face the facts. A "racial" society does exist in stark reality,
> and not with equality for black people; so we who are non-
> white must meet the problems inherited from centuries of
> inequalities and deal with the present situations as rationally
> as we are able.
>
> The exclusive ethnic quality of our unity is necessary for
> self-preservation. We say this because: Our experiences backed
> up by history show that African culture and Afro-American
> culture will not be accurately recognized and reported and
> cannot be respectably expressed nor be secure in its survival
> if we remain the divided, and therefore the helpless, victims
> of an oppressive society.
>
> We appreciate the fact that when the people involved
> have real equality and justice, ethnic intermingling can be
> beneficial to all. We must denounce, however, all people who
> are oppressive through their policies or actions and who are
> lacking in justice in their dealings with other people, whether
> the injustices proceed from power, class, or "race." We must
> be unified in order to be protected from abuse or misuse.[23]

Malcolm was no racist.

On February 21, 1965, Malcolm X was assassinated in the
Audubon Ballroom, not by the American Nazis or the Ku Klux
Klanners, but by black people. For a time it appeared that with
his assassination—and that of President John F. Kennedy,
Martin Luther King and Bobby Kennedy—the liberation struggle

would turn to dust and ashes like those assassinated bodies. But no, it went on. As if to say, "No," Mrs. Malcolm X, Betty Shabazz, came to Omaha in September, 1975, to participate in the dedication of the Black Museum of the Great Plains, a museum created in memory of Malcolm X. The museum is appropriate. Malcolm was concerned about the black past, and this preserving of documents and information about black people is truly a monument for which the credit goes to Mrs. Bertha Calloway, who has lived in Nebraska since 1940, migrating from Colorado, and who has had this idea of preservation as a burning desire, now realized (the museum is located at 2213 Lake Street).

The period around World War I which created such intensified expressions of racism as the Klan activities in Nebraska and white race riots may partly owe its bigotry not only to World War I and its heightening of prejudice against any culture other than white middle class "mass" cultures of all sorts; it may owe a part of its focused hatred to film statements. The incredible racism of D.W. Griffith's *Birth of a Nation,* with its praise of the Klan and its picture of black people as simply beneath humanity, a racism which in itself created riots in other cities, led to the creation of a counter underground film movement, first in the unsuccessful black movie *Birth of a Race* developed by Emmet Scott, and then in the Lincoln Motion Picture Company:

> The organization to pick up where Scott had left off, the first of the black company pioneers, was the Lincoln Motion Picture Company. Incorporated in 1916 (before Scott's film was even completed) and based in Nebraska, the organization was the brainchild of black actor Noble J. Johnson and his brother George. *The Realization of the Negro's Dream* was one of the company's first products. Like Scott's, this film extolled Negro achievements. Another release, *Trooper K,* was about the massacre of Negro troops of the famous Tenth Cavalry and the historic rescue of Captain Lewis S. Morey by the "unknown and unhonored" Trooper K. Both films were distributed to ghetto theaters. George Johnson had shrewdly

noted that because of·segregation in the South and de facto
segregation in the North, a number of all-black theaters were
opening. A growing black audience was anxious for black mer-
chandise. The Lincoln Motion Picture Corporation made
movies for the black market until the early 1920s, turning out
approximately ten films, each no longer than three reels.[24]

As we have mentioned, the 1919 Omaha race riots in which a
black man was pulled out of the jail by a mob of 5,000 people
and shot over a thousand times and then dragged around behind
an automobile was a culmination of a period of heightened repression of blacks in the teens, twenties, and thirties. The riot
broke out after an Omaha newspaper had been playing-up
supposed black crime for weeks, apparently as part of an effort
to focus white hatred. The growth of this feeling, on the white
side, is attributed in part to the effects of the media, but partly
to the influence of business leadership—its failure to stand
behind the "egalitarianism" which it promoted during World
War I, after that war, and into the period when the race riots
required that the business community support its verbal "egalitarianism" with public stands and action. A 1931 Urban League
study traces the responsibility which the business community
bore for the events of the teens and twenties:

> The development of the West attracted many of the
> former masters (of the slaves and their descendants) to Omaha,
> who sought the advantages of the West, as was the case of the
> Negro. Many brought with them inhibitions bearing on Negro
> life which up until the World War circumscribed the Negroes'
> social and industrial advancement.
>
> The desire for larger profits through industrial activities
> during the World War saw the heads of industries and the capi-
> talists' group break down many of these unexplained inhibi-
> tions at least for a period, and open the doors of opportunity
> for him, and give him an equal parity in the economic life of
> the community.[25]

The summary of the study then goes on to give an account of
the 1919 race riot and describes its effects:

The harmful effects of such exhibitions are too obvious for extensive elaboration. First, the loss of confidence by Negroes in the sincerity of the established forces to grant protection for a minority group; second, the disregard for established authority has struck roots in the minds of those who are inclined to mob violence. This occurrence has created in the minds of Omaha Negroes a sense of insecurity. With the growing numbers of Negroes in Omaha, there has likewise developed a growth in racial consciousness. This expression has found its outlet not only in the establishment of Negro business enterprises, and the insistence that they be patronized by Negroes, as a means of preservation, but in the field of politics. Negroes have been elected to represent their district in the legislature. . . . In 1927, two Negroes were elected to the lower house.[26]

The study goes on to note the appearance of discriminatory signs in downtown Omaha lunch-counters and the growth of white racist encounters in public swimming pools; it speaks of the prevalence of the color line in the world of work, the racism of the trade unions, and the exploitation of the black worker as 'problems' which do violence both to the black and white community. As the study notes, the teens and twenties encouraged the development of an independent base; this base was developed not only by the Garveyites in Omaha but by people who followed Booker T. Washington (without necessarily accepting Washington's view of an accommodative status for blacks). Chief spokesman for the Washington position was Reverend J.A. Williams, who published the *Omaha Monitor,* a black newspaper, until 1929, and exercised leadership in a variety of other areas.

When the depression came on between 1929 and 1932, the black community found itself even further at the end of the trail of oppression. A "Nebraska Conference on the Economic Life of Negro People" held the following:

The traditional concepts of 'jobs for Negroes' limit their opportunities for employment.

Negroes are limited to low-wage jobs requiring unskilled labor.

There is less demand for Negroes in domestic service.

The highest percent of unemployed is among Negroes.

Whenever possible Negroes are replaced by white workers in industry.

Negroes are denied membership in trade unions.

The standard of living among Negroes is generally low.[27]

The Committee recommended that black workers should organize to protect their interest and to give themselves the advantages of collective bargaining among other things.

Given the requirement for the development of black nationhood in Omaha, given the long-term development of this sense from the twenties on, it is perhaps not accidental that an Omaha black essayist, orator, and political leader had a major role in developing the ideology of black community power in education and in assisting the Kerner Commission to come to the conclusion that this nation was on the way to becoming two nations—one black and one white, separate and unequal— and that white racism was at the heart of the division.

Long, dark hours of slavery, of repression in the South and in Omaha, and a sense of independence through all of it lives in the heart of many older people in this area. Louvenia Butler, who lives in Omaha, loves to read her Bible, loves to tell you about God, and also loves to tell you about life. A recent interview with her reads as follows:

> . . . I visited Mrs. Louvenia Butler who was 102 years old. A wise old woman. Three events she shared are etched in my memory for all times. . . .
>
> First she spoke of her father and his brother in slavery. When asked about her father's brothers, and asked if she knew them, she said she knew nothing about them. The question was asked why didn't she know them. She replied: "Because when they got free they went home and was never heard from again." Where was home? She repeated the question with indignation at our ignorance. "Where's home? Home to Africa, where you think? They was free."

Secondly, she said she was a Christian, "and only God knows why." "My mother died when I was two years old and before she died she had the white lady she worked for to promise to take care of me so I would not be knocked around, mistreated, beaten or sold. She took it to heart, so that she moved me into the house with them, yes she took me from my family. My father moved near by so's he could keep an eye on me and on them. I never went to no back door, I ate at the table tho at first I had to stand on a box they made for me, my clothes was washed with theirs, and I had clean clothes everyday. I didn't do no work neither. I was treated like she treated her own children. But have you ever cried tears, have you ever cried 'vales' of tears, I have." When asked what did she mean, she answered with another incident. "When I was about six years old, the other children in the house said I should call them cousin, and I said you ain't none of my cousin, and they said if I don't, we gonna see to it that papa beats you with the bull whip." . . . But why would this make you cry a 'vale' of tears? She said, "Look at me . . . I'm black, I ain't white, I knowed who I was and they couldn't make me nothing else . . . and if it hadn't been for my daddy, I mighten cared for my own people, cause they was good to me."

The third event was shared when I asked her about her childhood and her education, with her being raised in the midst of the life style of the white children. "I was baptized a Catholic, and I went to Catholic school. That is until one day when the priest was teaching us, a man came in dressed all funny in white cloth from head to toe, he went up and said something to the priest, the priest kept on talkin, then he went away and came back with another one of them funny dressed people, and we started lookin all around and we could see outside that there were more of them and even the horses were dressed funny, and we could see guns stickin out from every picket fence. . . . Well, the priest kept on talkin and finally a third one went up to him and whispered something, we never did hear what they said . . . but this time the priest looked over at us colored children cause we sat apart from the white children. He said, 'Children you are to go straight home and you are not to return to the school until we notify you.' We all left and we all left running; I carry a scar to this day,

right here, cut by a piece of barbwire. I was so scared I
couldn't see. . . . That was my education and that was my
graduation. I never went to school again . . . and I never went
to the Catholic Church again; that is why I am a Methodist
today."28

Three Black Community Idioms:
Religion, Music, The Word

As black people turned to developing their own urban
communities, they turned to developing black business and
to using black religion as a center of the defense (with Mrs.
Butler), or to music which had behind it unique African,
Afro-Carribean, and black southern backgrounds. They also
turned to "the word"—as it could be turned to by poets, play-
wrights and novelists to shape the community's perceptions.

When the African-Americans migrated to Nebraska, they
came with desires of liberation, seeking that happiness, but they
also came with their religion. The earlier churches bear witness
to the fact that the black people held fast to their heritage. The
first churches carried as part of their name, "African": African
Methodist Episcopal, Zion African Methodist Episcopal, Quinn
Chapel African Methodist Episcopal, and so forth. There are
many other denominational churches of which black people
were members: United Methodist, Presbyterian, Baptist, Seventh-day Adventist, the Holy Church and the others. But the
names which expressed a sense of heritage tend to mean the
most. Why has the religious experience remained a constant
central element in black life? Maybe we can receive some
answers by looking at the tribute paid to Reverend O.J. Burckhardt of Lincoln in 1944 (Mrs. O.J. Burckhardt was Nebraska's
foremost black painter in the 1930's and 40's and Rev. Burckhardt, its foremost black pastor):

Burckhardt arrived in Lincoln coming from Jefferson
City, Missouri, where he had been attending Lincoln Institute,
a school organized by Negro soldiers who had served in the
Civil War. After being in Lincoln a few years, he noticed that

the members of his race were not showing proper concern regarding civic and political affairs of his race. [He took over the program.] This he has never regretted doing. He is known not only in Lincoln and Omaha, where he has given the greater part of his service, but throughout the country for his religious activities. Some years ago, he organized a church in Omaha which has proved a great factor spiritually to his own race. While engaged in such work in Omaha, he became associated with various social organizations . . . the Urban League, etc.

It seemed desirable for Lincoln to have a similar Urban League, an asset not only to the Negro citizens but to the city. [Burckhardt organized a successful Urban League in Lincoln] so much so that the Negro citizens of Lincoln have had given to them by the business men of the city a $30,000 building in which to carry on the affairs of the Urban League and other civic and social affairs [the present Malone Center] .[29]

The black churches in Lincoln and Omaha, churches which proudly recall their African relationship, have been the center of the sense of black nationhood: Earl Little's church, the Rev. A.L. Williams' church, the Rev. Burckhardt's church. Gayraud S. Wilmore remarks why this is the case:

Black religion has always concerned itself with the fascination of an incorrigibly religious people with the mystery of God, but it has been equally concerned with the yearning of a despised and subjugated people with the freedom of man, freedom from the religious, economic, social, and political domination which white men have exercised over black men since the beginning of the African slave trade. It is this radical thrust of black people for human liberation expressed in theological terms and religious institutions which is the defining characteristic of black christianity and of black religion in the United States, from the preacher-led slave revolts to the *Black Manifesto* of James Foreman and the 1970 "Black Declaration of Independence of the National Committee of Black Churchmen." . . . [30]

Do we have a witness!

Through the ears and the experiences they bring to us, from the sense of "who we are" so produced, we come to know that other undergirding of the black experience: music. From the very beginning, Omaha, Nebraska, was one of the key centers in the world of music because of its geographical location, as the most centrally located city in the northern midwestern area having any sizeable black population. Many black musicians came from other places and made Omaha their home from the 20's on. Bands were the rage, and these bands played to the biggest dance "territory" in the United States. From this "hub" thousands of pavilions, dance halls, and ballrooms engaged the bands from Omaha to play in a city or hamlet in Kansas, in parts of Missouri, Colorado, Montana, Wyoming, Wisconsin, the two Dakota's, Iowa and Minnesota. Minnesota, with its 1,001 lakes, was most profitable for the black bands because of the resort areas attached to the lakes, each having its own dance hall or pavilion.

Black bands were in demand! At this time jazz, rhythm, and blues belonged exclusively to the blacks, mostly because of their style, which was novel. The very essence of a people was being expressed in an idiom which was not understood by those who were not of African heritage. Another unique quality of the black musicians was the colorful, the emotional response to life, which others viewed as exotic. The emotion of black people was not confined or only contained in the music, but appeared in the demeanor of the people: black musicians were warm, outgoing, full of play—a play often reflected in their stage patter also. The nicknames, Big Daddy, Red, Moon Tate, which came to the fore as the black music world found a public outside the Omaha area, were representative of a larger world of black expression. Some of the earliest music came from Ted Adams, who died in the 1960's. His band was named the Omaha Nite Owls. Warren Webb and his Spiders was another band. In Nebraska, Preston Love made his debut playing drums. Lloyd Hunter named his band the Hunter's Serenaders. In 1931, his band went east and played with Victoria Spivey, and Preston Love, the local jazz musician in Omaha, played his first professional engagement as a fulltime saxaphonist. The DeDundes Band reached a rare height of popularity here and were promoted by "white benefactors." Nat Towles, who died in 1962, had musicians playing with his band who later, and because of their work with him, came to be known throughout the world. One of the few black female band musicians, Anna Mae Winburn, had a band named after her in which all the musicians were men (eventually, after having the band for about five years, she joined the Sweethearts of Rhythm in 1941); one of this country's very great musicians, Charlie Christian, played with the Anna Mae Winburn band in the 30's, the same jazz guitar player who went on to become one of the firsts with the Benny Goodman band. Then there is George Bryant (Bryant Community Center is named after him—located at 24th and Grant in Omaha), honored to be called the "biggest" music figure in the black community. He was an all-around musician, had mastered all of the musical instruments, and because of his many talents, was given the responsibility of directing the W.P.A. project for musicians.

Some of the key individual musicians presently living in Omaha continue this tradition: Charlie Williamson, trumpet player, is known and referred to as the Patriarch of Omaha; Sam Grevious, trombonist, was former president of the Black Musicians Union; Howard Tarrell was foremost on drums, etc. Throughout this musical history, the traditions of black music and of the black aesthetic continue on; on playground after playground in Omaha, one can see children playing circle games and clapping out chants and songs that manifest the cool of the group and the skill of the player in the ring. These games have, many of them, ultimate African or Afro-Carribean roots and create the sense of unity in the group. The same testing of cool, testing of capacity to elaborate somebody else's theme and of capacity to express the unity of the group while also expressing oneself, is the essence of black music in Omaha.[31]

The "man of words" has always had an important place in black life, besides the musician—in every black culture worldwide. The holy man, the charismatic preacher, the chant sermon preacher are all part of this and evident in Omaha. More recently, the oration and the essay have become central in the black civil rights movement. Several of Senator Chambers' essays have come to be celebrated in the literature of black consciousness: "We have wept, we have cried, we have prayed," the "Pride of Lions" speech, and the segments of Mr. Chambers' oratory reproduced in Eric Lincoln's *Is Anybody Listening to Black America* are justly famous.[32] Chambers is particularly excellent in using the animal fable or the historical exemplum to empower his statements and give them a luminous quality.

The more recent black writing in Nebraska centers in the literature of self-determination and emphasizes the Malcolm X thrust. In 1969, the Afro-Academy of Dramatic Arts was created, and since then it has put on the following plays—most of them plays which reflect Malcolm X's kind of perspective on black power and self-sufficiency: *Raisin In the Sun,* Lorraine Hansberry; *Ceremonies and Dark Old Men,* Lonne Elder; *Black Catharsis,* Academy Writers; *Happy Ending,* Douglas Turner Ward; *Mo-jo In String,* Alice Childress; *Uncle Tom's Revolution,* Darryl Eure; *Who's Got His Own,* Ron Milner; *Lay My Burdens Down,* Academy Writers; *God's Trombone,* James Weldon Johnson; *For Crying Out Loud,* Charlotte Eure; *Roof Top Monopoly,* Michael Dryver; *Every Man's Heart Lay Down,* Academy and WOW; *Malcolm X - The Last Hour,* Academy Writers and Malcolm X's poetry.

The same perspective appears in the writing of recent black writers, published and unpublished. The writing of Ray Shepard is particulary notable. Tyrone Eure, Clifford Like, and Harry Eure are also promising young writers achieving notice. With the new movement in the arts the building of black institutions has gone ahead apace, continuing the movement in that direction begun in the '20's and '30's. Tuskegee is still important. Vera Chandler Foster, an Omahan and an outstanding social worker, presently wife of the president of Tuskegee, and other civil rights activists, were recently honored in Omaha by Wesley House. Wesley House, under the management of Rodney Weed and others, was responsible for the organization of the Com-

munity Bank of Nebraska, the Franklin Credit Union, the
radio station KOWH, and the Wesley House Cultural Center,
all black enterprises. The mentor and inspiration to these young
black entrepreneurs is Mr. Charlie Washington, whose photograph with Malcolm X contained in this volume is a fit symbol
for his continued concern for justice and self determination
for black people.

Black community-building in rural areas in Nebraska
began shortly after the end of the Civil War. The culture took
its unique shape from the tradition brought to Nebraska from
the South and ultimately from what Mrs. Butler calls "home"
—Africa itself; the African-American people who came to homestead after the Civil War came with desire for land, for self-
sufficient community, and nationhood. At first the somewhat
separate rural communities developed while city blacks were
dispersed led the way. The notion in Micheaux is that nation
building should come first and the fight for rights later. With
the 1919 race riots and the establishing of the fact that nation
building could not go on without full rights, the Garveyite
movement came alive. Malcolm X's kind of figure appeared. A
new generation of nation-builders (inappropriately called
"separatists" in the white community) went about developing
black institutions of finance and economic development, black
productions in the media, in art and history, and in literature,
music and drama. Black people had determined that freedom
would be "now" and on their own ground.

But the search for freedom has been there always. As
Hildegard Hoyt Swift writes:[33]

My name was legion,
   I came in every slave ship to the Colonies,
      In every slave ship.

Mine was the long horror of the middle passage,
The cruel kiss of the whip, the darkness, the burden of chains.
Mine the stench of the hold, the groans of the dying.
Mine the queasy lurch of the ship, the hungry roar of the sea.
Mine the long, long horror and the hope of death,
   But still I endured.

I came in every slave ship to the Colonies,
Through the loss of my own freedom
To build a world for the free.

FOOTNOTES

1. John Hope Franklin, *From Slavery To Freedom* (Westminster: Vintage Books Edition, 1969).
2. George C. Cox, *African Empires and Civilizations* (African Heritage Studies, 1974), p. 3.
3. *Ibid.*
4. Langston Hughes and Milton Meltzer, *A Pictorial History of the Negro in America* (New York: Crown Publishing, Inc., 1970), p. 112.
5. Leo Wiener, *Africa and the Discovery of America* (Cambridge: Harvard University Press), Vol. I, pp. 116-17.
6. This information received from the Dusable Museum, Chicago, Illinois, Margaret Burroughs, Curator.
7. This is the subject of a dissertation recently completed at the University of Nebraska in Lincoln by Dr. Ernest Bradford, a Selma associate of King; the dissertation is entitled "Biblical Metaphors of Bondage and Liberation in Black Writing: A Study of Black Liberation as Mediated in Writing Based on the Bible."
8. Franklin, *op. cit.,* p. 128.
9. Lerone Bennett, Jr., *The Shaping of Black America* (Chicago: Johnson Publishing Co., Inc., 1975), pp. 66-68.
10. Senator Ernest Chambers, "I Speak In Parables: Your Child is a Reproach," *A Pride of Lions* (Lincoln: Nebraska Curriculum Development Center, 1968), pp. 61-99.
11. James C. Olson, *History of Nebraska* (Lincoln: University of Nebraska Press, 1966), pp. 126-27.
12. Bennett, *op. cit.,* p. 94.
13. Lillian L. Fitzpatrick, *Nebraska Places and Names* (Lincoln: University of Nebraska Press, 1960), p. 147. The name York appeared significantly again when a renowned Dr. Taylor died in Davenport, Iowa, February 17, 1974. The obituary indicates that Dr. Robert Taylor was born in Seward, Nebraska, in 1884. Later his family moved to York, Nebraska, where he completed his elementary and secondary schooling. Here he spent his boyhood, growing, playing, studying, maturing, with goals for achievement. Robert Taylor, like that venerable Paul Robeson, excelled in athletics and his academic pursuits; he went on to graduate at the University of Nebraska in Lincoln, Nebraska and Creighton University Medical School in 1912.
14. Frances J. Alberts, *Sod House Memories* (Hastings, Nebraska:

Sod House Society, 1972), I, p. 25.

15.   *Ibid.,* pp. 256-57.

16.   Malcolm X, *The Autobiography of Malcolm X* (New York: Grove Press, 1964), pp. 64-66; cf. Hughes and Meltzer, *op. cit.,* p. 267; the best account of the 1919 Omaha white race riot is to be found in Eldora Frances Hess, *The Negro in Nebraska* (Lincoln, 1932), pp. 62-67. Omaha mayor E.P. Smith was also strung up by the mob and later rescued by policemen. Over 1600 soldiers were called in, and General Leonard Woods' investigation found the police department in Omaha to be weak, to have failed to act to stop the gathering of the mob and to be so culpable as to require the removal of police chief Eberstein.

17.   Letters from Ara Speece Day to the author of this article.

18.   Micheaux' works related to this area of the country are *The Conquest* (Lincoln: The Woodruff Press, 1913); *The Forged Note* (Western Book Supply, 1915; republished Lincoln: The Woodruff Press, 1916); and *The Homesteader* (Sioux City: Western Book Supply, 1917). All have been reprinted. Oscar Micheaux was also a pioneer in the development of black film; the best account of Micheaux as a maker of films is contained in Donald Bogle, *Toms, Coons, Mulattoes, Mammies and Bucks: An Interpretation of Blacks in American Films* (New York: Viking Press, 1973), pp. 109-16. Micheaux is given fairly full treatment as a novelist in Hugh M. Gloster, *Negro Voices in American Fiction* (New York: Russell and Russell, 1965), pp. 84-91. Micheaux was much influenced by Booker T. Washington, and Washington had a strong following in Nebraska through his 1902 commencement speech at the University of Nebraska, which stressed the development of an economic base, and through the Reverend J.A. Williams of the *Omaha Monitor* who pushed Washington's views for over two decades through his paper. Washington and Garvey were, to a degree, allies and exchanged friendly correspondence.

19.   Donny Hathaway, "The Ghetto" (a recording, New York: The Atlantic Recording Corp.)

20.   *The Sunday World-Herald* (Omaha, Nebraska: Omaha World Herald Co., September 9, 1892), p. 13.

21.   Malcolm X, *op. cit.,* pp. 6-7.

22.   *Ibid.,* p. 1.

23.   George Breitman, *The Last Year of Malcolm X* (New York: Shocker Books, 1967), p. 119.

24.   Anonymous, "Looking Back on Black in Films," *Ebony* (June, 1973), XXVIII, 40; cf. Donald Bogle, *op. cit.,* p. 103.

25,   J. Harvey Kerns and T. Earl Sullenger, *The Negro in Omaha*

(Omaha: Urban League and Omaha University, 1931), p. 33.

26. *Ibid.,* p. 33. A number of studies of black people in Nebraska cities were done in earlier times; perhaps the most interesting is that by Mary Davies and Genevieve Marsh, "A Study of the Negro in Lincoln" (unpublished master's dissertation, Lincoln, Nebraska, 1904), in that it includes interviews with a sizeable number of black people who have been slaves (pp. 37-40). Other studies of Lincoln black community patterns were done in the 30's by Charles Blooah and Harvey Kerns.

27. Raymond Brown and others, *The Negroes in Nebraska* (Lincoln: Woodruff Printing Company, 1940), pp. 17-18; for an account of the *Omaha Monitor* and John A. Williams, see Eldora Frances Hess, pp. 70-72.

28. Lillian Anthony-Welch and Ann Ventry, interview with Louvenia Butler, Omaha, Nebraska, 1975.

29. Nebraska State Historical Society, "Program for Commemorative Service of 54 Years as Lincolnite."

30. Gayraud S. Wilmore, *Black Religion and Black Radicalism* (Garden City, N.Y.: Anchor Press, 1973), p. 21.

31. The best studies of the black aesthetic are to be found in Imamu Baraka, *Blues People* (New York: Morrow, 1963), *passim*; Jahnheinz Jahn, *Muntu* (New York: Grove Press, 1961); and Roger Abrahams, *Positively Black* (Salt Lake City: Prentice Hall, 1969). Cf. Abrahams' and Jahn's other essays on these topics. The motifs described were found in Omaha black playground and aesthetic practice by members of the University of Nebraska TTT project, particularly Professors Loretta Butler, Thomas Holland and Paul Olson. Some videotaping was done.

32. Ernest Chambers, "How It Looks From the Off Side," in C. Eric Lincoln, *Is Anybody Listening to Black America* (New York: Seabury, 1968), pp. 147-49.

33. Hildegarde Hoyt Swift, *North Star Shining* (New York: William Morrow Co., 1945), p. 6.

APPENDIX A

EARLY BLACK MIGRATION TO NEBRASKA

1842 . . . . . . .Tom Brown, the slave of a Missourian, accompanied his "master" to Nebraska on a Buffalo hunt. He escaped to Canada. He returned to Nebraska in 1907 and remained until his death in 1939.

1855 . . . . . . .Sally Bayne, settled in Omaha and is credited with being one of the very first settlers.

1862 . . . . . . .Homestead Act claim first filed in Nebraska.

1865 . . . . . . .Smith Coffey, a blacksmith, came to Omaha.

1866 . . . . . . .L.B. Mattingly, settled near David City, Nebraska.

1866 . . . . . . .Henry Burden, settled in Saline County.

1867 . . . . . . .George Conway, Missouri-born ex-slave came to Omaha.

1868 . . . . . . .The first "Negroes" settled in Lincoln, Nebraska.

1870 . . . . . . .Amos Harris, came to Loup Valley, worked as a ranch hand, becoming an independent rancher in Valley and Wheeler Counties.

1870 . . . . . . .Robert Anderson, ex-slave, one of the first Homesteaders in the state.

1973 . . . . . . .David Patrick, the first Negro homesteader in Hamilton County.

1876 . . . . . . .James Kelly, a rancher settled in Custer County.

1877 . . . . . . .Mrs. Emma Stewart and her mother, settled in Hastings, Nebraska.

1880 . . . . . . .Tom Cunningham, the first Negro policeman in Lincoln.

1883 . . . . . . .Jenny Morgan, faced homesteading alone.

1885 . . . . . . .Charles Meehan, settled in Overton, Nebraska.

1888 . . . . . . .Eliza Galloway, an ex-slave, settled in Kearney, lived there until her death in 1936, having reached 100 years of age.

1893-95 . . . . .M.O. Ricketts, House member.

1893 . . . . . . .Jules Miles, an ex-slave, and Civil War veteran settled in Omaha.

1894 . . . . . . .Jubilee Johnson, an ex-slave, died in Schuyler.

1848-1913. . . .Rev. George Maston, ex-slave, lived in Lincoln, Nebraska; Minister in Newman.

1907 . . . . . . .Charles Meehan, settled in Cherry County and the DeWitty Settlement was formed.

(Primary source: Nebraska Writers' Project, *The Negroes of Nebraska*. Lincoln: Woodruff Printing, 1940.)

APPENDIX B

BLACK POPULATIONS OF NEBRASKA CITIES

Population of African-Americans in Nebraska 1940 Census by Cities		*Population of African-Americans in Nebraska 1970 Census by Cities with Population of 10,000 or Over*	
City	**Black Population**	**City**	**Black Population**
Omaha	11,123	Omaha	34,431
Lincoln	997	Lincoln	2,215
Grand Island	120	Grand Island	94
North Platte	35	North Platte	75
Scottsbluff	62	Scottsbluff	56
Beatrice	82	Beatrice	23
Fremont	58	Fremont	21
Falls City	51	Norfolk	13
Nebraska City	61	Columbus	5
Alliance	203		
Hastings	70	*Total Black*	
York, 1974	200 families	*Population*	36,968
		In urban areas population increased; in the rural areas there was a noticeable decrease.	

(Primary source: Nebraska Writers' Project, *The Negroes of Nebraska.* Lincoln: Woodruff Printing, 1940.)

CATALOGUE

HOW TO FIND OUT ABOUT BLACK RESOURCES

Some of the specific institutions and places where one can find evidence of, and enjoy, black culture in Nebraska are noted here. The black church is representative of black culture. It was there where the spirit was rekindled, stoked and fired, so that survival was possible. It was there that our people were educated. It was there that we could "be" who we were—with no "airs" necessary (although we put on airs sometimes for other reasons). It was there that we could sing like we wanted to, say what we wanted as we wanted with the poetry, the drama, the pagentry, the walking and strutting, the pathos, the laughter, the joking—all rolled into one, which some people call "hoppin and hollerin" or making a racket. It was there where the businesses, the benevolent societies, the lending of money, the investments into stocks, and the banking began. It was there that the old time baking took place to raise money, but sometimes just for "good times." It was there that the "Old of Wisdom" kept alive our remembrances (e.g., the pillars of the church), kept our history and our heritage intact by telling us right from wrong, and demanded respect for who they were and the lives they lived: making us who we were.

This section is a cataloging of these aspects of black culture which are alive and "mean something to us" in our time:

Religious Institutions

Here, the cultural values are retained: preaching, music, education, self-knowledge, love of person, the family. The following is a list of protestant churches in the Omaha area:

Zion Baptist Church	Mt. Carmel Baptist
2215 Grant	5720 North 24th
Cleave Temple CME	Pilgrim Baptist
25th & Decatur	2501 Hamilton
Sharon Seventh-Day Adventist	Mt. Olive Baptist
3036 Bedford	3010 R

St. John Baptist
1118 South 12th

Ebenezer Baptist
2221 Fowler

St. Paul Baptist
1811 North 23rd

Metropolitan Missionary Baptist
5960 North 30th

Hope Lutheran
2723 North 30th

New Hope Baptist
1411 North 30th

Bethany Temple
2601 Seward

St. John (AME)
2402 North 22nd

Primm Chapel (AME)
18th & Binney

Grace Tabernacle Church of
    God in Christ
1801 Cuming

Mt. Sinai Baptist
4504 Bedford

St. Matthew Baptist
3332 Seward

Second Baptist
2531 Seward

Bethel Baptist
5318 South 30th

St. Mark's Baptist
3616 Spaulding

Allen Chapel (AME)
2842 Monroe

Church of God In Christ
2318 North 26th

New Light Baptist
2702 Pratt

Wesley United Methodist
2010 North 34th

Freestone Baptist (Primitive)
1316 North 26th

Pleasant Green Baptist
2002 Willis Avenue

Church of the Living God
2029 Binney

Greater Macedonia Baptist
3026 Hamilton

Faith Temple of God in Christ
2108 Emmett

Peoples Mission
1710 North 26th

Bethelehem Baptist
2320 North 28th Avenue

Fontenelle Chapel
1722 North 20th

Calvin Memorial Presbyterian
3105 North 24th

Corinth Memorial Baptist
3938 Florence Boulevard

Church of Christ
3723 North 37th

Bethel (AME)
2428 Franklin

Church of God in Christ Inc.
2901 North 30th

Greater Bethelehem Temple
    Jesus Only
2316 North 25th

St. Peter's Rock Baptist
1403 North 20th

Salem Baptist
3336 Lake

Paradise Baptist
2124 Lothrop

Zion Wheel Baptist
2620 North 45th

Mt. Nebo Baptist
3211 Pinkney

Immanuel Community
2761 Lake

Mt. Moriah Baptist
2602 North 24th

Morning Star Baptist
2053 North 20th

Tabernacle Holiness
2033 North 29th

Rising Star Baptist
1823 Lothrop

Gregg Memorial (AME)
1322 North 45th

Clair Methodist
2443 Evans

Church of Christ
2801 Sprague

Mt. Moriah Church of God in Christ
3901 Randelle Drive
Council Bluffs, Iowa

Calvary Baptist
4132 North 18th
Council Bluffs, Iowa

Tabernacle Baptist
1400 Avenue A
Council Bluffs, Iowa

Quinn Chapel (AME)
9th and C
Lincoln, Nebraska

Community Institutions

A sense of belonging, concern for the children, and the importance
of family are stressed in the following Omaha organizations:

Wesley House
2001 North 35th

Woodson Center
3009 R

Franklin Community Federal
   Credit Union
1732 North 33rd

Logan Fontenelle Multi Service
   Center
2211 Paul

Martin Luther King Center
7720 Wirt.

Nebraska Urban League
3024 North 24th

Six general organizations serve the Omaha black community:

O.I.C.
2802 North 24th
Mrs. Bernice Stephens (director)

Y.M.C.A.
430 South 20th
George Reid (director)

Urban League
3024 North 24th
James M. Evans (director)

Muhammad Temple
2934 North 24th

Martin Luther King Center
27th and Wirt
Jackie Chambers (director)

Bryan Center
2416 Grant
Mrs. Patricia Whitfield (director)

Two main parks also serve it:

Carter Lake

Martin Luther King Park

And two main lodges:

Masonic Temple
8223 North 30th
455-0106

Elks Hall
2420 Lake
451-9850
Ernest Turner (Exalted Ruler)

A number of clubs also serve the black community. Among them are the following (they may be located by checking in the Omaha telephone directory or with the community centers listed above).

Beauticians of the National Beauty
   Culture League Local 101
Citizens Coordinating Committee
   for Civil Liberties
Federation of Colored Women's
   Clubs
Interdenominational Ministerial
   Alliance
Kappa Alpha Psi Fraternity
The Links, Inc.
Mid-City Business and
   Professional Association
Nat'l Ass'n for the Advancement
   of Colored People (NAACP)
Central Branch of the NAACP
South Omaha Branch of the NAACP
Subordinate Branches-Division
   NAACP
The Afro Academy of Dramatic
   Arts
Urban League Guild
Amaranthus Grand Chapter OES
   Nebraska Jurisdiction
   Prince Hall Affiliation
The Iowa Buxton Club
Organizations of Africans-Nebr.
Southside Civic Club
Jack & Jill Club
Most Worshipful Prince Hall
   Grand Lodge of Nebr. F & AM

Benedict Club
Challengers Club
Delta Sigma Theta Sorority
Elks Lodge I.B.P.O.E. of W.
   2420 Lake Street
Ideal Improvement Club
Interdenominational Ministers
   Wives
Kellom Community Council
   1827 North 20th Street
Midwest Athletic Club
Negro Historical Society of
   Nebraska, Inc.
Northwest Branch of the NAACP
Iowa Branch of the NAACP
Youth Council of the NAACP
Omega Psi Phi
Lincoln, Nebraska Branch of the
   NAACP
Zeta Phi Beta Sorority
Sigma Gamma Rho Sorority
B-L-A-C (Black Liberators for
   Action on Campus-UNO group)
The United Black Federation
Club Reporters in Iowa
Twentieth Century Club
   Council Bluffs
Black Identity Educational Ass'n.
Alpha Kappa Alpha Sorority
   (AKA)

Eating Places

A partial list of Omaha eating places which feature black food follows. There, patrons can partake of greens, sweet potato pie, chitterlings, corn bread, black-eyed peas and ham hocks, and barbecued ribs.

   Skeets Barbecue Drive-In—2201 North 14th
   Metoyer Bar-BQ—2311½ North 24th
   Fair Deal Cafe—2118 North 24th

Cultural Centers

Drama, dance, creative writing, history, education, painting, sculpture, etching, pottery, jewelry making, music, mime and rhythm are perpetuated and kept alive by many Nebraska blacks. The following are sources in Omaha where information about black creativity can be found:

Great Plains Black Museum & Historical Society—2213 Lake
Afro Academy of Dramatic Art—1001 North 30th
Valentine Piano Studio—telephone 558-4908
Hinton Piano Studio—2409 Binney
Wesley House Cultural Center—2001 North 35th
The Association for the Study of Afro-American
   Life & History, Black Studies Department, University
   of Omaha—321 Administration Building

Annual Events

   Stone Soul Picnic (July)
   Links — Cotillion
   Ebony Fashion Fair (bi-annual)
   Black History Month Activities (February)

Literature

Aside from the authors mentioned (Micheaux, Malcolm X), the following writers have recently emerged in Omaha:

Herbert Renfrow - unpublished (plays)
Wayne Loftin - published (poetry)
Tyrone Eure - published (poetry); *Uncle Tom's Revolution*
Clifford Like - published (poetry); *America 76: Second Coming*
Sandra Booker - published (poetry)
Marcy Williams - unpublished (poetry)
Benjamin Gardner - published (poetry); *A Black Man Speaks of Hate*
Harry Eure - unpublished (plays)
Charlotte Eure - unpublished (plays)
Charles Bryant - unpublished (poet)
Preston Love - unpublished (writer); columnist *Omaha World Herald*
Burt Calloway - unpublished (writer)
Michael Driver - unpublished (plays)

A poet of long-standing in the Omaha community is Benjamin Gardner, whose publishing history goes back to 1933 at least. Ray Shepard of Lincoln has published two children's books, *Conjure Tales* (based on Chesnutts' *Conjure Tales*); and *Sneakers,* based on Lincoln experiences. He is writing a biography of Jack Johnson now. James Emanuel from Alliance is the editor of *Dark Symphony* and a poet of considerable consequence (now at City University of New York). Lance Jeffers, born in 1919 in Friend and raised there, is one of the "Howard" poets and writes 'black pride' poetry and poetry on social themes; his best known book is *My Blackness is the Beauty of This Land.* A Nebraska poet from earlier days was Mrs. Lela Northcross. A recent dramatist is Michael Randall of Lincoln and Kansas City; Roger Elliott of Lincoln has written some novels and short stories (unpublished).

Painting

Mrs. O.J. Burckhardt was a widely known painter in the 1930's. A retrospective exhibit of her works needs to be done. A number of younger painters and sculptors are working and can be reached through the University of Nebraska at Lincoln or Omaha, Wesley House in Omaha, or the Malcolm X Museum in Omaha.

Sources of Information for this Essay

The following older persons in the black community in Omaha were sources for the chapter which goes before and for related oral history projects being carried ahead by the author of this black catalogue and chapter. They are crucial to any exploration of black roots in this area:

	Age, 1976		Age, 1976
Mary Adams	87	Sally Addie	85
Erise Hayden Bailey	76	Mr. Baltimore	80
Mrs. Phydella Belford	85	Roy Benson	
LaVonne Blackwell	76	Zethro Brooks	86
Emanuel Brown	80	Harold Brown	
Ada Burton	107	Julia Caldewell	76
Mrs. Cheu	79	Lunded Crawder	91
Mrs. Crawford		Inez Cribbs	77
Mrs. Clara Dacus	76	Mr. Bose Dantzler	80

James Dortch	81	Earl F. Douglas	80
Mrs. Izora Douglas	81	Rev. H.W. Fetch	80
Estelle Gray	80	Wade Spencer Gray	72
Fabian Hayden	80	Mr. Harris	75
Darun Harris	75	Mrs. Olive B. Hawkins	85
Mrs. Ella Mae Higley	84	Beulah Jackson	76
Olivia Kartley	85	Eula Lonam	75
Mrs. Nette Lotte	80	Charles Mason	76
William Monday	76	James Neal	75
Myrtle Collier Newland	81	Mrs. Willie Reed	95
Mrs. Lula Mae Scott	75	Miles Speese	81
Lonnie Stephan	79	Mary Ellen Swillie	91
Belle Taylor	70	Weoma Teal	80
Odie Williams	97	Mrs. Woods	75
Lola Woods	79	Susie Yancy	79
Charles E. Young	80		

IV

Czechs: The Love of Liberty

By Joseph G. Svoboda

ACKNOWLEDGMENTS

I wish to express my gratitude to the many Nebraska Czech senior citizens who allowed me to tape their reminiscences over the past several months. The insight they helped to provide into the varied aspects of Czech community life in the state was invaluable. I also wish to thank Dr. Vladimir Kucera and Ms. Dorothy Stepan, both of Lincoln, for their help in compiling the catalogue. Mrs. Emil Kostka and Mr. Walter Baer of Wilber, Mr. Roger Rejda of Lincoln, and Mrs. John Pospichal of Clarkson were kind enough to loan me photographs. The staff of the Nebraska State Historical Society was also helpful in providing photographs from their collection.

NEBRASKA.
B. & M. RAILROAD
LANDS
THE START.
2ND YEAR.
3D YEAR.
4TH YEAR.
5TH YEAR.
6TH YEAR.
600.000 AKRŮ
B.&M. DRÁHY
POZEMKŮ
VE VÝCHODNÍ
NEBRASCE
NA PRODEJ
ZALEVNÉ CENY
A PŘI
MÍRNÝCH PODMÍNKÁCH
NEJLEPŠÍ POZEMKY NA ZÁPADĚ PRO ROLNÍKY
A DOBYTKÁŘE - NEJDELŠÍ LHŮTY NEJNIŽŠÍ
ÚROKY A NEJLIBERÁLNĚJŠÍ PODMÍNKY
JAKÉ KDY OD KTERÉKOLIV SPO
LEČNOSTI NABÍDNUTY
BYLY.
ČTĚTE OBSAH.
A. GAST & CO. ST. LOUIS
Karel Ludvík Büdeker, úřadně koncess. výpravčí lodí v Bremách.

THE CZECH MOVEMENT TO THE LAND

Above.

The John Safařík farm, an early Czech homestead, in 1887, near St. Paul, Nebraska, represents one of the early prosperous homesteads. It perhaps resembles the fourth year farm pictured on the ad opposite; few farmers achieved the grandiose empire assigned to sixth-year owners. (Courtesy of Joseph Safařík, Murray, Nebraska.)

Opposite.

Burlington and Missouri R.R. advertisement—Handbill for lands in Nebraska written in Czech. Translation: "600,000 acres of B & M railroad land in eastern Nebraska for sale for cheap price and easy terms. The best land in the west for farmers and ranchers—the longest terms—the lowest in interest and most liberal conditions ever offered by any company. Read the contents. Karel Ludvik Budeker, official shipper in Bremen (Germany)."

HOSPODÁŘ

Časopis pro hospodáře, dobytkáře, zahradníky, včelaře a domácnost.

ENTERED AT THE POST OFFICE AT OMAHA, NEB., AS SECOND CLASS MATTER.

ROČNÍK I.　　　　　OMAHA, NEB., DNE 15. BŘEZNA 1891.　　2 5　　　　SEŠIT

Naše vyobrazení.

Vyobrazení na této stránce představuje hřebce Gilberta 5154 druhého. Týž jest dobře známý a jětkem p. Leonarda Johnsona a byl již mnohého vyznamenání v

ké nohy a spěnačky, široké hnáty, prosty všech vad, jest dobré stavby těla, silných údů a pohybuje se tak lehce a bystře, že by ani nikomu nenapadlo, že váží přes tunu.

Rytina tohoto znamenitého hřebce byla nám poskytnuta laskavostí vyd. čas. Western Resources.

duje stejné práce a opatrování, stejně vyžaduje pastvin a zásob píce k jeho vyživení, ale odměna, výtěžek z prodeje, je nepoměrně rozdílný. Proč by se měl vyživovatel a pěstitel takových, chatrné odměny poskytujících, ale té samé práce a obsluhy vyžadujících, od-

host aneb vytrvalosti proti nám povětrnosti, slovem, vlastnosti chceme zdokonaliti vyvinouti. Známo již každé že dobytče toho neb onoho meue nikterak nemůže vyho veškerým požadavkům své stitele, z příčin na snadě

GILBERT (461)

zuých výstaváčí, mezi nimiž dru- u cenu při výstavě v Lincoln, eb. Jest to hřebec dobrého ple- eue, spřibuzněn jsa z daleka s stokracií La Belle z Francie. Je f 7 roků stár, je barvy jabkovité razíkové, s dlouhým ohonem a lnou hřívou, skoro bílou; má vel-

Zušlechtění domácího dobytka.

Pro Hosp. napsal J. V. Holeček.

Snahou každého pořádného rolníka jest a má být zušlechtění domácího dobytka, nechť již druhu jakéhokoliv, neboť obojí druh vyža-

rud a plemen držeti, oproti jiným docela rozdílný výnos poskytující, při těch samých podmínkách?

Vodítkem ovšem hlavním při zušlechťování nám musí být účel, totiž, zdali chceme dosíci oným zlepšením plemene, statné postavy, chuté jich výrobku a mno-

cích. Může velký, těžkonohý závoditi v běhu s lehkonoł Aneb může-liž malý indianský ník (pony) táhnouti náklad p ný onomu u koně francouzs (Norman-Percheron)? Nemol tak jako nemožno očekávat v mlékonosnou dojnici z druho

Above. Czech Catholic Church of Holy Trinity, Heun, Saunders County, completed in 1878. (Jan Habenicht, Dějiny Čechů Amerických. St. Louis: "Hlas," 1909.)

Below. South Omaha Sokol Hall, built in 1904 by ZČBJ lodge Hvězda Svobody, later served Sokols in South Omaha. (Courtesy of Nebraska State Historical Society.)

Left. Mallat brothers of Wilber in early Sokol uniforms (about 1880). John K. Mallat formed the first Sokol gymnastic society in Nebraska in 1875. (Courtesy of Mrs. Emil Kostka, Wilber, Nebraska.)

Below. Women Sokol Group, Saline County, about 1900. (University of Nebraska-Lincoln, Archives.)

Above. Wilber Women Sokols ready to perform, 1920's. (University of Nebraska-Lincoln, Archives.)

Below. Catholic Sokols in Omaha, about 1900. (Jan Habenicht, Dějiny Čechů Amerických. St. Louis: "Hlas," 1909.)

INTELLECTUALS AND THE ARTS

Above. Komensky Club, University of Nebraska, 1911. Pictured are Orin Štěpánek and Šárka Hrbková. (University of Nebraska-Lincoln, Archives.) Šárka Hrbková made an ardent effort to encourage Czech language studies in the face of World War I personal opposition. Orin Štěpánek was one of the University's great teachers and is presently honored by a University fund named after him.

Below. Czech band in Wilber, 1915. These bands still are very much alive. (Courtesy of Walter Baer, Wilber, Nebraska.)

Above. Czech oldtimers in Wilber (about 1919). (Courtesy of Mrs. Emil Kostka, Wilber, Nebraska.)

Below. Czech cemetery at Wilber. It was established in 1874. (Courtesy of Mrs. Emil Kostka, Wilber, Nebraska.)

CESKE DIVADLO

VE DWIGHT

V NEDELI 16HO LISTOPADU

"Nasledky Prviniho Manzelstvi"

Fraska v Jednom Jednani

———— OSOBY DEJI ————

TREBUCHARD, ...	V. J. Kabourek
BLANKA, Nevlastni Dcera	Blanche Pospichal
PRUNDEVAL, Soukro mnik z Remse . . .	Joe Augusta
KLARA, Jeho dcerca	Agnes Kabourek
PIQUSISEAN, Kapitan Francouske Armady .	Pan. A. J. Prenosil
FINNETA, Sluska Trebucharda . . .	Pani. Kate Korinek

Pohyblive obrazky pred divadlem zacatek presne 7 hodin

DOSPELY 50c   DITKY 15c

PODIVADLE TANECNI ZABAVA

HOME TALENT PLAY

———— at Dwight ————

SUNDAY, NOV. 16, 1930

Theatre announcement of a Czech play presented in Dwight (1930). (Courtesy of Mrs. Blanche Pospíchal, Clarkson, Nebraska.)

Above. Czech Dramatic Club "Mošna" in Omaha, 1924. (Courtesy of Mrs. Blanche Pospíchal, Clarkson, Nebraska.)

Below. Czech language summer school in Clarkson, Nebraska, 1936. Mrs. Blanche Pospíchal is still presently teaching Czech classes in Clarkson. (Courtesy of Mrs. Blanche Pospíchal, Clarkson, Nebraska.)

"Štastná rodinka"

zpěvohra o třech jednáních, kterou předve-
dou děti České Školy za pomoci
ochotníků dram. klubu v operní síni
v Clarkson

v neděli, 28. července '40, ve 2 hod.

Dostavte se k tomuto divadlu v hojném počtu. Ditky se na vaši
návštěvu těší a spolehají. Listky jsou poměrně velmi levné.
Dospělá osoba pouze 15c.   Ditky 10 c.   Každý jest uctivě zván.

Czech operetta "A Happy Family" presented by the pupils of the Czech summer
school at Clarkson in 1940. (Courtesy of Mrs. Blanche Pospichal, Clarkson, Nebr.)

Above. Scenes from the Dwight Czech festival; the regional peasant costumes still are used, though the ties to the old country and its customs have largely been cut by a series of international changes and catastrophies.

Below. The bands still have their place in the festivals and the dancing—the European polkas and other folk dances predominately.

Above. The heart decoration, prominent in the 1880 Sokol costumes, is still used.

Below. The very youngest generation is learning some of the people's arts.

IV

Czechs: The Love of Liberty

By Joseph G. Svoboda

If I were of the Gypsy race and its very last descendant, I would still do my best to ensure that an honorable memory of my heritage remained in the history of mankind.

František Palacký — Czech Historian

The Struggle for National Existence

Karel Zulek became the first permanent Czech settler in Nebraska when he set foot in the little town of Arago in Richardson County on the Missouri River. The date was August 27, 1856.[1] In the next six decades some fifty thousand Czechs settled permanently in Nebraska. This was a large percentage of the total Czech immigration into the United States. By 1910 the number of first and second generation Czechs in Nebraska was nearly 51,000 or approximately ten percent of the state's population of foreign birth and foreign parentage, and almost five percent of the total population of the state. It has been estimated that in 1910, one-eighth of all Czechs in the United States resided in Nebraska.[2]

Who were the Czechs, or Bohemians as they were more often called? Why did they leave their homeland? Why did they come to the United States and why did they settle in such numbers on the Nebraska prairies? These and related questions must of necessity be answered first to better understand the way of life of Czech settlers in Nebraska, their struggles in the new environment, their Americanization, their generation problems, and their heritage.

The highlights of the historical development of Bohemia provide a clue to the formation of the characteristics of the Czech people. Two historical factors shaped the philosophical outlook of the Slavs of Central Europe. The first is evident in the dawn of Czech history when Constantine and Methodius, on invitation of the Czech Prince Rostislav, came in 863 A.D. from Byzantium to Moravia to introduce Christianity to the Czechs in the old Slavonic language. The two Greek missionaries with their indefatigable zeal prevailed in their work despite the pressure of German bishops who were there to Christianize the western Slavs under the auspices of German princes and in their interests. This early conflict heralded a long history of Czech struggle for survival as a nation against the predominant German influence which was at times subtle, but often brutal.

While these struggles could not be wholly successful within the framework of a medieval Holy Roman Empire dominated by the Germans who continued their penetration into Bohemia, the Czechs did essentially preserve their cultural and political identity. The fourteenth century brought a new element into the Czech struggle for survival. Toward the end of that century the corrupt practices of the Catholic Church came under attack by John Huss, a priest and the rector of the recently established Charles University at Prague. Huss, influenced in his teaching by the early English reformer Wycliffe, was called to defend his criticisms to the currently sitting Church Council in Constance, and on refusing to recant he was burned at the stake as a heretic in 1415.

The ensuing revolt of the Czechs, who successfully defeated the crusades sent against them by the popes, is one of the most crucial periods of Czech history. Inevitably, the struggle for religious freedom against the power of the Catholic Church supported by German princes became a part of a more general conflict for Czech independence against the German threat.

Although lacking ideological cohesion, the Czech Hussites, led by able generals, defeated waves of invading armies of Catholic Europe. Finally, divided among themselves, they fought a fratricidal battle at Lipany in 1434. This disastrous event demonstrated for the first time the difficulty of achieving a *modus vivendi* and unity among the stubborn and differently motivated free Czechs. Still, a limited victory was gained by the moderate Hussite party which lasted for almost two hundred years, in spite of the ascension of the German Hapsburgs to the throne of Bohemia in 1526. By then, reformation movements were springing into existence in various parts of Europe and the Czech evangelical Bohemian Bretheren, the spiritual heirs of the earlier Hussites, flourished in the Czech lands.

Gradual encroachment on Czech rights by the Hapsburg monarchs led to the last stand the Czechs made for their national liberties. Their tragic defeat at White Mountain in 1620 left the Czech nation spiritually and materially broken, at the mercy of the absolute power of the German Hapsburgs bent on exemplary revenge. Their leaders either executed or exiled, their lands confiscated, their writings burned, the Czechs for more than two centuries lived in an age of darkness. The oppressed peasants, with the support of a few patriotic priests, kept the Czech language and the Czech freedom spiritually alive. The towns and cities were fast becoming Germanized. Even the Patent of Toleration granted by the enlightened Emperor Joseph II in 1781, allowing religious freedom to recognized Protestant denominations, did not stem the tide of national lethargy. In fact, Germanizing tendencies increased. But the ideas of the French Revolution carried throughout Europe by the armies of Napoleon ushered in a new era of hope, particularly to subjugated national groups. Although pessimism still prevailed to a large extent under Metternich's absolutism following the defeat of Napoleon, the impact of liberalizing ideas was generally felt among the Czech intelligentsia. With the restoration of intellectual leadership, an awakening among the Czechs began.

The revolutions which next swept across Europe in 1848 undermined authoritarian regimes, and the Austrian Empire was no exception. Metternich's despotic regime came to an end, and with it the last vestige of feudalism. Although the repression asserted itself again and the dissatisfaction of Czechs with their inferior political and economic position in the Austrian Empire grew, the national renaissance was now in full swing. Liberal journalists (foremost among them Karel Havlíček), writers, politicians, and scholars, writing first in German and later in Czech, began reaching more and more of their countrymen. Primarily it was an increasing awareness of Czech history, particularly the glorious era of the Hussite Reformation with its deeper meaning of freedom, humanism, democracy and justice, as well as the endless struggle against the German might, that made the Czechs proud and self-reliant.

Since the Czechs immigrated to America in the decades between 1848 and the founding of an independent Czechoslovakia in 1918, the struggle against the German power and against the Catholic Church are important for understanding the Czechs in the United States. The struggle against the Catholic Church had a lasting impact on the religious attitudes of Czechs in America, while reaction to the German Hapsburgs produced a liberal ideology which was carried to America.

Adjusting to Freedom, Hardships and Responsibilities

While there were a few residents of Bohemia who entered the American colonies as early as the seventeenth century as a result of the persecution of the Moravian Brethren after the White Mountain disaster,[3] the Czech immigration to the United States did not begin in earnest until the second half of the nineteenth century.

Despite awareness of past oppression and existing uncertainty, it was neither primarily political nor religious reasons that accounted for Czech immigration. The foremost cause was the economic condition prevailing in Bohemia.[4] The nationalistic leaders discouraged people from leaving for whatever reasons, arguing, in one instance, that "love of fatherland, if nothing else, should deter Czechs from emigrating."[5] But the urge for greater economic security was too strong. Stories of the discovery of gold in California, sensationally magnified in newspapers, lured some Czechs. Somewhat later, the Free Homestead Law provided a very real inducement to peasants who had to eke out an existence on inadequate land holdings. The wars in which the wobbly Hapsburg Empire was continuously engulfed, and which offered nothing but a speedy death for the glory of the Emperor, encouraged some Czech lads to avoid military service by quietly slipping to the promised land across the ocean.[6] There were some political refugees, too, but their number was insignificant.[7] As more immigrants settled in America, they wrote to their families and friends back home, describing the living conditions, climate and existing opportunities, thus inducing thousands of others to leave. Some midwestern states, anxious to increase their population, encouraged emigration from European countries by publishing pamphlets in newspapers in Bohemia about the wonderland in the American prairies.

The majority of early immigrants were peasants who had owned very little land, usually not more than 25 acres. These cottagers, as they were called, represented the rural lower middle class who had very little opportunity to improve their lot in a strictly stratified society. They could, however, sell their land and thereby afford transportation for themselves and their families to America, and still have enough money left to pay for land registration fees and immediate necessities. The peasants with larger land holdings managed quite well and did not have the urge to leave. On the other hand, landless day laborers simply did not have the necessary funds to leave.

Other Czech immigrants came from various trades—shoemakers, tailors, cabinet makers, harness makers, blacksmiths—while others had no particular trade or occupation at all and worked temporarily in manufacturing plants as unskilled laborers.

Educationally, the Czech immigrants rated high.[8] This was due to compulsory education existing in Austria in the middle of the nineteenth century. However, the education consisted for the most part of five grades of elementary school. Only a few could attain a high school education, and only the select few could attend a university. Still, a sprinkling of Czech immigrants possessed higher education backgrounds, sometimes acquired in Catholic seminaries.

The attitude of Czech immigrants toward religion is most perplexing to American observers. Unlike the immigrants of other nationalities who generally retained their native religious persuasion, the Czechs in large numbers abandoned their allegiance to the Catholic Church to which they customarily belonged in Bohemia. While over ninety percent of the population in Bohemia was considered Catholic according to official Austrian statistics, less than half the Czech immigrants retained their membership in that church in the United States. In some communities the percentage of secularists (freethinkers) was even larger.[9] One writer, Rose Rosický, defined the term "freethinkers" as "all the groups ranging from atheists (or more properly speaking Pantheists, for Czech atheists believe in Nature as the guiding force) to those who believed in a Creator but did not attend church."[10]

The reason for many Czechs' rejection of organized religion lay in their experience with the Catholic Church in Bohemia, where it represented an arm used by the Hapsburgs to keep the Czechs in political subjugation and economic misery. In the United States, they simply expressed their freedom by not joining any church or by formulating spiritual alternatives. These "unchurched" were far more numerous among the freethinkers than were the doctrinaire atheists. The latter, however, organized themselves, first in the Unity of Freethinkers and later in the Association of Freethought Societies. By their press, they propagated rationalism and atheism with the missionary zeal of early Christians. Their vitriolic attacks against Christianity in general, but aimed at the Catholic Church and Czech Catholics in particular, made cooperation among various Czech-American groups often difficult.

For the purpose of self-help the Czechs organized themselves into fraternal benevolent associations which paid a benefit to members in case of illness or death. The benevolent low-premium insurance associations, the best known of which were the Czech Slavonic Benevolent Society (CŠBS) and its offshoot, the Western Bohemian Fraternal Union (ZČBJ), had hundreds of lodges across the United States and proved to be a real boon to many Czech immigrants who could not otherwise afford life and illness insurance. Next to benevolent associations, the Czechs formed social interest groups, such as reading societies, dramatic and singing circles and gymnastic associations (most prominent among them Sokol). Since the orientation of most of these groups was "liberal" and in some cases—for example the Czech Slavonic Benevolent Society—had an anti-Catholic bias, the Catholics often organized themselves into separate groups usually centered around the local church. František Sokol-Tůma, a Czech writer who arrived in the United States in 1904 and spent some five months visiting Czech communities, made an interesting observation: "The Czechs in America are brought together only for mutual protection . . . necessitated by lack of American social legislation. Above that, they are interested only in social gatherings, concerts, stage plays, but all their activity is not motivated for the national (i.e. Czech) good but it is dependent upon other, often personal reasons and circumstances."[11] While this, as well as observations of other Czech visitors about the life of Czech-Americans, is superficial and lacks understanding of American conditions, it also strikes a true note about the Czech immigrants: they were aware of the need for their security on one hand, and they loved social life and group activities on the other.

The Czechs did not leave their native land to establish a Utopian society in America.[12] They came to make a better life for themselves and their children. It is true that many of them were exposed to various social and labor ideas which, with increasing industrialization, were discussed and written about in

Bohemia. Those who opted to settle in large American cities often experienced extreme difficulties. Poor labor conditions and substandard housing coupled with the tendency of employers to take advantage of non-English speaking immigrants, provided an opportunity for establishing Czech labor groups. The first such Czech Workers Club was founded in Chicago as early as 1866. It was followed by similar groups in Cleveland and New York, where in 1870 the first Czech trade union was organized. The new movement had established as early as 1870 its weekly newspaper spokesman, *Narodni Noviny,* published in Chicago. It is interesting to note that this newspaper antedated by two years the first Czech socialist newspaper in Prague. The early labor movement suffered a temporary setback when a wave of Czech exiles, radicalized by their persecution and suffering in Austria, turned to anarchism and assumed control of the Czech labor groups. Efforts were made to improve the organization of the unions after the Haymarket tragedy in Chicago. Credit for many of the improvements must go to Czech immigrants of the 1890's who were already members of labor unions and the Social Democratic Party in Bohemia. Czech workingmen joined the Knights of Labor (later the American Federation of Labor) and set up Czech speaking branches in their respective trades.[13] Thomas Čapek, in his study of the Czech press in the United States published in 1911, gives the Czech labor movement a respectable place: "The less initiated see only two ideological mainstreams continuously poised against each other—freethinking and clerical (i.e. Catholic and protestant). There is however a third stream which is concerned with society's ills. I for one was surprised at the many aspects of social problems dealt with in the anarchist and socialist literature and newspapers."[14]

By and large the political orientation of Czech immigrants leaned towards the Democratic party, although there was no apparent general pattern. The reason most often given was the fact that "Republicanism meant the Administration, and that Bohemians were readily led by their past experience to join the opposition."[15] It was also argued that "the Democratic party

managed to acquire an image as the friend of immigrants"
and that for slow assimilators such as the Czechs "it made more
sense."[16]

The newspapers were the most important medium keeping
the Czechs aware of happenings in other Czech settlements in
the United States and about the developments in their native
land. Between January 1860 and the spring of 1911, 326
Czech newspapers and journals (predominantly weeklies) were
published.[17] Most of them had a life expectancy of less than a
year. The publishers and editors were for the most part self-
educated men dedicated to helping and advising the new immigrants. Their leadership role was not always appreciated. The
readers often failed to pay subscription rates, causing the
financial failure of many sincere and useful journalistic efforts.
One editor, in announcing the demise of his short-lived weekly,
wrote bitterly in 1874: "It is hard to make a living in America
with a pick and shovel, yet it is even harder for a journalist. I
am throwing away the pen which made three prime years of my
life so miserable . . . I will not even say whose fault it is. I
mention only that I could not publish the farewell issue of the
paper because I lacked money to buy newsprint, even though
the Czechs owed me $800. . . ."[18] On the other hand, reli-
gious, political and ideological animosities among some com-
peting newspapers ran high and, in many instances, contributed
to bitter relationships among their readers. This intolerance and
lack of unity was criticised by the visiting Czech writer Sokol-
Tůma.[19]

Regardless of the problems and the criticisms, the impact
of the Czech press was tremendous. It is estimated that in 1900
about 150,000 Czechs subscribed to one Czech newspaper or
another (according to 1900 census there were 156,891 Czechs
in the United States) which indicates that almost every Czech
immigrant, including men, women, and children read Czech
newspapers.[20] While the first generation of Czechs needed and
enjoyed reading in their mother tongue, the interest in the
second generation diminished, and it virtually ceased with the
third generation.[21]

Czech Culture on the Prairie

The Czechs settled in Nebraska for the same reason they settled in Wisconsin, Minnesota, Iowa, Kansas, and the Dakotas. They migrated for the most part from the villages of Bohemia and Moravia and they hungered for land they could till and own; and the land was there in abundance. Three acts passed into law by the United States Congress or made effective in Nebraska between 1854 and 1873 enabled a prospective settler to take possession of up to 480 acres of land within a few years.[22] The early Czech newspapers directed the newcomers interested in farming to the most favorable, unsettled parts of the Midwest. Many Czechs who settled first in Wisconsin and Iowa moved farther west on learning of excellent conditions for farming and readily available land. The first Czech newspaper in Nebraska, *Pokrok Západu* (Progress of the West), published in Omaha from 1871 by an enterprising Czech Jew, Edward Rosewater, served in its early stages as a land advertising sheet. The railway companies, especially the Burlington and Missouri, and the Union Pacific, were very active in their efforts to bring more settlers to Nebraska. Frank Sadílek, an early Czech settler from Wilber, claimed that "up to 1880, fully three-fourths of the entire number of Czech immigrants came to our state."[23]

Along with the pioneers of other nationalities, the Czechs suffered much in their new homes. They lived in dugouts or sod houses, busted the stubborn prairie, fought droughts, grasshoppers, prairie fires and blizzards—and often without reward. How sad sounds the story by a third generation Czech recollecting the experience of her grandparents in Nebraska. They arrived too late in the season to plant crops,

> . . . so both grandpa and grandma went and helped their neighbors and worked for seventy-five cents a day. The next year they started to farm for themselves; and not being used to hard work, found it awfully hard. That summer they mostly lived on bread and butter and Irish potatoes. Grandma did not like it here and often cried and wanted to go back to Europe. They made a nice crop that year and also the following two,

so grandpa paid most of his debts. And they got used to hard work and began to like it here. The fourth summer was dry and the crop was small, but they did not mind that, so they thought the coming year would be better; but it turned out to be still worse. The summer was hot and very dry and the crops were smaller than the year before. The grasshoppers came and ate most everything there was, so many of them that the people could not see the sun for three days. The only thing grandma saved in her garden was a head of cabbage over which she put a wash tub. She could not help but cry, for she worked so hard over it. Everything was like after a cyclone. The times were hard, but still the people forgot about that and every Sunday they would meet and dance and talk and enjoy themselves. The only music they had was a mouth harp, and they often thumped on the floor with a broom stick for a bass. Most of them danced barefooted so that they wouldn't wear the soles on their shoes.[24]

This particular family gave up and left Nebraska to start farming in Virginia. But a vast majority of others stayed even though a few would have preferred to return to their homeland. A 95-year-old son of a Valley County pioneer recollects that his father would have gone back to Bohemia with his family if he had had enough money for the journey.[25]

Along with economic hardships and the rigor of pioneering, settlers faced extreme isolation and loneliness. Although the minds of Czechs were for centuries exposed to westernizing influences, their inner makeup remained Slavic, inscrutably complex and sentimental. Their love of music, dance, and beer occasioned joyful celebration, and the release from monotony of day-to-day existence. Here, on the plains of Nebraska, they were in many cases denied this kind of escape. Willa Cather in her poignant story of a Czech immigrant family in Nebraska writes: "I knew it was homesickness that had killed Mr. Shimerda, and I wondered whether his released spirit would not eventually find its way to his own country."[26] To others, the suicides of fictional Shimerda and other Czech immigrants are attributable to their lack of religion and their fatalistic outlook on life. "It appears that when a crisis comes, there is no sustaining force to guide the individual to a more settled mind."[27] It was the combination of both, the ever present Slavic fatalism as an underlying recognition of man's helplessness and the more immediate loneliness in the often beautiful but seemingly cruel natural setting of their new prairie home that accounts for the high suicide rates of the Czech settlers.[28] This mental conflict between a desire for the greatest possible personal freedom and economic security on the one hand, and a sentimental longing for the homeland on the other, did not prevent the Czech pioneers from staying. The initial psychological and economic difficulties were slowly overcome by a dogged determination and a willingness to adjust and to make the best of it. Their isolation became bearable by occasional visits to their Czech neighbors and to the growing number of predominantly Czech villages.

The village settlements growing since the late 1860's in the counties of eastern Nebraska, particularly in Saline, Fillmore, Saunders, Butler, Colfax and Knox counties, and in the growing city of Omaha, provided the necessary means for social life the Czechs desired. There they recreated an image of a Bohemian setting as they remembered it: houses adorned by flower beds, the vegetable gardens in the back, the benches lining the main street where older citizens could sit and talk, halls to stage the plays, to dance polkas, to drink beer, and to argue, and churches for worship. This Czech-American setting gave them security and social satisfaction. They viewed it gratefully and were proud of it. Czech customs prevailed. People spoke Czech, danced Czech music, cooked Czech dishes, and read Czech newspapers. Even at death a person could expect to be buried in the Czech cemetery following a eulogy or prayers in the Czech language spoken to the soft sounds of Czech music. Božena Němcová, an outstanding Czech writer who suffered a great deal in Bohemia for her convictions, wrote to her friend who left for America regarding this need for the cultural unity of Czechs: "Live happily in that new country and never regret that you had to leave. . . . The fatherland is everywhere where there are people of one language, morals, and endeavors."[29]

Like Czechs in other parts of the United States, the settlers in Nebraska had organizations which served their needs. Every Czech settlement had its fraternal benevolent lodge which was concerned not only with providing insurance but with numerous social activities as well. The halls of the Western Bohemian Fraternal Association were used for gymnastic exercises of the Sokols of all ages, musical and dramatic performances, and community celebrations such as Christmas.

Religiously, the Czechs in Nebraska were divided about equally into freethinkers and Catholics, with a relatively small number of evangelical protestants. Saline and Fillmore counties in particular were strongly secularist, while in Butler, Saunders and Colfax counties Catholics predominated. Though occasional friction arose among them, the Czechs in Nebraska were less affected by their religious convictions and did not allow them to prevent harmony in business and social life. While the unchurched were generally active in the fraternal lodges and Sokol organization, the Catholics participated in their group activities, which usually centered around the church and were organized by the priest.

Both the Catholics and the freethinkers, each in their own way, pursued the goal of retaining the traditional Czech culture and transmitting it to the next generation. The Czech language was to be the primary vehicle used in attaining this goal. The schools were to play a significant part in that effort.

While even the most outspoken Czech traditionalists favored the American public school system with English as the language of instruction,[30] they advocated some supplementary education for their children in Czech. The children of Czech immigrants, after all, learned the native language in the home before going to public schools. They had the background and the feel for the Czech language, and they saw no reason why they should not continue to use it. It was part of their ethnic identity. Eventual dissipation of that culture was inevitable, however, and perhaps even desirable. But would not its retention enrich at least the second generation of ethnic Americans, and would not that implantation of different ideas help to promote better understanding among all Americans as well?

The protagonists of supplementary instruction in Czech saw it as a means to instill into the children's minds a better understanding of their parent culture. In the long run, these efforts have failed. But during the nineteenth and perhaps even the first two decades of the present century, hundreds of Czech schools, operating mainly during the evenings, weekends, and summers, were in evidence across the United States wherever Czechs were settled. The classes met in Czech lodge halls, Sokol halls or public schools. In most cases there was little continuity, and the lack of competent teachers created problems. According to a partial survey in 1910, Nebraska had five supplementary schools (all conducted by freethinkers), located in Omaha, South Omaha, Humboldt, Schuyler, and Bruno, with a combined enrollment of about 300 pupils.[31] The latest effort to revive interest in the Czech language belongs to Dr. Vladimír Kučera, who with great dedication taught hundreds of Americans of Czech descent the language in Omaha, Milligan, Dwight, Schuyler, Clarkson, Wilber, Abie, North Bend and Table Rock in the 1960's and 1970's. The public school at Wilber now offers an optional Czech class, and there is some volunteer teaching of Czech in two or three other communities. On a higher level, the Czech language and Czech literature was taught at the University of Nebraska at Lincoln between 1907 and 1919, when it was discontinued ostensibly because of small enrollment.[32] The teaching was later resumed by Professor Orin Štepánek, and in 1959, as part of the University extension program, by Dr. Vladimír Kučera. At present there are regular Czech classes offered by the Department of Modern Languages and Literature.

Future of the Czech Heritage

The Czech life in Nebraska, which manifested vitality for several decades, had by the 1920's begun to show signs of weakening. The changes were slow, often imperceptible to contemporaries. Nevertheless, these changes pointed to the permanent disappearance of the Czech way of life in Nebraska. The effects of assimilation are particularly evident among second generation Czechs, those born and educated in the United States. Extracurricular instruction in the Czech language may have slowed the process, but it could not stop it. Children born in America often resented their parents' ways of thinking and acting, and preferred in their place the culture of America. They did not want to stay in the "old-fashioned" world which their parents created to satisfy their social needs. They did not have first-hand recollections of the authentic Czech culture, and therefore had nothing to long for. Instead, they aspired to full participation in the American way of life which to them seemed to offer so much. Ironically, this reaction was similar to that of their parents, who left the native land they loved in search of a better way of life. Now it was the younger generation's turn to search for the same in the rapidly growing American economy. And not all parents discouraged this trend.

As the second generation began to outnumber the first, the Czech language slowly began to disappear. World War I and the antiforeign feelings which resulted led to the enactment of strict language laws in Nebraska.[33] This further discouraged the younger generation from improving their basic knowledge of the language and culture of the parents. To what extent a distinct culture of white European stock can survive in the American setting without the native language may be a matter of conjecture, but it appears that in the case of the Czechs the language was a primary force in the preservation of a cultural identity. Without it, the assimilation and acculturation of a group becomes inevitable. It is just a matter of time.

Listen to the sentimental narrative of a member of the Czech community at Warsaw, Nebraska, in the late 1920's:

> The Czech language is seldom heard in the Warsaw [Catholic] Church. No longer do the beautiful Czech songs of a by-gone era echo over the Warsaw plain. . . . The time is not distant

when the dear Czech language will vanish and only the Czech inscriptions and the names on the monuments in Warsaw cemetery will remind the passer-by of the fact that there lie loyal Czech pioneers, who struggled for a livelihood and a better future for their descendants.[34]

The main source for the survival of the Czech language was the steady flow of Czech immigrants. This flow to Nebraska was relatively strong until the outbreak of World War I. Following the war, it declined rapidly. The immigration laws of the 1920's establishing nationality quotas prevented the influx of new blood to replace the older Czechs.[35] A marked decline in the actual number of first generation Czechs in Nebraska began in the 1940's. And it should be emphasized again that it was primarily this generation which was interested in the preservation of Czech culture in America.

The establishment of an independent Republic of Czechoslovakia at the end of World War I was another, perhaps more psychological, reason for declined interest in the retention of Czech culture in the United States. For many older Czechs it was the climax of their sentimental involvement with their native country dominated by the Germans when they left. Now, with the Hapsburgs gone and the country free, they felt their role in the Czech struggle for freedom had come to an end. They proved their devotion to the country of their birth by providing material, political and moral support to the leaders of Czechoslovak resistance abroad, and by volunteering by the thousands to join the United States expeditionary forces during the war. Now, with Masaryk, who epitomized the noblest ideas of the Czechs' historical struggle, at the helm of a democratic Czechoslovakia, they experienced a sense of relief and deep gratitude to their adopted land for the opportunity to participate in this struggle and its outcome.

Finally, intermarriage between Czechs and non-Czechs proved a very effective means for fast assimilation and acculturation. Generally, the only solution for both the parents and the children in such marriages was to accept American attitudes from the outset to prevent conflicts. An interesting observation about intermarriage among first generation Czechs can be made at this juncture by referring back to the two streams that dominated the course of Czech history. First was the almost continuous struggle for survival against German domination, and second was the reformation effort against the universalism of the Catholic Church. While the Czechs in large numbers carried their anti-Catholic sentiment to America, they apparently did not feel the same about their historical anti-German mission. At least this did not manifest itself in their interpersonal relationships with fellow immigrants from Germany. By far the largest number of Czechs who intermarried in the United States selected Germans as their mates.[36]

The effect of the Czech assimilation pattern becomes progressively more evident as the history of Czech life in America lengthens. Nebraska is no exception.

The decline in use of the Czech language has already been mentioned. It resulted from the phasing out of Czech language books, newspapers, and periodicals. At one time, Nebraska had Czech newspapers published in Omaha, Wilber, Clarkson, Schuyler, and elsewhere. Now there is only one in the entire state: the *Fraternal Herald,* official organ of the Western Life Association. And this monthly is only partially in Czech.

Another example may be seen in the disappearance of Czech plays, formerly presented by volunteer dramatic clubs in many Nebraska communities.

Declining usage of the Czech language as the common means of communication among the Nebraska Czechs has contributed to the demise of other cultural forms. It helped to change the ideological and spiritual contents of institutions that, for reasons of their own, either survived or on occasion were revived by efforts of a few dedicated individuals.

In an 1897 convention in Omaha, the Western Bohemian Fraternal Association came into existence as an off-shoot of yet another American Czech benevolent society. Originally, only persons of Czech extraction were permitted to become members. The Czech language was used exclusively. Various social functions, performances, dances—all distinctly reflecting the composition of the Czech membership—were organized by local lodges. Today, however, the name has been changed to the Western Fraternal Life Association and anyone can join, just as long as he abides by the rules and pays the premiums. Social activities have been greatly curtailed. Of the 51 lodges in Nebraska, only nine still conduct their meetings and keep their minutes in Czech.[37] In all probability, these lodges are more inclined to traditional Czech activities. Even so, the Americanization process will likely continue until complete absorption takes place.

Sokol, the Czech patriotic gymnastic association founded in Bohemia in 1862, with the professed ideal that there must be a vigorous mind in a healthy body, spread rapidly among the Czech-American communities. It was extremely well organized and its programs were well attended, particularly by young Czech-Americans of both sexes. Sokol chapters were active not only in gymnastics, but also sponsored educational and cultural programs including Czech language classes, gymnastic displays (festivals), dances, and picnics.

Only a few Nebraska chapters are active today. The object of the present day Sokol in America is "physical, mental and moral development of young men and women in accordance with the civic and progressive patriotic principles toward attaining the highest standards of American citizenship regardless of their ancestry."[38] Even modern day Sokol, open to everybody, is apparently not able to prevent losing its members. There is simply not enough appeal in its traditional program, and the competition from similar sports-related organizations is strong. There remain, however, many dedicated individuals, most of them of Czech descent, who carry on the activities in the existing chapters. How long will Sokol survive? This depends upon young people of today. They must develop the desire for participation in Sokol activities. Without that desire Sokol will eventually cease to exist.

A similar argument applies to almost all other traditional activities brought into existence by and for the social and economic benefit of first generation Czechs. At times it seemed that the second generation, with its genuine interest and capable leadership, would create a permanent base for the survival of the Czech culture. One such promising undertaking was the establishment of the Komenský (Comenius) Educational Club at the University of Nebraska in 1904. Within a few years, 29 chapters were established. The primary purpose of the club was the preservation of the Czech language and culture through educational endeavors. The club's monthly organ, capably edited by Šárka Hrbková, professor of Czech at the University of Nebraska, served its purpose well. The clubs suspended their activities because of the war and by 1918 were out of existence. More than 50 years later Dr. Kučera revived the Komenský Club in Lincoln in conjunction with the Czech classes offered by the University's extension program. The Club was successful for a number of years. It resulted in many worthwhile presentations, and featured Czech music and folk dances intended to make the participants aware of the Czech heritage in Nebraska. In recent years, this club too has passed out of existence. There is currently no one to maintain the organization, and little apparent interest among students of Czech background.

Some Czech heritage remains alive in present-day Nebraska despite the odds against it. It has been suggested in this essay that the disappearance of the Czech language was the primary reason for declining interest in this heritage. It may be also suggested that there is only a minor difference between the inevitable assimilation and the optional voluntary acculturation of ethnic white groups in America. The second, third, and fourth generations have, by continual adjustment to the needs of the prevailing society, developed new sensitivities regarding their cultural heritage. Americanization does not necessarily lead to a total obliteration of the ethnic cultural pattern of which they are a part, and it should not prevent continuation or even revival of activities aiming at the retention of this identity. Some scholars indicate that the ethnic factor is really genuine and that it is particularly evident in the third generation In the words of one authority,

They (i.e. third generation) have everything that their grandparents and great-grandparents came for, but the price they
paid is the lack of feeling of belonging, a lack of social psychological roots. There develops, then, what Hansen chose to
call third-generation interest, a principle which makes it
possible for the present to say something and do something
about the future in the name of the past. It is an impulse
which forces many different people to interest themselves in
the one factor which they have in common: heritage.[39]

It remains to be seen whether enough interest can be generated
by the descendants of Czech pioneers and immigrants to stimulate a revival of this cultural heritage in Nebraska. They would
contribute much to the multi-cultural America if they did revive it, and to the memory of their pioneer forefathers as well.

The appended catalogue of Czech resources available today
in Nebraska indicates the existing possibilities for young Czech-
Americans in Nebraska. There are numerous ways in which they
can revive this fading culture if they wish to do so. They can
learn the Czech language, read Czech literature (some is available in English translations), study Czech history, learn about
Czech artists, listen to Czech music, join and support the activities of existing Czech clubs and organizations, visit annual
Czech festivals sponsored annually in several Nebraska communities, attend predominantly Czech churches retaining some
of the Czech past, or visit with old-timers and learn from them
the customs of the past. It is quite possible that by involving
themselves in these traditions, they will find a degree of satisfaction never before experienced. "Why are you so enthusiastic
about so many Czech traditions?" one third generation Czech,
very fond of Czech music and Czech dances, was asked. Her
answer was very simple: "Quite frankly, I enjoy them."[40]

Perhaps by doing this they will come to understand and
appreciate the American culture even more, and will learn to be
better citizens in a free and responsible society.

FOOTNOTES

1. Vladimír Kučera, ed., *Czechs and Nebraska* (Ord, Neb.: Quiz Graphic Arts, Inc., 1967), p. 51. Actually the first Czech to enter Nebraska was Joseph Francl, who crossed Nebraska in 1854. *Ibid.* p. 48. Šarka Hrbková writes in *Bohemians in Nebraska* (Lincoln, Neb.: Nebraska State Historical Society, 1919), p. 143, that Libor Alois Slesinger was the the first Czech who came to Nebraska on April 15, 1857.

2. Problems relating to estimating the number of Czech immigrants into the United States have never been satisfactorily resolved. See particularly Kenneth D. Miller, *The Czecho-Slovaks in America* (New York: George H. Doran Co., 1922), pp. 47-48; Thomas Čapek, *The Czechs in America* (Boston and New York: Houghton Mifflin Co., 1920), pp. 56-68; Šarka Hrbková, *op. cit.,* p. 143; Jar. E. Salaba-Vojan, *Česko-Americké Epištoly* (Chicago: n.p., 1911).

3. See Thomas Čapek, *Památky Českých Emigrantů v Americe* (Omaha: Narodni Tiskárna, 1907), particularly the story of August Heřman, who was already in the area of the present day Philadelphia in 1633, pp. 17-61.

4. One early Czech immigrant writes that Bohemia experienced good times after the Napoleonic wars, with plenty of opportunity for employment and low prices. In the 1840's potato crops failed, resulting in hardships which led the people to consider leaving the country. See Thomas Čapek, *Padesát Let Českeho Tisku v Americe* (New York: Bank of Europe, 1911), p. 4.

5. Quoted in Čapek, *The Czechs in America,* p. 32.

6. Austria lost Lombardy in two bloody battles at Solferino and Magenta in 1859. In 1866 she suffered a military defeat from the hands of the Prussians at Sadowa.

7. In the mass escape in 1847, 39 Czechs of the 35th Pilsen Regiment escaped to America from the Mainz fortress. Another political refugee, and an early Nebraska settler, was Libor Alois Slesinger, participant in the 1848 revolution in Prague.

8. According to the survey regarding illiteracy among immigrants 14 years of age and over for the year ending June 30, 1900, the percentage of Bohemian and Moravian immigrants who were illiterate was only 3.0 percent. Only Finns, Scots, English and Scandinavians had a lower percentage of illiterates. See Emily Green Balch, *Our Slavic Fellow Citizens* (New York: Charities Publication Committee, 1910), p. 479.

9. In Chicago, which had the largest block of Czechs, it is estimated that as many as 70 percent of all Czechs avoided not only the Catholic but also the protestant faiths. See *Panorama: A Historical Review of Czechs and Slovaks in the United States of America* (Cicero, Ill.: Czechoslovak National Council of America, 1970), p. 31. In Milligan, a village in Nebraska comprised almost entirely of Czechs, three-fourths of the Czech people did not belong to any church. See Robert I. Kutak, *The Story of a Bohemian-American Village: A Study of Social Persistance and Change* (Louisville, Ky.: The Standard Printing Co., 1933), p. 148.

10. Rose Rosicky, *A History of Czechs (Bohemians) in Nebraska* (Omaha: Czech Historical Society of Nebraska, 1929), p. 279.

11. František Sokol-Tůma, *Z Cest po Americe,* Vol. I (Moravská Ostrava: F. Tůma, 1910), p. 144.

12. Ladimir Klacel, a former Augustinian monk, who immigrated to the United States in 1869 at 63 years of age, was an exception. He was an ardent Utopian Socialist who dreamed of founding a "community of free and just men," similar to the Utopian communes founded here by French, German, and Swiss immigrants. He failed because the community, planned for the Black Hills in Dakota, was not established. In *Panorama,* p. 85.

13. *Panorama,* pp. 85-86.

14. Tomaš Čapek, *Padesat Let Českeho Tisku v Americe,* p. V (Introduction).

15. Balch, *op. cit.,* p. 395.

16. John R. Kleinschmidt, "The Political Behavior of the Bohemian and Swedish Ethnic Groups in Nebraska, 1884-1900 " (unpublished Masters Thesis, University of Nebraska, 1968), pp. 38-39. It is interesting to observe that in a quantitative study made in several counties in Nebraska, the second generation Czechs reversed the political allegiance of their fathers and generally favored the Republican Party. *Ibid.* pp. 40, 46.

17. Tomaš Čapek, *Padesat Let Českeho Tisku v Americe,* p. 185.

18. *Ibid.,* p. 113.

19. Sokol-Tůma, *op. cit.,* p. 71.

20. Tomaš Čapek, *Padesat Let Českeho Tisku v Americe,* p. 51.

21. Sokol-Tůma, *op. cit.,* p. 176.

22. Under the Preemption Act of 1841 (U.S. Statutes at Large, Vol. X, p. 283) and applied in Nebraska in 1854 when President Pierce signed the Nebraska-Kansas Bill (U.S. Statutes at Large, Vol. V, p. 454), a "citizen of the United States, or one who has declared his intention to become a citizen was entitled to settle upon the public domain and secure 160 acres by improving it, making his home upon it and paying $1.25 per acre to the

United States." Under the Free Homestead Act of 1862 a settler could take 160 acres for a $14 filing fee on condition that he make it his home and improve it within five years. Under the Timber Claims Act of 1873 a settler could obtain 160 acres by planting ten acres of trees on it and taking care of them for eight years. See Addison E. Sheldon, *Land Systems and Land Policies in Nebraska* (Lincoln: Nebraska State Historical Society, 1936), pp. 25, 75, 97.

23. Rosicky, *op. cit.*, p. 30.

24. Edmund de S. Brunner, *Immigrant Farmers and Their Children* (Garden City, N.Y.: Doubleday, Doran and Co., Inc., 1929), p. 187.

25. Nebraska Czech Oral History Collection, University of Nebraska-Lincoln, Library. Interview with Anton Adamek, Ord, Nebraska, November 11, 1975.

26. Willa Cather, *My Ántonia* (Boston: Houghton Mifflin Co., 1954), p. 101.

27. Alfred R. Jensen, "European Background Influences on Education in the Milligan School" (unpublished Masters Thesis, University of Nebraska, 1952), pp. 25-26.

28. The suicide rate of Bohemia, and later of Czechoslovakia, has always been one of the highest in the world. In 1972 only Hungary, East Germany and Denmark had higher rates. See *Information Please Almanac, Atlas and Yearbook,* 1976 (New York City: Simon and Schuster), p. 733.

29. Letter from Božena Němcová to Joseph L. Leskar, August 12, 1856. Quoted in Kucera, *op. cit.* p. 14.

30. Salaba-Vojan, *op. cit.*, p. 153.

31. *Ibid.*, p. 161.

32. Letter from Chancellor S. Avery, University of Nebraska, to Šarka Hrbkova, May 13, 1919, University of Nebraska-Lincoln Archives. There is some evidence to suggest that small enrollment was only partly responsible for abolishing the linguistic classes in the Slavic languages. Šarka Hrbkova's involvement in the action pursued by the Nebraska State Council for Defense on the loyalty question during World War I was a major cause. See S. Hrbkova to Chancellor S. Avery, May 17, 1919, University of Nebraska-Lincoln Archives.

33. Nebraska. Laws, Statutes, etc. Laws Passed by the Legislature of the State of Nebraska, 1919-21, pp. 244-45.

34. Rosicky, *op. cit.*, p. 327.

35. According to the Immigration Laws passed by the United States Congress on May 26, 1924, the Czech annual quota was 3,073. See U.S. Bureau of the Census, *Statistical Abstract of the United States, 1975*

(96th edition), Washington, D.C.

    36. Balch, *op. cit.*, p. 476.

    37. *Fraternal Herald*, April, 1975, pp. 32-33.

    38. Joseph A. Kučera, "Sokols in America," in *Sokolsky Slet* (Crete, Neb.: Western District of American Sokols, 1964).

    39. Wayne Wheeler, *An Almanac of Nebraska. Nationality, Ethnic, and Racial Groups* (Omaha: Park Bromwell Press, 1975), p. 6.

    40. Interview with Dorothy Stepan, Lincoln, January 13, 1976.

CATALOGUE

HOW TO LEARN MORE ABOUT NEBRASKA CZECHS

Libraries Containing Czech Materials

If you wish to explore further some aspects of Czech history, arts, music or literature, the libraries listed in this section can be consulted for holdings. In addition to monographs, journals, and newspapers, some local libraries in Nebraska may include materials relevant for exploration of family histories and genealogical research.

Libraries Outside Nebraska

Chicago, University of
20,000 volumes, primarily in the humanities and social sciences. Special collection includes the Czech and Slovak Immigration Archives, containing some 8,000 items relating to Czechs and Slovaks in the United States, Canada, and other countries.

Columbia University (New York City)
15,000 volumes in Czech and Slovak. The Russian Archives contains materials relating to Czechoslovakia.

Harvard University
Contains an outstanding Slovak collection, particularly in the 19th century. Almost all Beneš and Masaryk titles have been collected. Major additions concerning John Huss and the Hussite movement. The Jakum Deml collection is probably unparalleled outside Czechoslovakia.

Indiana University at Bloomington
18,000 volumes in various languages in the humanities and social sciences. Rare book collections devoted in part to Beneš, Masaryk, Bezruč, and Czech Bibles.

Library of Congress
80,000 volumes, of which 80 percent are either in Czech or Slovak. The remaining 20 percent are in other languages. 2,400 titles of

periodicals, and 175 newspapers. Of significance is the Czech Renaissance Collection, consisting of several hundred volumes imprinted in the 16th and 17th centuries.

New York City Public Library
10,000 volumes in Czech and Slovak. Volumes in English are distributed throughout the collection. Major Czech newspapers, with extensive backfiles.

Slavonic Benevolent Order of the State of Texas (Temple, Texas)
Books and archival materials relating to Sokol festivals, Czech history, etc.

The Archives of the Moravian Church - Northern Province
Located on the campus of Moravian College, Bethlehem, Penn. Extensive research collection relating to the history of Untias Fratrum, with special emphasis on the Moravian Church in America since the 18th century.

Other institutions having extensive Czech and Slovak collections are:
Hoover Institute at Stanford University
University of California at Berkeley
University of Illinois at Urbana
Western Reserve Historical Society in Cleveland
The Balch Institute in Philadelphia
University of Minnesota Immigration History Research Center in St. Paul (includes archival materials pertaining to Czechs in the United States).

Libraries in Nebraska

Clarkson

Creighton University (Omaha)

Crete
Small collection of Czech books and pamphlets (history) and books about Bohemia and Czechoslovakia in English.

David City
Small collection in Czech covering history and literature.

Dwight

> *Approximately 125 volumes in Czech language (history, literature and travel) and 50 books and magazines in English dealing with the history of Bohemia and Czechoslovakia.*

Milligan

> *Small collection in Czech covering fiction.*

Nebraska State Historical Society (Lincoln)

> *Numerous pamphlets about Czech settlements in Nebraska; particularly strong in Czech newspapers published in Nebraska; also included are manuscripts relating to Nebraska Czechs and their careers.*

Schuyler

> *Small collection of fiction in Czech.*

Serpan Memorial Library (Omaha)

> *Located in the Sokol auditorium, the library contains over 3,000 books in Czech language.*

University of Nebraska - Lincoln

> *The University has approximately 2,000 volumes in Czech, with literature and the social sciences predominating. The University Archives has recently been involved in an oral history project designed to preserve the heritage of the Czech pioneers in Nebraska. The audio tapes of interviews are available in the University library in Czech and English. Archival materials documenting the history of Czechs in Nebraska and the United States are also included in the Special Czech Collection. These materials include pamphlets, letters, written reminiscences, histories of Czech settlements, and related items. The library has a nearly complete set of a Czech newspaper, **Hospodar**, published from 1891 to 1960 in Omaha. Substantial backfiles of other Czech newspapers published in Nebraska have also been received.*

Wilber

> *The Dvoracek Memorial Library contains a Czech Heritage Room housing Czech books, Czech art and Czech music collections. Extensive backfiles of Czech newspapers published in Nebraska are main-*

tained. General collection of Czech novels and nonfiction, many relating to the history of Czechs in the United States.

Museums

A few local museums illustrate in pictures and three-dimensional objects the life styles of Czechs in Bohemia and early settlers in Nebraska. You will likely find there photographs of homes of Nebraska settlers and framed large pictures of Czech historical figures (Cyril and Methodius preaching to Czechs, murder of St. Wenceslaus by his brother, Huss defending himself at the Council of Constance, blind Hussite general Žižka leading the Taborites, Comenius and Bohemian Brethren leaving their native country, Havlíček's arrest by Austrian police, Masaryk's return to Prague in 1918). In addition, the museums usually have recordings of musical groups, products of various old Bohemian crafts, costumes worn in different parts of Bohemia, musical instruments, home-made furniture and Czech cut glass.

Clarkson

Table Rock

Wilber

Organizations

The presently active groups offer to members social activities (dances and occasional get-togethers). A few organizations also sponsor annual Czech festivals in several Nebraska communities. Many fraternal lodges maintain small libraries containing Czech books which are available to members.

Western Fraternal Life Association
Zapadní Česko-Bratrská Jednota (ZČBJ)

Asterisks (*) mark lodges which conduct their meetings in Czech.

*Abie	Havlíček Borovský
Barneston	Budějovice
Brainard	Čecho-Moravan
Burwell	Josef Jungman
*Clarkson	Zapadní Svornost
Comstock	Slavín
*Crete	Nebraska Crete
David City	Dobroslav
Dodge	Jan Amos Komenský
*Dorchester	Tábor
DuBois	Jan Kollár
Dwight	Dwight
Elba	Elba
Exeter	Zbirov
Farwell	Čech
Hemingford	Box Butte Lawn
Lincoln	Lincoln
Lindsay	Jan Hus
Linwood	Ratolest Mladočechů
Lynch	Lipany
Milligan	Milligan Svatopluk Čech
Morse Bluff	Plzeň
Niobrara	Vyšehrad
Odell	Králové Hradec
*Omaha	Hvězda Svobody *Jiří Poděbradský Mladý Rozkvět *Omaha

	Pathfinder
	Zest
*Ord	*Dennice
	Loup Valley
Pierce	Český Prapor
Plattsmouth	Tyrš
Prague	Vladislav I
Ravenna	Žižkův Palcát
*Sargent	Sargent
Schuyler	Blaník
Spencer	Karlín Junior
St. Paul	Kutná Hora
Swanton	Vlastenec
Table Rock	Přemysl Otakar II
Tobias	Křivoklát
Verdel	Sladkovský
Verdigre	Bílá Hora
Virginia	Osvěta
*Western	Saline Center
Wilber	Libuše
	Praha

Catholic Workman

Katolický Dělník

Catholic fraternal society organized to promote the spiritual, moral social welfare of its members, and to help the widows and orphans of deceased members.

Abie	Sts. Cyril & Methodius
Appleton	Sts. Cyril & Methodius
Bee	St. Wenceslaus

Brainard	St. Ivan
Bruno	St. Anthony
Cedar Hill	Sacred Heart
Clarkson	St. Joseph
Crete	St. Joseph
Deweese	St. Joseph
Dodge	St. Procopius
Dwight	Nativity
Heun	Sts. Peter & Paul
Howells	St. John Nepomucký
Leigh	———
Linwood	St. Wenceslaus
Loma	St. Luke
Lynch	St. Wenceslaus
Milligan	St. Joseph
Netolice	St. Wenceslaus
Omaha	St. Albert
	St. Clement
	St. Joseph
	Sts. Peter & Paul
	St. Procopius
Plasi	St. Procopius
Plattsmouth	St. Bartholemew
Prague	St. Wenceslaus
Ravenna	St. Joseph
St. Paul	St. Wenceslaus
Schuyler	St. Joseph
Stanton	———
Tabor	St. Wenceslaus
Thornburg	Sts. Cyril & Methodius
Touhy	St. Ladislaus
Ulysses	———
Valparaiso	———
Verdigre	St. John Nepomucký
Wahoo	Sts. Cyril & Methodius
	St. Wenceslaus
Warsaw	St. Joseph
Weston	St. Mark
Wilber	Sacred Heart
Wilson	St. Joseph

Nebraska Czechs Incorporated (state-wide organization)

Its purpose is "to develop and encourage interest, research, and inquiry into the culture, traditions, and history of the Czech immigrants to the United States and to Nebraska only as they and their descendants brought them to America . . . not as they might have existed in Czecho-slovakia or as they might exist today."

Local chapters have been formed in the following communities: Wilber, Dwight, Schuyler, Omaha, Lincoln, Saunders County (Wahoo).

Sokol

Active branches today:

Omaha

South Omaha

Crete

Wilber

Brush Creek

Churches and Cemeteries

Churches (For historical background see Vladimír Kučera, ed., *Czech Churches in Nebraska*, n.p.: 1976.)

Although none of the churches are any longer purely Czech and none conduct services in Czech, a few traditions originally brought from Bohemia are maintained by priests and ministers.

Catholic

Abie	Sts. Peter & Paul
Appleton	Blessed Virgin Mary
Bee	St. Wenceslaus

Brainard	Blessed Trinity
Bruno	St. Anthony of Padua
Cedar Hill	Sacred
Clarkson	Sts. Cyril & Methodius
Colon	St. Joseph
Crete	St. Ludmila
Dodge	St. Wenceslaus
Dry Creek	Assumption of the Blessed Virgin Mary
Dwight	Assumption of the Blessed Virgin Mary
Fairfield	St. Aloysius
Heun	Blessed Trinity
Howells	St. John
Lawn	St. Wenceslaus
Linwood	Blessed Virgin Mary
Loma	St. Luke
Lynch	Blessed Virgin Mary
Milligan	St. Wenceslaus
Netolice	St. Wenceslaus
Odell	Blessed Virgin of Perpetual Help
Omaha	Assumption of the Blessed Virgin Mary
	St. Adalbert
	St. Rose
	St. Wenceslaus
Ord	Blessed Virgin Mary of Perpetual Help
Plasi	Sts. Cyril & Methodius
Plattsmouth	Blessed Virgin Mary of the Holy Rosary
Prague	St. John the Baptist
Ravenna	Our Lady of Lourdes
Schneider	St. Wenceslaus
Schuyler	St. Mary
Spencer	Blessed Virgin Mary
Tabor	Nativity of the Blessed Virgin Mary
Tobias	St. Joseph
Touhy	St. Vitus
Verdigre	St. Wenceslaus

Wahoo	St. Wenceslaus
Warsaw	St. Wenceslaus
Weston	St. John of Nepomuk
West Point	Assumption of the Blessed Virgin
Wilber	St. Wenceslaus

Protestant

Clarkson	New Zion (Presbyterian)
	Zion (Presbyterian)
Omaha	Bethlehem (Presbyterian)
	Bohemian Brethren (Presbyterian)
Thurston	Jan Hus (Presbyterian)
Weston	Wahoo Church (Presbyterian)
	Weston Church (Presbyterian)

Cemeteries (For historical background see Vladímir Kučera, ed., *Czech Cemeteries in Nebraska*, n.p.: 1972).

The gravestones contain data of interest to individuals interested in compilation of their family histories.

Abie	Bohemian National Cemetery
	Sts. Peter & Paul Catholic Cemetery
Appleton	Catholic Cemetery
Bee	St. Wenceslaus Cemetery
Brainard	Bohemian National Cemetery Association
	New Catholic Cemetery
	Old Holy Trinity Cemetery
Bruno	Catholic Cemetery
	Czech National Cemetery
Clarkson	Bohemian Catholic Cemetery
	Bohemian Slavonian Cemetery
	Midlands Bohemian Slavonic Cemetery Association
	Protestant Cemetery (Zion)
Crete	Jindra Cemetery

Deweese	Czech Catholic Cemetery
Dodge	Bohemian National Cemetery
	St. Wenceslaus Cemetery
Dwight	Assumption Cemetery
Farwell	Czechoslovak Cemetery
Heun (rural Schuyler)	Holy Trinity Cemetery
Howells	Catholic Cemetery
Humboldt	Bohemian National Cemetery
Jelen	Bohemian National Cemetery
Lawn	Bohemian National Cemetery
	Catholic Cemetery
Linwood	Linwood Hill Cemetery
	St. Mary's Cemetery
Loma	St. Luke Catholic Cemetery
Lynch	Bohemian National Cemetery
Milligan	Bohemian Brethren Cemetery
	(North Milligan Cemetery)
	Czech National Cemetery
	(South Milligan Cemetery)
Morse Bluff	Sacred Heart Cedar Hill
	Catholic Cemetery
Nimburg	Bohemian National Grave Yard
	Association
Odell	Czech National Cemetery
Omaha	Bohemian National Cemetery
	Holy Sepulcher
	St. Mary's Cemetery
Ord	Bohemian National Cemetery
	Protestant Cemetery
	St. Wenceslaus Catholic Cemetery
Plasi	Sts. Cyril & Methodius Cemetery
Pleasant Hill	Pleasant Hill Cemetery
Prague	Bohemian National Cemetery
	Evangelical (Presbyterian)
	Cemetery
	St. John's Catholic Cemetery
Ravenna	Bohemian National Cemetery
Schuyler	Dry Creek Catholic Cemetery
Spencer	Bohemian National Cemetery

Stanton	Bohemian Catholic Cemetery
Sunol	Bohemian Slavonian Cemetery
Swanton	Swan Valley Cemetery
Table Rock	Česko Slovanský Hřbitov
Tabor	Bohemian Catholic Benevolent Society Cemetery
Tobias	Atlanta Center Cemetery
	Tobias Cemetery
Touhy	St. Vitus Cemetery
Valparaiso	St. Mary's Cemetery
Verdigre	Bohemian Catholic Cemetery
	Bohemian National Cemetery
	Riverside Cemetery
Wahoo	Czech Presbyterian Cemetery
	St. Francis Cemetery
	St. Wenceslaus Catholic Cemetery
Warsaw	St. Wenceslaus Bohemian Catholic Cemetery
Weston	Bohemian National Cemetery
	St. John's Cemetery
	Znojmesky Cemetery
Wilber	Big Blue Cemetery
	Bohemian Slavonian Cemetery
	National Cemetery
	Waymire Cemetery
Wilson	St. Mary's Cemetery

Czech Classes

Clarkson: *Classes taught by Mrs. Blanka Pospichal.*

Lincoln: *University of Nebraska offers regular day classes. Instructor is Dr. John Kochik.*

Omaha: *Evening classes taught in Sokol Hall by Dr. Vladímir Kučera and Mrs. Stella Webb.*

Wilber: *Public School offers optional Czech language classes. Teacher is Mrs. Irma Ourecky.*

Czech Festivals (Czech Days)

The festivals of the last fourteen years constitute perhaps the most significant revival of Czech folklore in Nebraska. The best known is the festival at Wilber, a town proclaimed by the governor of the state as the Czech capital of Nebraska. All festivals present a glimpse of Czech folk costumes, dances, songs, and music of the by-gone era. The dishes served (roast duck, roast pork, sauerkraut, dumplings, and kolače) demonstrate Czech cuisine.

Clarkson: *Czech Days (Chamber of Commerce)—end of June*

Dwight: *Spring Day—early in April*
Summer Day—mid July

Lincoln: *Czech Day (Western Frat. Life Assn.)—mid-May*
Czech Day—mid-May

Lodgepole: *Czech Day—last Sunday in October*

Omaha: *Czech Day—early in May*
Czech Festival (South Omaha Sokol)—early in June

Saunders County Festival *(Czech Kolače Days)—summer*

Verdigre Czech Kolace Days—*July*

Wilber Czech Days—*first weekend in August*

Music

"Co Čech, to muzikant" (every Czech is a musician) is an old Czech saying. Although it is obviously an exaggeration, it does indicate the love of Czechs everywhere for music, song and dance. In Nebraska, Czech bands playing old-time Czech music, mainly polkas and waltzes, provided entertainment to thousands and they continue to do so today. Some of the better known Czech bands in existence for many years, in some cases for many decades, include:

Abie	Ernie Kucera
Bruno	Ernie Soufal
Clarkson	Clarkson Czech Band
Crete	Leonard Becwar
	Uneta Orchestra
Grand Island	Czech Masters (Joe Lukesh)
Omaha	Eddie Janak
	Dick Janek
	Vern Luddington
	Frank Hazuka
	Frankie Remar
	Ron Nadherny
Prague	Adolph Nemec
Schuyler	Al Grebnick
	Frank Kucera
Waverly	Math Sladky

Some of the more recent bands playing Czech music:

Columbus	Moostache Joe
Lincoln	Red Jisa
	Slechta Boys
	Olivers Polka Concert Band
PlaMor	PlaMor Polka Queens
Odell	Bill Hayek
Pawnee City	Bouncing Czechs
Prague	All Stars
Seward	Polka Dots

Newspapers

In the past, there were several Czech weeklies. The first of these was *Pokrok Západu,* beginning publication in 1871. *Hospodář* was the last regularly published Czech newspaper in Nebraska, beginning in 1891 and currently published in West, Texas. *The Fraternal Herald* is the only periodical relating to Czechs still published in Nebraska. It carries articles, notes and obituaries on Czechs and is currently published in Omaha. Some back files of Czech newspapers published in Nebraska are available in the

Nebraska State Historical Society, the University of Nebraska–Lincoln Archives, and the Dvoracek Memorial Library at Wilber.

V

Germans From Russia:
A Place to Call Home

By Roger L. Welsch

ACKNOWLEDGMENTS

John Carter, a former student of mine—and now a friend and colleague in the field of folklore—worked heroically to help me gather the information and photographs for this essay. My father and mother, Chris and Bertha Welsch, provided me with hundreds of personal details about German-Russian life. Ruth Amen, president of the American Historical Society of Germans from Russia, was generous with time and information not only about that organization, but about German-Russians in general. Officers of American Forward and the Welfare Society were interviewed about those organizations and gave us answers to a good many of our questions. Theodore Wenzlaff was a great help in our search for historical and cultural information about Sutton, Nebraska and its Germans. Opal Jacobsen of the Nebraska State Historical Society's Picture Room was, as always, very helpful in our search for early photographs. Finally, thanks to William Peter for information about his German-language newspapers. I sincerely appreciate this help given by these people.

Above. A home typical of the variety found in traditional German-Russian settlements throughout the Plains states.

Below. Behind many German-Russian homes stood the summer kitchens, cool places for cooking during the hot Plains summer months. Few are in use today.

Above. Sugar beet workers in western Nebraska. From the files of the Nebraska State Historical Society.

Below. Cracked and worn photographs of beet-tenders' children standing in front of a beet shack in western Nebraska have two kinds of meaning. They tell all of us about the typical life of an important cultural group and they carry powerful emotional loads when, like this one, they are rare photographs of our uncles and aunts. This is the Welsch family and my father, who's words occur so often in this essay, stands at the right.

These two photographs are typical of the ancestral portraits that still hang in many German-Russian homes. The photographs are provided by the courtesy of the American Historical Society of Germans from Russia; the subjects are unknown.

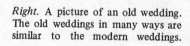

Right. A picture of an old wedding. The old weddings in many ways are similar to the modern weddings.

Above. Ray Stahla (accordian) and Hans Klein (hammered dulcimer) playing a dance at the Welfare Society Hall in Lincoln.

Below left. A feature of the two-day German-Russian wedding is to pin money on the bride for each dance. (John Carter photo of Vogel-Martinsdale wedding in Melbeta.)

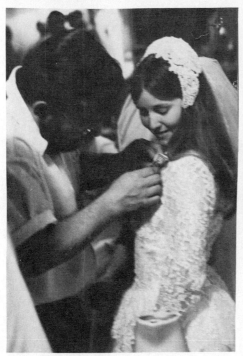

Above. Less typical, but certainly more practical for the bride who expects to dance a hundred dances in the two days, are tennis sneakers under the wedding gown.

V

Germans From Russia: A Place to Call Home

By Roger L. Welsch

Few Americans understand a real *lust* for land. If you have money in this country, and the ability to acquire that kind of money is not beyond the reach of most middle-class Americans, you can buy land. Few white, protestant Americans can imagine the impact of oppression and yet it was people who were oppressed and lusted for land who constituted the bulk of this country's pioneer population.

How then can we understand the Plains' German-Russians, who have spent two centuries struggling to own land, to escape oppression? Is their history believable in the absence of an Abraham Lincoln or Willa Cather? Is their history exciting enough to be of interest or value, the story of these small farmers, minor merchants, and fieldworkers? Obviously I believe the answer to those questions is "yes," because I am writing this now. And my reasons for the positive response are manifold: I am myself a German-Russian and feel a need to respond to my people's hunger for self-respect; the history of these people is, moreover, typical, and its retelling thereby underlines the inevitable impact of America on its immigrants and of the immigrants on America; and a massive departure of good workers for unknown areas where land is not a monopoly and where free political and religious expression is at least a theoretical potential carries a clear message for America's future.

The Migration to Russia

From the time that Europeans ceased their nomadic wan-
derings after 800 A.D., land has been wealth. Land became the
base of power and wealth and was therefore reserved for the
rich and the powerful. The men who walked behind the plows
and the women who gathered the sheaves came to know and
love the land, but it could never be theirs. Never. Nor would it
ever be their children's. Ever. The hunger that is generated by
that kind of unrequited love and exposure to the object of unrequited love is devouring. In 1750, as today, German farms
were small and modestly productive; they were sustained only
by virtue of the careful stewardship of the people who worked
the soil.

But beyond that, Germany was shattered into myriad
small principalities. This one was ruled benevolently and this
one—the more common—was savagely despotic. Survival at best
was marginal. The continual struggle between the small political
states sapped the strength of the countries. Many a family was
also weakened through the death of its young men in battle or
of its young women in the starvation and rapine. Progress was
not even a concept. Progress implies change and there could
be no question of change. This is the way things had always
been and this is the way things would always be. The rich
would be forever rich, the poor forever hungry, landless, exploited. To wish for change would have been viewed as madness. As in fairy tales, success came only through dumb luck
(usually of birth) and mystic intervention, and "it never happens here."

If the internal consumption of human spirit and flesh were
not enough, the American Revolution and Napoleon's wars
were chewing up Germans faster than they were Americans,
English, or French. In addition to the well-known Hessian mer-
cenaries purchased by the English, a substantial proportion of
the "French" troops supporting the American side of the Revolution were in reality also Germans, from much the same southwestern areas of Germany as those mentioned above.

If you can drum up a modest appreciation for the sixteen-year-old in that situation, anticipating—if that's the word—a lifetime of misery before an early death, then you can certainly understand the almost insane enthusiasm that greeted the news that Catherine the Great, Czarina of the Russias from 1762 to 1796, *a German,* was offering her people land—*free* land, and land for their sons. And this was good land along the Volga River. Moreover, she offered free, German-run schools for their children, and freedom of religion, and transportation to this new Eden. Why, even today an offer of that sort would draw hundreds of thousands of prospective settlers, and it was no less the case then.

The provisions of Catherine's Manifesto, issued in 1763 (the year the Seven Years' War ended on the European continent), were:

1. that the immigrants were to enjoy full religious freedom but they were forbidden to evangelize among the native Russians;

2. that the settlers were to be exempt from military service;

3. that they were to be granted total autonomy in local government, schools, and churches;

4. that they were to receive free transportation from Germany to the Volga Valley;

5. that each family was to be granted thirty dessiatines of land (about 80 acres, an enormous piece of land in comparison to what the Germans had been accustomed to);

6. that the government would provide interest-free loans of 500 rubles and total tax exemption for a period of ten years.[1]

The response to the invitation was so staggering that the German government had to choke off the emigration in 1768 to avoid a depopulation of the countryside. From 1764 to 1768, 104 German colonies were established along the Volga River in the area of Sarotov, 59 on the east bank, 45 on the west, with a

total population of 23,019; by 1798, by increase and more immigration, the population had risen to 39,193. (For later reference, it should perhaps be noted here, too, that by 1895 the
population had swelled to 391,000, and by 1914 to 668,896.)[2]

The migrants were often disappointed to find that Russian
promises of developed farms and villages were not met, that
more often than not they had to build their farms and villages
from the ground up, but there can be little doubt that the
Russians were probably as overwhelmed by the inrush of Germans as were the Germans left behind who saw their countrymen fleeing eastward like stampeding cattle before a range fire.

But the villages and farms grew, mostly with German
names, and a Russian Germany developed on the Volga. German was the language of the streets, of the village governments,
of the schools and churches. The culture was German, and the
sharp edge between the Germans and the neighboring Russians,
discussed further below, never blurred.

One might well ask about the source of this generous
altruism on the part of the Russian government, a generosity
so rare in international politics! Nobody gives away a huge area
of productive land and bestows upon the recipients yet a further program of privileges without some sort of expectations.
(American homesteading, it must be recalled, was not a matter
of a government giving away its own lands, since the land in
question was that of the native Indians.)

There were reasons, some benign, some sinister. There was,
for example, a strong desire on the part of the Russian national
government to realize the potential agricultural wealth of the
Volga Valley. Russian farmers had not shown the industry or
ingenuity required, and Catherine was naturally partial to the
frugal and industrious farmers of her German homeland. One of
the fears of the European Russians of the western half of Russia, moreover, was of the incursions of the aggressive eastern,
Asiatic peoples—the Cossacks, the Khirgis, the border Chinese—
a factor which perhaps had also accounted in part for the dispir-
iting of the previous occupants of the Volga Valley. The
Germans were to serve as a buffer population between the East

and the West, a function they still fill today in another geographic location.

Life in Russia

The German colonies grew and prospered. While they were subjected to much the same hazards of any community of the time and region, life was good for the Czarina's Germans. Gradually the perquisites began to fall away, but even a hundred years later the life of the colonies was viewed as idyllic. The villages, each arranged roughly along religious lines, functioned well, the crops were good, and despite very little contact with the German motherland, German culture prospered.

As stated, the provisions of the Manifesto were in the passage of the century slowly dissolving, a "breach of promise" still bitterly recalled by German-Russians in Nebraska today, but in all fairness it must be viewed as remarkable that any government was still observing even fragments of that commitment made over a hundred years before, especially when one remembers that the United States government was during the same period making a practice of breaking Indian treaties within the hour.

Most of the hardships on the Volga and the Black Sea were taken in stride. The weather there was more severe than that in Germany—but then, farmers have always had to deal with the weather. They were not rich, but they were nowhere as poor as they had been in Germany. The raids by the nomadic tribes were brutal but relatively infrequent, and the losses—a couple of dead colonists, perhaps, a few stolen women—seldom approached the depredations that had become commonplace in European warfare. And until the end they had their language, their schools, and their churches.

Perhaps the greatest cause for injury and pain came from within the colonies themselves. The villages were built primarily of religiously homogeneous units. One town was predominantly—*very* predominantly—Catholic, the next Lutheran, the next Mennonite. Marriages across religious lines were considered impossible disasters, of somewhat the same frequency and magnitude of tidal waves! Other communities of even the same religious leanings were regarded with contempt and suspicion. Because of this isolation, each village developed a distinctive dialect form so that a few words or sentences would immediately identify the speaker as a "Kukkuser" or "Norgra"[3] —and the distinctive language form could be submitted as *prima facie* evidence of inferiority. "Everyone talks funny except me," seemed to be the general attitude of the day. In addition to the geographic, linguistic, and religious factionalism, additional cause for tavern brawls and field fights was given by the divisions within the villages themselves. Each village, no matter what its size, was divided into the "unnergasse" ("downtown") and "ivergasse" ("uptown"), the terms sometimes describing a real difference of a couple of feet of altitude but sometimes being simply an artificial division apparently designed only to facilitate street fighting allegiances.

The sense of isolation was profound. The break with the homeland was clear and final. Few had the money or inclination even to visit Germany, and as is almost always the case, those left behind felt that they had been deserted by the migrants, and arguments that those remaining had simply been too chicken-hearted to seize the opportunity to go to the Volga did not settle the dust.

Nor did the German colonists establish lines of contact other than governmental concerns and minor commerce with their Russian "hosts." Few Germans ever bothered to learn Russian and few items of culture other than some common peasant foodways became a part of colony life. The reluctance was not dispassionate either. Russians and all things Russian were regarded as inferior if not barbaric, uncivilized, contemptible, and disgusting. Experience from the Middle Ages on had taught the Germans that little but misery comes from strangers; they bore diseases, brought armies, robbed, cheated, and had barbaric habits—and the Germans had little reason to believe otherwise of their Russian neighbors.

The feeling was of course mutual. Obviously, the taxes not

paid and the soldiers not produced by the Germans had to be
made up for by the Russians. The Russians regarded the Germans as impossibly arrogant, ruthlessly ambitious, and culturally intransigent—all of which was true.

The telling factor, however, lay in the dynamics of those
relationships. As the provisions of the Manifesto fell away, the
Germans came to be more like the conventional Russian citizen.
The loss of the privileges was not met with much enthusiasm,
but it is no different anywhere else in the world, after all.

The factors were, however, different from anywhere else
in the world. The economic situation was deteriorating in Russia, and the political situation was growing ever more tense. In
1904 a war broke out between Russia and Japan and the colonists were drafted to serve in the military along with other
Russian citizens. The Germans resented the elimination of their
decades-long exemption from the military, especially the
Mennonites, for whom it became a matter of conscience. The
Germans felt that they should not have to participate in an
Asian war that seemed so remote and of so little consequence
for their own lives.

Finally, promotional information had been filtering into
the colonies from America. Land speculators, the railroads,
labor brokers, and money lenders were eager to find new groups
of the discontent, disenfranchised, ambitious, frightened, or
exiled to bring to the American Promised Land. There were
some of each of these categories among the Volga Germans, and
so the dream of the Volga was reborn in the dream of the American Great Plains.

The Migration to America

Representatives of various groups, colonies, families, and
associations were sent to look over the new land, and probably
to the frequent amazement of the land hustlers, they liked what
they saw. Volga Germans came to Nebraska in 1874, to Colorado in 1880, and soon were pouring into all western states.
With the boost given migration by the Russo-Japanese War by

1910 there were 243,361 German-Russians in the United States. By 1920, there were 79,000 Protestant Odessa Germans, 37,000 Catholic Odessa Germans, 100,000 Protestant Volga Germans, 19,000 Catholic Volga Germans, 31,000 Mennonites, and 37,000 Wolynian and Lithuanian Germans (first and second generations).[4]

In part the attraction was the land itself—these Germans were farmers and they understood the land's potential—and it was in part the historical context: the worsening conditions in Russia, building toward the climax of the great Revolution in 1917, and the developing conditions here—growing rural populations, cheap land, a chance for renewed isolation, and few Russians.

So they came by the hundreds of thousands, rebuilding the hopes, good and bad. Families and villages clustered again but it was impossible this time to avoid some "mixing" with the swirl of Norwegians, Czechs, and Poles on the Plains. The Catholics tended to go into Kansas, the Evangelical Lutherans into Nebraska, and the Mennonites into the Dakotas and Canada, but again mixture was inevitable. The Kukkusers were still alien if intelligible to the Norgras—but now they lived next door to each other and fought against a common enemy—the non-Germans or the Germans (probably a mixture, too, of former rivals from Dinkel and Frank!) who lived on the other side of town, a renewed and regenerated rivalry of the old "ivergasse"/ "unnergasse" variety.

Moreover, they were not only fighting among themselves as before but, as mentioned, they were still faced by a surrounding sea of inferiors—the "Englischer," as anyone who was not a German-Russian was called. This term, one of the most civil of a wide selection of possible terms, referred to Russians, Swedes, Greeks, and Italians alike, and these "Englischer" all called the German-Russians "Rooshens," and often still do.

Thus, a substantial proportion of Lincoln's and Nebraska's population was made up of Germans from Russia who were fiercely German, and yet so little was known about them that commercial flyers were printed for the community in Russian;

it might as well have been in Japanese, for few of them knew any Russian at all.

By 1870, 36 percent of the state's foreign-born population—which was, of course, predominant—was German, but only a handful of this population was German-Russian (less than 1 percent). In Lincoln before the turn of the century, Germans (almost all of them German-Russians) represented only 12.1 percent of the total population. But, as Hattie Plum Williams reported, that population and proportion swelled dramatically: by 1903 the percentage read 17.4; by 1908, 27.3; and by 1913, 43.2 percent. The specific numbers of individuals migrating to Lincoln in each year during the crucial four decades also reveals the explosion of German-Russian settlement: [5]

1872: 1	1886: 9	1900: 124
1873: 0	1887: 30	1901: 107
1874: 2	1888: 16	1902: 124
1875: 6	1889: 15	1903: 141
1876: 4	1890: 32	1904: 101
1877: 5	1891: 91	1905: 157
1878: 3	1892: 113	1906: 224
1879: 0	1893: 32	1907: 346
1880: 4	1894: 5	1908: 127
1881: 3	1895: 1	1909: 138
1882: 1	1896: 4	1910: 156
1883: 7	1897: 8	1911: 278
1884: 1	1898: 76	1912: 366
1885: 4	1899: 114	1913: 576

Narratives of the passage from the Volga to the Platte are powerful and agonizing even today. The long weeks in the stinking holds and steerages of filthy ships, the burials and births at sea, the refusal of admittance at Ellis Island for the sick—such motifs still bring tears to the eyes of the migrants and their children, even this long after the real event. Tales are still told of men who came to America to earn the passage for their wives and children left on the Volga, and who then found more

attractive mates here and used the passage money to pay for an
American wedding.

Life in America

The Rooshens, old beyond their years from hard years in
Russia, murderous weeks on the voyage to the Plains, and hard
times in the heavy manufacturing shops or sugar beet fields of
America, were seen by "Americans" as quaint, even crazy.
These aliens talked funny, conducted their own schools and
churches, and they were arrogant. They dressed funny, with felt
boots and head kerchiefs. In the summer the women cooked
for their large families in the airy, cool summer kitchens and the
entire Rooshen parts of town—entire towns sometimes!—gave
off the heavy, peasant odors of cooking cabbage, ryebread,
pickles, and homemade beer. The small frame houses were uniformly white in some communities, uniformly garish in others
(for example, one Nebraska town has the term "Rooshen blue"
for a particularly brilliant powder blue that distinguishes
German-Russian houses there even today).

Today such enclaves of relative poverty might be called
ghettos or slums, but they were nonetheless absolutely immacu-
late in those days. Every day, rain or shine, throughout the
year, until death did them part, German-Russian hausfraus were
out on their hands and knees scrubbing the sidewalks; on
Monday they vied to be the first to have their laundry flapping
on the clotheslines.

It is a temptation for me to suggest that with German-
Russian mothers, cleanliness was not next to, but rather equiva-
lent to or maybe even three points ahead of, godliness—that is,
it would be a temptation if their concept of godliness had not
also been so intensely well developed. While the rest of the
week was an unending pageant of man-killing labor, Sunday was
a day of absolute rest. Church attendance was a matter of fact.
Pietistic zealots like the "Brüderschaft" intensified the power of
faith and religious intimidation and contributed in large part to
the death and weakening of secular German-Russian culture on

the Plains. In towns like McCook, Nebraska, music, laughter, and traditional culture in general were the principal victims of the Brüderschaft's stern view of life.

Possibly one of the main reasons the Rooshens so mistrusted the "Englischer" and persisted in maintaining their tight communities was the threat they saw American culture posing for what they felt was decent. Here the children were embarrassed by their German-ness and therefore began to drift away from one of the most visible manifestations of that German-ness: the church. And there were other things too. One of my aunts told me about a time when she found a deck of cards in her son's garret room. Here she paused while I contemplated the enormity of that depravity. She had, she told me, marched right down to the basement for an ash shovel, not being willing, of course, to touch the cards with her bare hands. She went back to the attic, scooped up the cards, and huffed back down to the basement where she threw the Devil's Playthings into the furnace. Looking me right in the eye, she slowly and deliberately described how the deck of cards had exploded in a blast of smoke and fire that reeked distinctly of *brimstone*!

A story that was told to me by an uncle, with equally deliberate drama, was of a group of card players who had welcomed a stranger to the gaming table. At one point in the game one of the players uttered the most common of German-Russian blasphemies, "Ach Herr Jesus in Himmel noch einmal" (pronounced however in a split second: "Achhadajesusimimmel-nochamol!"). The stranger leaped frantically to his feet, at this mention of the Lord's name, clawed the door open, and dashed out into the night screaming. He left behind him the distinctive smell of brimstone, and the next morning the shaken card players found his tracks in the snow—cloven-hoof prints!

If towns like Sutton could maintain their autonomy by geographical and linguistic isolation, and towns like Henderson could add to that their homogeneous religious beliefs, then places like Lincoln and Grand Island prolonged and intensified their isolation by their work habits: in the summer the families packed up and moved west to the sugar beet fields, thus insuring that the children rarely finished a complete grade of school, let alone an entire education. The "beet trains" would load up what could have passed for a cargo of European peasants to journey to the seasonal work in the Nebraska panhandle. Perhaps my father's words best describe the situation:

> Each year on May 13 the "Bollingtone" Railroad parked a long train, made up of boxcars and passenger cars, under the North 10th Street viaduct. There the beet tenders loaded their household goods, dogs, cats, rabbits, chickens, geese, ducks, etc., in the boxcars, the people in the passenger cars. The train pulled out about noon. There usually was a long layover in the middle of the night at Alliance, Nebraska. The next day people arrived at their destination. A separate boxcar was used for each town. Some of the more prominent towns for beet tenders were Bridgeport, Minatare, Mitchell, Morrill, Scottsbluff, and Henry in Nebraska and Torrington and Lingle in Wyoming.
>
> There was no diner on the train. Each family brought along their own food. It had to last the entire trip. Most beet tender families were large families. The more children a family had, the more beets they could work. The more beets they could work, the more money they could make. These large families made it necessary to take large quantities of prepared food along on the train to the beet fields. We had no refrigeration or thermos bottles or pop coolers or such. It was necessary to prepare food that would not spoil. Such as well-done fried chicken, homemade white and rye bread, hard salami, minced ham, homemade dill pickles, and cans of pork and beans. This was washed down with water, which was furnished free on the train. Some families did have a good supply of homemade "hootch" to keep them in good spirits throughout the trip.[6]

To this day, railroad workers recall having to sweep out one and two-foot drifts of sunflower seed hulls from the floors of the beet train passenger cars—and to this day, sunflower seeds are still popularly called "Rooshen peanuts" in parts of the Plains.

That is a sight I wish I could have seen: the tumult and color of those beet tender trains. I would even like to have been able to ride along with them a while, sampling some of that fine old-fashioned food. But I would add to that request the clear rule that I would be able to get out of the train before it reached the beet fields or to ride it on to California or Arizona. The work in the fields of Wyoming, Colorado, Kansas, and Nebraska was back-breaking. Down endless rows of choking dust they crawled or stooped, planting beets, thinning beets, weeding beets, harvesting beets. There was no thought of day-care centers for the children; the entire family worked as a unit in the furnace-like heat. The pay was minimal and my father once wrote that his family had worked an entire summer only to find on the morning that they were to be paid that the employing farmer had left, lock, stock, and barrel, abandoning his beet workers utterly without resources. They did not even have sufficient money to pay for return fare, and they spent the next few years working in the area to recover from the stunning loss.

On the other hand, my father, Chris Welsch, was not immune himself from a bit of sugar beet field financial chicanery:

> The first hoeing was done by hoeing out a 10 or 12-inch space of beets, leaving a very small space or group of beets and so on through the length of the row. This hoeing was done by the adults and older children. They walked upright and used long-handled hoes which were kept very sharp. The younger children followed on hands and knees and thinned the beets which were left in the spaces or groups, one beet to each space, no more, no less. If you were caught pulling them all out or leaving more than one beet in a block or space, you were threatened with the hoe handle. The first hoeing had to be finished by the 4th of July. The family that was not through by the 4th was looked down on. The adults got blisters on their hands from the hoe handles and the children who had to crawl on the ground got very sore knees. Sometimes they were raw, open sores. If a child did a good job of thinning and worked real fast he sometimes found money on the

ground in the row he was thinning. I was so slow I usually was
so far behind that I was crawling in the opposite direction of
all the others. One day my dad placed a silver dollar in the row
my older brother was thinning. I was thinning southward and
my brother was thinning northward. I happened to glance over
into his row and found myself a silver dollar![7]

The literal and figurative scars of those years were never
erased from the minds of the German-Russian people. The
shame of being poor and scorned can be seen in the pugnacious
pride or total rejection the Rooshens now seem to feel for their
native culture. Another illustrative passage from my father's
memoirs:

[In] 1921 Mr. Harry Grant wrote my folks a letter asking them to come back and work for him. This was considered
a great compliment by beet tenders. A few beet tenders
worked for the same farmers many years. Usually one year was
all that could be tolerated because most farmers thought beet
tenders were very inferior people. When we arrived at Mr.
Grant's farm we found the beet tender's shack had been
moved about a half mile away from his house. There was no
well, no outhouse. Mr. Grant['s] . . . promise was not kept.
We learned that Mrs. Grant made him move the shack because
she didn't want those "Rooshin" (sic) kids running around in
her yard.[8]

My father bears *real* scars from his encounter with a
lightening bolt while working in the fields of western Nebraska:

We [were] swimming and playing around [early Sunday
morning] . . . . Mr. Anest drove up and said I was to go home
with him and help him and his brother stack hay. I told him I
didn't want to but he insisted. I never could understand why
he wanted me to help instead of [my older brother] John. Nor
could I understand why my folks told him where we were because they were so opposed to working on Sunday. That
evening after work Mr. Anest took me into Bridgeport and
bought me a dish of ice cream and a box of three-inch firecrackers. There were eight or ten large firecrackers in a card-

board box and some matches in my front pocket. Monday, July 2, we were doing second hoeing and Mary got the hiccups. She tried everything she could think of but the hiccups wouldn't stop. I finally dropped back a ways behind her and lit a firecracker and threw it toward her. When it exploded it frightened her so bad that she forgot all about the hiccups.

That turned out to be the only firecracker out of that box that I got to shoot. The following day, July 3, 1928, we were doing second hoeing in a beet field that was down in a valley. We were unable to see very far in any direction. We could hear a thunderstorm coming but we could not see how close it was. We decided to hoe to the end of the field and then go home. Before we got to the end of the field lightning struck. We were all knocked to the ground. The others . . . were only stunned. I was knocked unconscious and remained unconscious for three days. The bolt of lightening hit me on the left side of the head and went through my body into the ground. It tore all of my clothing off of my body including my large straw hat and shoes. My clothing and shoes were tore to small shreds. The box of firecrackers was not damaged. I received a small burned spot on the left side of my head and the front of my body from my neck to my pelvis was burned. The burn separated and went down the front of my legs for about eight or ten inches where it stopped. It then seemed to jump across my ankles where I received deep burns. The soles of my feet were burnt also where my feet were standing on the ground; two holes were still there after the storm.[9]

In the fall, after the harvest and with all the fieldwork finished, many of the workers would return to their homes in the eastern part of the Plains, usually to work in the factories or in the railyards. The migrant Germans did not share the shame of their children, who naturally took the brunt of the humiliation in the classrooms and on the playgrounds, but instead took great pride in their peasant labors. The work in the sugar beet fields did, after all, represent a real step up from their roles in Russia during the later years of colonization. From my own memory I can recall my Uncle Henry, who used to take me occasionally to the shoot-'em-up westerns he attended every week at the Colonial Theater, once stopping off with me at the Burlington railyards where he worked. He showed me his locker, all his own, and then, absolutely glowing with pride, he demonstrated how he oiled the huge, glistening steam engines when they pulled into the station.

In fact, the few times I can recall when a German-Russian elder talked with me, a child, were moments of such inordinate pride in work that the normal rules of non-communication with children by adults were unselfconsciously disregarded. Little wonder then that it became a standard ritual when we visited my Aunt Anna that she would have to fix two lunch buckets when my Uncle Henry went to work at the railroad—one for him and one for me to take home and eat in bed in faithful imitation of the laborer's ideal I had seen in him standing by that engine in the gloom of the railyards.

So, through the winter the German-Russians worked, drank, got married, went to church, fought, cured all internal ailments with Alpen Kräuter, a patent nostrum that tastes so bad that it *has* to be good for you; all external ailments with Denver Mud, a potion certain to heal man and beast. (Upon finishing this paragraph I resolved that as a part of my long concern with the German-Russian past I really should find an old bottle of Alpen Kräuter and a jar of Denver Mud to place strategically as a curiosity in our bathroom. I was astonished to find that both are still available—and are still being purchased at Barth Drugstore, where three generations of German-Russians have bought them!)

Springtime, so far as I can recall, was marked primarily by rising waters. In Lincoln, the Rooshen area was labeled "The Bottoms" with good geographical reason. The Salt Creek flood plain precisely defined the area occupied by the German-Russian settlement, so every spring there was at least the threat—and all too often the reality—of that turbid, rolling cesspool of a creek running right through my grandmother's front room. There was a brief period of tension that was disquieting but a little exciting for a child, as the Rooshens gathered in knots on the corners and at H.J. Amen's grocery store to talk, always in muted tones, about the rising water. The night would jerk with flashlights as the people walked to and from the bridges over the creek where they would peer down into the yellow, angry water or try to remember which stick on the bank it was that marked the level of the river an hour before.

Then everyone would simultaneously relax, drink home-brew or coffee, and talk away the remainder of the night with stories of previous floods. Or they would, on the other hand, begin the tearful gathering of a few pitiful treasures and begin to move to the higher home of a relative or friend. I remember our home, high enough to be totally immune from the flood waters, packed with round-faced relatives, listening to our radio and crying.

They were crying because they knew what was happening in the Bottoms; they knew because it had happened only last spring or perhaps the spring before that. The basements were filling up with backed-up sewer water and a cellar's full of pre-served fruit, meat, and vegetables, made during long hours over a witheringly hot woodburning cookstove, was being ruined. Now the women could hope that the jars were not being broken. Mud was being deposited one or two feet thick on the floor, on the shelves, in the furnace (if there was one), on the stairs from the cellar.

Then the basement's disaster faded into insignificance as the water moved up into the main living area and the same stinking muck covered the rugs, the chairs, the stove, the dishes, the clothes, the beds, everything. Now the hope was for the house and the neighbors: let the house not be swept from its foundations! Let Old Tante Maria be safe!

The return when the waters retreated was stunning. The filth was everywhere. The stink was incredible. I still shudder to think what the sight of that must have done to the souls of my dear aunts and grandmothers, who could not abide a dirty side-walk, yet seeing a dead and bloated chicken in fetid slime, plastered against the kitchen table where tomorrow she would feed her children. Women who would cluck their tongues about the slovenly housekeeping of a neighbor who tolerated water-spots on her windows saw their homes filled with filth.

The cleaning operation began with shovels. Then brushes and brooms, mops, and rags, brought the customary order and cleanliness back, with perhaps only a faint odor remaining. The veneer on the furniture was perhaps slightly separated in a motif characteristic for the German Bottoms. And now they could begin to forget, at least until next spring when the snow melted and the rains came.

I grew up thinking that iron-bound family Bibles *came* with the outside of each page wrinkled and stained. And one way for a young rowdy to get a quick response from the sleeping Rooshen Bottoms on a Saturday night was to shout out, "Steig auf, du Leit! 'S'ist hoch Wasser!" "Up, everyone! The water's rising!" It would work every time.

I can anticipate the protesting argument that such was the lot of the German-Russians in Lincoln, but what does that have to do with their countrymen in Hays, Kansas, Yoder, Wyoming, or Yankton, South Dakota? Well, that manner of burden is representative. If it was not floods, it was duststorms, or grasshoppers, or flu epidemics, or bindweed, or any of the myriad of agonies the Plains serve up to its would-be conquerers and that America dishes up to its migrant peasants.

If floods were a peculiar agony of life in the Lincoln Bottoms, another kind of slime was encountered by all Germans and, as an apt tribute to the stupidity of its generators, by all manner of other migrants, Danes, Czechs, and Germans alike. The Volga colonists had the singular ill fortune of becoming Americans shortly before this country entered into thirty years of bitter enmity and two disastrous wars with Germany. Here were people who were fiercely German, when the Ku Klux Klan and other "100 percent Americans" were closing down German schools and churches, attacking German language instruction in the schools, and worse. The German Bottoms in Lincoln saw burning crosses and Germans were forced to show their "allegiance" by putting their money into war bonds. There were threats of tar and feathering. And Berlin, Nebraska became Otoe, Nebraska. The attention of Swedes was called to signs reading "We speak American here," and so they did.

If the children of the migrants had been ashamed of their peasant-laborer heritage, now they had good reason—fear—to obscure their German background. Few first-born American German-Russians remained to live in the Bottoms; although their first language had been German, not another word of that language crossed their lips (and then some, like my own parents, had to pay a university professor to teach their children the language they had grown up speaking!). The foods that had once characterized the German-Russian kitchen became only ritually acceptable. The German newspapers died (note the closing dates on the German newspapers listed in the accompanying index). Only in the past three or four years, primarily through the agency of the American Historical Society for Germans from Russia, has there been a reversal and a new-found source of ethnic pride—or better, a lack of ethnic shame—in being German-Russian. Only during these past few years have politicians found a German name to be an advantage during election years.

This process suggests an important—perhaps crucial—distinction, that between heritage as a source of pride or as a reason for a lack of shame. I fear the first and welcome the second. I am, you see, not a cheerleader for the German-Russian people. I find little pride in the fact that the German-Russians' own thirty years (actually nearly two centuries!) of persecution have not prevented them from nurturing their own prejudices, especially a virulent anti-semitism. "All Jews Stink" is still a popular dance tune. Few children and grandchildren of the migrants have remembered that their parents and grandparents were draft dodgers from an Asian war, and I almost wept for my people's history a few years ago as I listened to a petty politician from the Lincoln Bottoms excoriate the Vietnam resisters in terms that could have been applied quite precisely to his own father. This man is not to be respected or receive my vote simply because he is a German-Russian kinsman. But, on the other hand, I do believe that he should be free of any shame of his peasant, draft-dodging background; his short historical memory reflects shame, not pride.

Nobody eats a whole watermelon; we eat the flesh, discard the seeds and the rind, and that's what we must also do with the German-Russian experience. That history has to be combed for lessons that can serve us today, good and bad. We can examine the good and learn from it and discard the bad, remembering what about it made it bad.

Perhaps the greatest single potential for a rational and productive organization of German-Russian cultural resources lies within the future of the American Historical Society for Germans from Russia. In only a few years, riding on the crest of developing ethnic awareness and pride, it has grown from a faltering and hesitant skeleton into a hale and vigorous organization with a firm base of scholars and the crucial framework of enthusiastic amateurs. For a few years the Society showed the distressing symptoms of misdirected chauvinism, but it is now producing work papers with firm information along with the nostalgic reminiscences. Individual local chapters throughout the continent have developed oral history programs and repositories for artifacts and documents. The annual meeting, like the work papers, combines the subjective with the objective, to the enhancement of both.

The activities of individual chapters vary of course in substance, but my own experience with the Lincoln Chapter suggests that the potential is being realized. When the Smithsonian Institution's Old Ways in the New World program planned to bring a group of German folk musicians and dancers to Lincoln, the local chapter of AHSGR, along with several other agencies discussed below, met and worked with the State Bicentennial Commission's office to coordinate feeding, housing, transporting, and presenting the musicians. It was one of the first explicit statements I have ever witnessed in which the German-Russians said without reluctance, "We are Germans," and then proceeded to use that recognition in a productive and positive direction.

Two other agencies participated in the cooperative efforts with the Smithsonian Institution on that occasion and they have for decades served as the backbone of social life among

Lincoln's German-Russians. The Welfare Society at 1430 North 10th Street, representing the North Bottoms, and the American Forward at 745 D Street, representing the South Bottoms, are fraternal organizations whose primary purpose was funeral finance; each member contributed to the funeral expenses of other members, anticipating that the program would then similarly take care of their own funeral costs.

But the societies came to be much, much more. Their halls were the center of secular community activity. Actually, the Welfare Society originally was known as the Neighborhood House and was established with the help of the Congregational Church. At that time it was located at the corner of 9th and New Hampshire Streets and provided showers for members as well as recreational facilities. Moreover, it provided room for classes in American history, civics, and English, meant to lead the members toward citizenship.[10]

The American Forward Association was organized initially in 1922 and incorporated in 1925. Membership was limited to Volga Germans but soon this limitation was abolished and the organization opened its doors to any person of German-Russian extraction. In its early years the major purpose of the organization was to speed the transculturation of the new immigrants. All members were expected to be either American citizens or actively working toward citizenship.[11]

The vigorous peasant music and dance of the German-Russians once rang almost weekly from the halls, while the good smells of food and drink poured from the basement windows. A fine piece of evidence of what the dances were like is the sign that still hangs above the door of the Welfare Society: "Please! No Smoking. No *stomping*." (my italics)

The American Forward had the distinct disadvantage of occupying as a lodge a hall in a building that had previously been the Immanuel Lutheran Church, and many members of the severely pietistic German-Russian community felt that it was improper to dance and drink beer in a building once sanctified.

These halls were places where meetings, classes, and

gatherings of all manner were held. They often functioned as a community government. They aided charities and served as clearing houses for flood relief. Wedding dances and receptions were held here. I can remember an aunt and uncle celebrating their 25th wedding anniversary at the Welfare Society Hall. And, in fact, it was in the Welfare Society that some of the Smithsonian Institution's functions were held in the summer of 1975. The American Historical Society for Germans from Russia has met in both halls and has sponsored "Brode," traditional roast beef dinners with overdone roast beef and the ever-present rye bread, dill pickles, boiled potatoes and beer.

To my own great personal regret, the lodge halls rarely sponsor large community celebrations now. The once weekly dances have faded away to occasional and lightly attended dances.

It's hard to understand why. The blame is often laid on the absence of young people, and it is true that toward the last few years, beginning in the fifties, the median age of the drinkers and dancers began to rise to fifty. But the question *why* there were ever fewer young people remains. Changes in dance styles perhaps? Changes in musical tastes? I think these are not the ultimate answers. On numerous occasions I took friends or students, or even whole university classes, to Welfare Society dances, and the response was almost universally enthusiastic. Moreover, the newcomers seemed to enjoy the skill and warmth of the old-timers and the old-timers, in turn, seemed to welcome the young visitors—who, significantly, often became regular attenders of the dances. Perhaps the answer to the Society's decline lies in the fact that it was the young German-Russians who were not participating, still bearing the stigma of being Rooshens and having no intention of destroying many decades of name changing and neighborhood hopping by once again dancing to the jingle jangle of the hammered dulcimer and thereby admitting again that they are indeed Rooshens.

A hopeful sign is the vigorous activity within the societies in other directions. They are becoming ever more involved with the cultural activities of the German-Russian community and, most importantly, have begun to cooperate and function as complementary units within the German-Russian community.

The unstructured social life among German-Russian young people was in some regards of the Old World but was inevitably colored by intrusions from the surrounding American culture. Perhaps again the best way to describe that social life would be to turn to the description written by one of its practitioners. My father grew up, as I have mentioned, in Lincoln's South Bottoms and worked in the western counties of Nebraska and the eastern edge of Wyoming. His experiences, I believe, are typical:

> After the children in the [Church] confirmation class were confirmed they were "ledig." They could sing in the church choir, go to shows, dances, and even start dating and stay out late at night. They could also become members of the Jugend Verein, a church organization for single teenagers or young folks. Some called it "Christian Endeavor." The Lutherans called it "Luther League." They met Sunday evening, 6 to 7, and then we went "up the line. . . ." "Staying out late at night" usually consisted of "going up the line." This was F Street up to 11th Street, never 9th or 10th. North on 11th Street to O Street, west on O Street to 10th and then north on 10th to the north side of the 10th Street viaduct. This was done on foot. If nothing interesting turned up before we reached the north side of the viaduct we turned around and slowly took the same route home. We usually hung around the west stadium for a while to watch the lucky guys walk and drive by with their dates. We usually met the same boys and girls on this route and got to know them on a first-name basis. As we got older and braver, and if we had a little money, we would ask the girls for dates. Very few of these girls were allowed to have a date pick them up at their home. You had to meet them on a street corner a few blocks from their home. When you took them home you took them to the front gate, kissed them good night, and said goodnight very softly and walked away before she went to the door, so her parents would not see you.
>
> A date on a weekday night usually consisted of a show,

which cost from 10 cents to 25 cents each and if you were really trying to impress the girl you would buy her a 5 cent bottle of pop and a 4-ounce candy bar for 5 cents. If you really liked her you might buy her a banana split for 15 cents. For a dollar a boy and girl could have a very nice evening.

As we got a little older and braver we let some of the girls talk us into going to the "Russian Hops" at the Welfare Hall and a dance hall on the second floor of a building on the northeast corner of 9th and M Streets. They usually charged 25 cents to get in and very few of us had two bits, so one of us would pay to get in. They stamped your hand. The one who paid his way in got stamped on the palm of his hand, then waited a while and went back out and moistened his palm and gently put it on the back of the other fellows' hands until the stamp or print got quite dim. On several occasions we found an open window at the Welfare House and some people inside who helped by giving us a pull while our buddies outside gave us a push. After learning how to do the "Russian Hop" we had to learn how to dance "American." We then had to get transportation to get to the "Starlight Ballroom," which was eight miles south on 14th Street, or the "Sunset Ballroom" in Emerald, or the "Plamor Ballroom," which is still in existence.

In the summer time the F Street Park, which is now "Cooper Park," was the site of many exciting ball games between North and South Lincoln. Both hard ball and soft ball. The area north of the Welfare House was an open field and the return matches were played there. These games were for real. Many of the players could have been professionals had they had the opportunity and the right training. . . .

Many of the young men who came over from Russia soon learned how to shoot craps. Weather permitting, below the 10th Street viaduct was a favorite spot for a Sunday afternoon crap game. The police soon learned of this and tried desperately to catch these boys. One Sunday afternoon they did catch Jake Henry and a buddy of his. They both pretended they could not speak English. They kept on conversing in German and were satisfied the police could not understand them. Two police officers started marching them over the viaduct to the police station, which was only a few blocks away at 10th between Q and R.

Jake Henry said in German, "I think I can knock this one down with one blow." His buddy said, "I think I can do the same to this one."

Henry said, "When I say 'Now' let him have it and run."

On signal they both knocked the police down and ran away. Jake Henry then got himself a watchdog and taught him to bark when anybody approached and they had their crap games in open fields. . . .

After many of the young folks got married they managed to buy a used car. Then they couldn't afford to go anywhere. Their favorite pastime then was to park on O Street Sunday evenings between 11th and 12th, watch the people walk by, and honk everytime somebody walked by that you knew. One got to visit with many of the old gang that way. If one was wearing nice new clothes it was smart to window shop up the south side of O Street from 10th to 14th and down the north side of O Street on Sunday evenings. That way all those people parked on O Street could see your new outfit. Much like an Easter parade. It seemed that Sunday evenings the Germans from Russia had the downtown business district to themselves.[12]

I referred above to the pietistic nature of the German-Russians and the secular functions of the fraternal societies. The spiritual complement was, of course, the church. A few people in the German-Russian community might reject the church, a few others would have nothing to do with the fraternal societies, but very few rejected them both. The Sunday church services historically served as far more than an hour's religious exercise. The gatherings before and after the services were important too for the exchange of information within the community and as one of the few situations for courtship. The function of the minister as an arbiter and true leader was crucial. The church bells announced weddings and deaths—the tone of the bells sometimes indicating the sex of the deceased, or whether the victim was a child or an adult, the number of the toll sometimes counting out the age of the deceased. For many years the churches also served as the last bastion of the German language, as Theodore Wenzlaff notes in his *History of the Hope*

Reformed Church: 1908-1968.[13] This church moved on February 6, 1934, to hold every other service in English. By 1960 only one Sunday a month had a German service, and by 1967, all services were in English with only an occasional hymn sung in German.

The churches have shown the same tendencies toward superannuation that we have seen within the fraternal organizations. There is no more willingness on the part of second and third generation German-Russians to take up the old church ways than there is to dance and sing like their parents and grandparents.

Perhaps there is hope, however, for those of us who have a romantic attachment to those old ways. Anthropologists and folklorists have long recognized the factor of re-enforcement that comes from attention given some ordinary thing by outsiders. So, a German-Russian community will listen and dance for decades to its own traditional music without giving it much thought or regard one way or another—until a field worker from the state university, from the state arts council, or from a prestigious organization like the Smithsonian Institution comes along and takes pictures and tape recordings and invites the artist or craftsman to participate in national, international, or state festivals. Suddenly the community realizes, "Hey, we have art and music too, and somebody who apparently knows thinks they are valuable and beautiful!"

So it is that I want to emphasize in this guide the importance of traditional arts and crafts. Little in the way of high, sophisticated, elitist art has come out of the German-Russian Bottoms of America, but the skill and beauty of the materials and ideas produced by nameless folk craftsmen and artists are no less important. Perhaps the German-Russians have not produced artists who produce art but they have instead produced, *as a people,* some things of real, artistic beauty.

Even traditional materials are hard to find in the area of graphic or plastic arts. The migratory economy, the grinding poverty, and the precariously balanced residence patterns of the German-Russians discouraged the accumulation of material art. But even under these circumstances one finds a drive for artistic expression, finding an outlet in functional items, perhaps. There was little hope of having a piece of fancy sculpture or a fine painting in a German-Russian home (recall, if you will, my father's description of the beet tenders' training loading up for the long trip to the beet fields!), but my grandparents did have one magnificent piece of glassware and a popular print now in my parents' possession. My maternal grandfather did write poetry even while he was working in the beet fields. Since bed coverings were going to be a necessity anyway, why not, the folk mind reasons, produce art there? So the quilts were resplendent with color, design, abstraction, and craftsmanship. That kind of artistry can be found in carpentry and gardening, canning and runza-making, tatting and dulcimer construction. When my mother carefully filled her canning jars so that they were attractive as well as functional, and when she neatly arrayed the jars on the shelves, wasn't she after all using the same kind of aesthetic judgements as Rembrandt? I have never seen more beautiful woodwork in any furniture or in any musical instruments (and I got into the business of folklore by way of collecting musical instruments) than that I see in Albert Fahlbusch's hammered dulcimers; he is our German-Russian Chippendale, our Stradivarius. Moreover, he is also our Yehudi Menuhin, since he rivals that man's skill in his playing.

Epilogue: The Fate of the Colonists Left in Russia

The story of those German-Russians left behind in Russia is even more moving than that of the migrants. Severe famine followed the Revolution of 1917, leading to epidemic starvation through the 1920's. Of course a century of resentment boiled up in Russian hearts and the German colonists were the last to eat and the last to rest, the first to go to the front, the first to starve. All of us have heard and trembled with the fear that went along with the Nazis' and the Communists' policies described as "the knock in the night." We have all imagined the horror of a father or son being whisked away in the night to prison, of mothers and daughters imprisoned under inhuman conditions; perhaps in our worst dreams we have also thought of the terror of whole families being torn away, as was the case with the Nazi holocaust. But in Russia, whole colonies were loaded at night into boxcars, carrying only what they could rake together in the last few moments, and they were taken eastward—eastward, where they once more were to serve as a buffer population between European Russia and Asia, this time on the Chinese-Russian border.

When Germany invaded Russia during the Second World War, every possible resource was thrown into the battle, including soldiers recruited from the German colonies. It was a strange situation: Germans fighting Germans. Desertions were massive in number. The Wehrmacht needed men too, however, and the deserters were quickly re-outfitted, given short training sessions in Germany and then reassigned to battle for the German army. The repatriated combat troops were usually sent to the Eastern Front against the Russians, for it was reasoned quite logically that they would, without question, fight to the death; if they should be captured and their identity discovered, their fate would be even worse than that of the common German soldier, which was nothing to be anticipated, as it was.

In one case, a German-Russian soldier, drafted into the Russian army, was captured by the Germans and once retrained, sent back against the Russians in the East. He was again captured by the Russians, but using a photo with a photographer's stamp, given him by a girl in Munich, he convinced the Russians that he was German rather than a German-Russian; then as a prisoner he worked in the Russian mines until the early 1950's when he was released to Germany. The irony was that he had been working in Russia only a few kilometers from his home and the remnants of his family, but any effort at contact would have revealed his true identity as a Russian deserter and he and his family would have suffered awesome consequences.

Following the war, large numbers of German colonists fled Russia and entered Germany. They were, of course, glad to escape the horrors that were being inflicted on them in Russia where there was a virulent and justifiable hate for Germans, but even in Germany they were strangers. Indeed, it must be remembered that since the beginning of the century there had been a constant trickle of refugees flowing from Russia into Germany. The following passages are excerpts from an article "German-Russian Refugees in Berlin" in *Deutsch-Amerika,* April 22, 1922,[14] but the scene described here was repeated many, many times from 1917 to 1950. The complete translated text of this article and another one describing German-Russian refugees arriving in Germany in 1930 are scheduled for publication in a future work paper of the American Historical Society for Germans from Russia. The translation is mine:

> At the beginning of March a group of German colonists who had fled from scenes of the Russian famine arrived at the Silesian Railroad Station in Berlin. They were taken under the protection of the Red Cross, which had made every possible effort to provide means to relieve the suffering of these pitiable countrymen of ours. . . .
>
> They had come from the area of Sarotov, a great regional center of German settlement. In peace time the Germans there occupied no less than 15,000 farms, associated with 63 villages and including approximately 200,000 to 300,000 inhabitants. Then came war and revolution. . . .
>
> At the end of the year 1920 people began to die of hunger. Things had become so drastic that people were eating dead draft horses. Since there were no potatoes or cereals, nor any other form of food for that matter, the completely inedible meat was cut into small pieces and boiled. People who ate such food swelled to the point where they were no longer recognizable and died by the thousands within a few days, with great pain.
>
> These three families [of refugees] belonged to the upper classes and had owned leather factories and shops in the city. They had been in prison for months, under the most horrible conditions. Huge sums of money were constantly being extorted from them. If the Bolsheviks did not find the father of a family at home with the demanded money they would take the children away to prison until the money was delivered.

At the first of the year, 1921, the German colonies began to disintegrate. The majority of the inhabitants had been slain by starvation or bullets and others had fled aimlessly in every direction. The main trail, for not immediately obvious reasons, led to Moscow, another through Poland to Germany. On the 28th of May, 1921, the three families began their journey to Germany, which was to take them nine months. They chose the route through the Ukraine and Roumania. When they left the site of fifty years of labor, the entire colony possessed only two pounds of flour, but still quite a bit of valuable properties.

For half a year they trudged through the states of that enormous land. Finally they arrived at Dnjestr, the Roumanian border. Of course it was not simply a matter of stepping across, since the family would in that case share the fate of many thousands of refugees who had been shot down by the border guards. They therefore established a small leather shop so that they could earn a living and wait until the river froze over.

One night then they packed and sneaked away. They stumbled over steep drops and climbed—the three fathers with their wives and children—down the banks to the river. They made the crossing with pounding hearts. They lay on the banks and waited for a changing of the Roumanian guards. They got through the watchposts undetected and reached the woods. There they became confused and lost. The families had to sleep in the open, buried in the snow. One child . . . died. The next night they were challenged by Roumanian soldiers, who first gave them food and some milk for the children. The officer in charge however wanted to send them back to Russia since they had no contacts in Roumania. It was clear to all of them what a return to Russia would mean.

At about the same time 300 Russian and Jewish refugees had crossed the border. Forty of these had been returned and they were immediately shot down on the other side of the border before everyone's eyes. Therefore, with great effort, an acquaintance was found who would inform the German diplomatic offices in Bucharest of their fate. The intercession of the German envoys was immediate and even before the reply telegram had arrived, a staff officer was in the appropriate town, fishing refugees from the general tumult of the fleeing crowd. It was not long before the passes to Germany were in good order. In this relatively short time the Germans had to surrender their collective valuables under the threat that they would otherwise be sent back to Russia. They even left behind a debt of 35,000 Lei with their helpers.

And now here they were, completely abandoned, in the German capital city, waiting to be admitted to a camp for repatriots. But still in the eyes of the adults there was a quiet terror of a memory of a time when the little children bit their own flesh out of hunger and when they dared the death dash across the Dnjestr that snowy night.

The reader will have to remember while reading this passage that journalistic style was more florid then than now and that the writer was clearly using this opportunity to comment on the cruelty of the Soviet government, but the general mood and facts surrounding the family's flight and plight are, I believe, quite accurate.

Following the war the German colonists remained in the new settlement sites along the Chinese border, and there they remain yet today. The removal was traumatic, but perhaps even worse is the continuing program of cultural dilution and eradication pursued by the Russian government. Misguided patriots in America have tried to make everyone here "100 percent American" by destroying the rich cultural traditions which are the real wealth of our heritage, but unfortunately this same kind of mentality has exercised far more power and influence in Russia.

The German colonists are still German and many of them cling to the old ways. But I have learned in correspondence that German communities are discouraged by scattering housing, and many of the older Germans feel that military service and general commercial diffusion have led young people away from the good old ways, a situation analogous with the conditions of the German colonies in America.

CATALOGUE

HOW TO FIND OUT ABOUT GERMAN-RUSSIANS

Developing a Family History

Conventional views of history have sometimes clouded the real issues
of the historical contribution of Germans on the Plains. As I once wrote in
an essay for the Midwest Center for the Humanities:

> The impact of the German-Russian peoples on the
> northern Plains is hard to gauge because it is not measured in
> statesmen, buildings, wealth, inventions, or books. By their
> fierce independence they have strengthened the independence
> of America: in their rock-hard conservatism they have pro-
> vided a powerful counterpart to hasty change. But perhaps
> their greatest contribution is to the diversity of America. The
> beauty of a fine patchwork quilt, after all, is not the result of
> all the patches being alike but in their diversity; and no one
> patch is beautiful in and of itself, but only within the context
> and differences of the other patches in the quilt. So it is with
> the German-Russian people. Their principal impact on the
> Plains has been in their being—and remaining—what they are.[15]

If we are then to record and depict the most important contributions of Germans to Nebraska and Plains history we must document the
lives, attitudes, and products of the common German. We must record the
biographies of the most ordinary of beet tenders and railroad workers,
for therein lies our real glory. We need careful examination and documentation of the most ordinary of summer kitchens, churches, or meeting
halls, the most typical of meals.

There are many ways to attack such a project, depending on resources and your own interests. You perhaps could follow the lead of my
family and assemble a photographic family tree: copy all photographs you
can find of your family's ancestors and assemble them into a striking wall
display in your home. As I like to note in my classes in oral history, in this
way my children are not bored by the conventional lines, squares, and
numbers of the usual family tree, but see their past as *people*. My son can
see a man in a Russian cavelry uniform—with a certain kind of nose. Then

he sees that nose again in the next line, on his grandfather. He can look across the room and see that same nose on me, and in the morning, in the mirror, he will see that nose between his own two eyes. Thus he becomes an organic part of a dynamic family history made up not of names and numbers but of people and noses.

A beautiful way to develop a gift for the future is to make a project of assembling photographs or photographing every living member of your family. You will instantly have an important historical document and within a few years it will be invaluable. Think of what a prize you would have if your father or grandfather had done a project like this!

At very little expense copies of the photos can be made for every member of the family and you will be the hit of the Christmas Eve gift opening and you probably will inherit three million dollars from Aunt Clara for your thoughtfulness.

A similar (and similarly exciting) project can be done on recording tape. Record, for example, one hour of memories from your grandmother. Duplicate the tapes for a cost of less than $2 each, and distribute the recordings as a $2 Christmas present that will endure long past the $20 sweaters or $4000 automobiles. Or spend a couple of weekends interviewing uncles and aunts about, for example, Christmases on the family farm. You will become an instant hero of the family.

If you would like to avoid the problems that go along with family research, concentrate on that family farm. Do a history of the homestead, or of the family business building in your town, or of the family's tenure in town. Go through the local newspapers (an extensive file of newspapers is retained by the Nebraska State Historical Society) and every little town and village once had two or three newspapers (and they reported every time anyone so much as got the hiccoughs) and trace your family's record in print. There is no end of possibilities once you have the energy and initiative. Perhaps the saddest situation is all of those good intentions that fade away to nothing when the resources are in the grave.

For those of us who are Germans, the starting point is so close that it may for the moment escape our attention—the place to examine our history on the Plains does indeed lie within our own families. If the strength of our people does rest with the common elements, then those of us who come from common farm and small merchant backgrounds are in the best positions to do some detective work about German culture.

These pages are not the place for a thorough examination of the techniques for genealogical or family history research, but I would like to underscore a few points that are vital to research among the German and

German-Russian people on the Plains (see Bibliography).

1. Avoid thinking of a family project of this sort in terms of a family tree alone. A family tree is a worthy enough project, but it is like a road map: it falls far short of transmitting the real beauty of the scenery. I would urge the interested family researcher to develop a family *history,* not just a genealogy. Interview living relatives, neighbors, and friends. Record the story of your family in Russia, in transit, and in America. Record the joys and sorrows of the family. This kind of approach is all the more important because often with our German-Russian people it is very difficult to trace a family line back very far because of Soviet or East German intransigence or because records were so frequently lost or destroyed during the Second World War.

Note the texts from my own father's memoirs that I have included within this essay. They represent the really interesting materials that rarely accompany a simple family tree.

2. Do not limit the pleasures that come from your research to yourself. Xerox or mimeograph your findings and distribute them—perhaps as Christmas presents—to other members of the family. In this way you will:

A. Create a real family heirloom.

B. Be remembered for a valuable but inexpensive gift.

C. Arouse more interest and response for your project and thereby possibly uncover even more information (and a family history is never *finished!*).

D. Provide for yourself some insurance; if something should happen to your own records of your research you will be able to refer to others' copies—if you have been generous.

3. In terms of the points above, the family researcher should also consider using the files of the Nebraska State Historical Society's genealogical library and those of the American Historical Society of Germans from Russia—and then repaying them for that help by filing copies of family histories with those societies' archives.

Other Resources for Historical Research

The problem, if the real culture of Plains Germans does indeed lie within the common man and his products, is how to recognize it and how to get it and what to do with it once it is recognized. We all know how to read books and find high culture—art, music, and drama—which are usually assembled in some special place (a gallery or concert hall), so that even the least sophisticated, least appreciative observer can nonetheless see and recognize what high art is.

A number of alternatives can be found within any area's universities and colleges. Perhaps a secondary lesson of this is that college is not only for young people. If you are interested in history, folklore, anthropology, or ethnic studies beyond the stage of "interested amateur," look through the various catalogs and schedules of schools in your area. New and experimental courses are being added to a school's program every teaching period, so keep checking. Indeed, if you and several friends would like to have a course in oral history, folklore, or field techniques, let the dean or the president of the college know; he will work with his business office and faculty to develop public service courses that will improve the program and income of the school.

If you cannot be sure if a particular course will meet your needs, call the teacher and ask about it. Most teachers understand that you do not want to waste your time and money and they do not want dissatisfied students, so they will outline what their approach will be in a course for you.

At the University of Nebraska at Lincoln, courses in folklore are offered in the English Department, in fieldwork in the anthropology and English Departments, in ethnic and regional history in the History Department, and many courses in ethnic culture are provided within ethnic studies programs and the institutes. In my experience faculty members are always willing to consider the development of a new course if there is a clear need and sufficient interest.

Nor should other educational outlets be ignored: smaller colleges (in Lincoln, for example, Nebraska Wesleyan and Union College offer relevant courses), community programs (Southeast Community College in Lincoln offers courses in genealogy), service programs (the YMCA, YWCA, and city recreation department in Lincoln occasionally offer courses in this direction), and, finally, evening courses and extension courses (the University of Nebraska Extension Division offers a non-credit correspondence course in Nebraska folklore and workshops in genealogy and family history).

If a community has sufficient combined interest in developing a program for oral history or folklore collection, it is entirely possible that supporting funds can be obtained from the Nebraska Arts Council or Nebraska Committee for the Humanities to bring in a professional to give you a start, to instruct community members in collection and archiving techniques, and to provide help in the early stages of collection and archiving. A program I am personally familiar with was developed in Exeter, Nebraska with help from the Nebraska Committee for the Humanities. This project worked from two directions—the first to draw the community's attention to its own resources, and the second to initiate a collection program within the schools. My own impression was that this program was successful; if nothing else, a large number of children were left with tape recordings of themselves interviewing their grandparents and parents about their heritage. If you had such a recording, wouldn't it be one of the most precious of your possessions? Now is the time for you or your children to create just such an heirloom for yourself.

Because we Plains Germans are so close to our past we have the advantage of having access to much of our migrant history. In fact, some of you reading this *are* perhaps migrants. You who came from Russia or who were the first generation born here, you who have worked in the beet fields, should consider at once recording or writing down your own memories. By your own efforts you can create an important historical document. My father has written over 125 pages of his memories, some excerpts from which I have used in this paper. These pages are the single most valuable item my family possesses and I have made several Xerox copies to insure against the loss of the information. I see real potential for publication of this set of memoirs, and if nothing else, they will constitute an important legacy for my children. It was in these laboriously written pages—my father probably wrote more in recording his memories than he had written altogether in the previous ten years!—that I first understood any number of things about him, about me, and about the German Russians. Insights like that are rare in a lifetime.

I hope that I have briefly covered the possible scope of the ways to approach a study of our German heritage. The main point to keep in mind, I believe, is that we can work from our own minds with absolutely no training but we must also consider the possibilities of collecting materials from a wide variety of sources and arming ourselves with the sophisticated techniques taught by professionals through the universities and colleges.

Festivals

Festivals have become increasingly a form of expression of renewed ethnic pride, but all too often the would-be festival organizers have little more than enthusiasm—a good start, but not enough to carry through a good, solid festival. Perhaps the single most important consideration is that the community or organization considering a festival must avoid at all costs the temptation to develop a "new ethnic culture" based on what they wish their culture or history had been rather than what it actually was or is. Far too often the result is thin and plastic, not to mention deceptive for outsiders, when a simple reliance on the real folk cultural assets of the community might have produced a presentation of real value and interest.

The American Historical Society for Germans from Russia has produced its own festivals and has been helpful for other communities in their planning. A limited number of items are available for loan and display where a historical motif is desired. The same is true of the Nebraska State Historical Society, where sufficient assurance of security can be developed for the artifacts and displays.

Funding for such festivals is available in small amounts and under special conditions from the Nebraska Arts Council, 7367 Pacific Street, Omaha, Nebraska, or the Nebraska Committee for the Humanities, Highway 30 West (RR 2), Kearney, Nebraska. Contact the offices of these agencies regarding the appropriate preparation of proposals and the requirements currently followed regarding matching funds. In many cases groups or communities can cover their portion of festival expenses with "in-kind" money, that is, with work, time, local supplies, and so forth, rather than with hard cash. It is crucial to contact these agencies as soon as possible since there are deadlines for grant proposals and considerable time is necessary to process and screen proposals and establish priorities.

Where there is plenty of planning time and where there is a willingness and ability to invest some money in the presentation of a cultural festival, a source of information regarding German groups touring America is available from the Consulate or Embassy cultural officers, addresses listed below.

The Smithsonian Institution's Festival of American Folklike is, without question, the most ambitious and professional of America's folk festivals, and some idea of the scope of the festival and how it works can be obtained from the Division of Performing Arts, Smithsonian Institution, L'Enfant Plaza, Washington, D.C. The Festival of American Folklife is a huge operation and covers every aspect of American folklore from truckers and telephone workers to native American Indians, from regional materials to ethnic lore. A major component is the "Old Ways in the New World Program," which searches America for, say, German music and then looks for the music of the cognate area in German (or in Russian, if possible).

Following the appearance of the visiting groups at the Festival on the Mall in Washington, D.C., many of the performers are sent on a national tour. When Germany is participating in the Festival, it is possible for any group or community to apply for the appearance of these folk performances at a moderate cost. Requests for information should be directed to "Old Ways in the New World" (Touring), Division of Performing Arts, Smithsonian Institution, L'Enfant Plaza 2100, Washington, D.C.

Some idea can be gained about the festival and how a festival can be operated from a film produced about the Smithsonian's festival. It is a 16 mm film, 28 minutes long, and can be borrowed at no expense except for the return postage, which is quite inexpensive.

If you wish to see the film, you should contact the appropriate regional office of Association-Sterling Films, as listed below:

5797 New Peachtree Road Atlanta, Georgia 30340 404-458-6253	serves: Alabama, Florida, Georgia, North Carolina, Mississippi, South Carolina, Tennessee
8615 Directors Row Dallas, Texas 75247 214-638-6799	serves: Arkansas, Colorado, Missouri, Kansas, Louisiana, New Mexico, Oklahoma, Texas
7838 San Fernando Road Sun Valley, California 91352 213-767-0200	serves: Alaska, Arizona, California, Hawaii, Idaho, Montana, Nevada, Oregon, Washington, Wyoming, Utah
600 Grand Avenue Ridgefield, New Jersey 07657 201-943-3855	serves: Connecticut, Delaware, Kentucky, Maine, Massachusetts, Maryland, New Hampshire, New Jersey, New York, Ohio, Pennsylvania, Rhode Island, Vermont, Virginia, West Virginia
512 Burlington Avenue LaGrange, Illinois 60525 312-354-7422	serves: Illinois, Indiana, Iowa, Michigan, Minnesota, Nebraska, North Dakota, South Dakota, Wisconsin

Those living in the Washington, D.C. area should contact Anne Evans at the Smithsonian, at 381-6525.

Festivals already underway are useful for those who are interested in planning festivals of their own and for those of us who enjoy participating in the music, dance, and color—and the inevitable eating of good food. McCook, Nebraska has developed a festival, "German Days," but unfortunately it relies far too much on commercial enthusiasm and slick presentation and far too little on a soundly researched concept of what German culture in the area (or anywhere else) truly was. Henderson, Nebraska, on the other hand, has done a brilliant job of presenting to the outside world the real substance of German culture in that Mennonite community. By accident or design they have captured the real value of the festival, presenting to others the actual customs, traditions, crafts, and arts that go on in that community on a day-to-day, continuing basis—or once did—accurately reproduced. The Henderson festival has traditional cookery of the area, butchering as it is still practiced, soap making, and so forth with little in the way of artificial stereotyping. Perhaps there were people in the community who wished that their ancestors had had the good taste to wear Bavarian clothes and frilly dirndls and dance colorful dances, but the point is that they didn't; instead they baked, butchered, and made soap. And, the festival is no less a success for its historical honesty.

A "Septemberfest" is irregularly practiced in Gering, Nebraska, and the two I have attended were superb. The food and music were first-rate and, like Henderson, there was little effort here to "fancy up" German-Russian culture. It was instead an honest celebration of the realities of it.

A less obvious German festival can be found imbedded within the county fairs of Plains counties where there is a strong German representation. Here, within the context of an activity which is not strickly speaking German, can be found German art, cookery, customs, and music.

Finally, in many communities the best festivals of all can be found in church basements and bars and on farmsteads, if you have the energy to do the looking. Churches have fund-raising "Brode," bars have German music and dances, and small groups of Germans gather to make sausage, bottle home-brew, or butcher. It is in these small "festivals," totally unemcumbered with the destructive ornamentations added by promoters, chambers of commerce, and special pleaders, where the real essence of German culture in Nebraska can be seen, smelled, tasted, felt, and enjoyed to its fullest.

Photographs

Historical photographs of Germans in Nebraska, German settlements, German farms and buildings, and so forth can be found in the Picture Room of the Nebraska State Historical Society, 15th and R Streets, Lincoln, Nebraska 68588. For a moderate expense, the Historical Society will duplicate or make slides of photographs for patrons.

A small but growing collection of German-Russian photographs is on file with the museum of the American Historical Society for Germans from Russia, 615 D Street, Lincoln, Nebraska.

A fairly large collection of historical and contemporary photographs, especially of German-Russian house types, summer kitchens and so forth in Lincoln, Sutton, Henderson, and Scottsbluff has been assembled as a part of this catalogue project and will be deposited with the developing Center for Great Plains Studies at the University of Nebraska-Lincoln.

Photographs from all three of the sources cited above appear as a part of this essay.

General Cultural Information

General information regarding German culture and history, especially in Germany, can be obtained from the Cultural Officer of the German Embassy, 4645 Reservoir Road, Washington, D.C., 20007—or from the German Consulate, 104 South Michigan, Chicago, Illinois. A private American agency that can also be contacted for information, and in some cases organizational help, is the Carl Schurz Society, 339 Walnut Street, Philadelphia, Pennsylvania 19106. The Carl Schurz Society can sometimes be of help also in arranging for appearances of German culture groups on tour in the United States.

The German-American Society in Omaha, Nebraska (3717 South 120th Street, telephone 402 333-6615) has an extensive formal program of German culture, language, and resources education. They sponsor a German folk dance group which meets regularly at the Society's headquarters. On the first and second Saturdays of each month the Society sponsors parties featuring German food, drink, music and dance. On Saturday mornings there are German language classes for children and on Wednesday evenings for adults. On Thursdays there are gymnastics classes for children, in keeping with true German cultural traditions. The Society publishes a monthly newsletter with information about cultural events in the area and within the Society. Each Labor Day the Society has a two-day festival featuring, once more, German food, music, and dance. For information regarding membership and attendance at the Society's events, contact the address or phone number above.

The American Historical Society of Germans From Russia

I have stated elsewhere that the single greatest effort toward the study and preservation of the German-Russian past has come from this organization. I therefore feel that it is important as a part of this resources catalogue to list officers and local chapters of the organization. Readers who are interested should feel free to contact the International Headquarters or local chapters or to consider the establishment of additional local chapters.

With the help of Ruth Amen of the Society, John Carter has put together the following brief history of the organization:

> The American Historical Society of Germans from Russia was officially founded on October 8, 1968, in Greeley, Colorado. The organization was the result of the work of three people, David J. Miller, William F. Urbach, and Theodore Wentzlaff. Assisting this group from "long distance" was Joseph H. Height.
>
> The basic function of the group is to collect and preserve German-Russian heritage and history. The organization works extensively in the areas of genealogy, local history, and folklore, and events relating to German-Russian culture. The major activity of the local chapters revolves around "fellowship" activities and genealogy. It is hoped that the future will bring a more intense interest from youth and a more active collection of material culture artifacts. Local chapters now have several displays of material artifacts in museums and work is in progress to erect a display at the Smithsonian Institution.
>
> The Society publishes three periodicals during the year. The work papers are the publications that deal with topics of a diverse nature, from European history to genealogical methodology. *Clues* is a publication dealing with specific genealogical problems and more specifically with Germans from Russia. The Society also publishes a newsletter that deals with Society events and business.
>
> A rough estimate of the number of individuals participating in the organization at this time would fall somewhere around four thousand.

The officers of the American Historical Society of Germans from Russia as of June, 1975:

H.J. Amen, Honorary President (dec.)
601 D Street
Lincoln, Nebraska 68502

Arthur E. Flegel, Vice-President
1895 Oakdell Drive
Menlo Park, California 94025

Dr. Karl Stumpp, Honorary Chairman
7000 Stuttgart 71
Florentiner Str 20, Apt. 5117
West Germany

Dr. Adam Giesinger, Vice-President
645 Oxford Street
Winnipeg 9, Manitoba, Canada

David J. Miller, Past President
  and General Counsel
Post Office Box 1424
Greeley, Colorado 80631

Edward Schwartzkopf, Secretary
2020 Park Avenue
Lincoln, Nebraska 68502

Miss Ruth M. Amen, President
601 D Street
Lincoln, Nebraska 68502

Jake Sinner, Treasurer
3115 Kucera Drive
Lincoln, Nebraska 68502

Presidents of local chapters of AHSGR on the Plains:

Denver Metropolitan Chapter
Mrs. William Cook, Jr.
4190 Marshall Street
Wheat Ridge, Colorado 80033

Northern Colorado Chapter
Mrs. David J. Miller
2319 21st Avenue
Greeley, Colorado 80631

Lincoln, Nebraska Chapter One
Ralph L. Giebelhaus
3931 No. 13th
Lincoln, Nebraska 68521

Mid-Nebraska Chapter
Mrs. Ona Short
137 Lakeside Drive
Hastings, Nebraska 68901

Southwest Nebraska Chapter
Miss Carolyn Lenhart
311 West 4th Street
McCook, Nebraska 69001

Northeast Kansas Chapter
Isadore Appelhanz
3216 West 11th Street
Topeka, Kansas 66604

Southeastern Wyoming Chapter
Mrs. Albert N. Simpson
1513 E 19th Street
Cheyenne, Wyoming 82001

FOOTNOTES

1.   As outlined in *Sixtieth Anniversary of the Free Evangelical Lutheran Cross Church of Fresno, California: 1892-1954* (Fresno, 1952), p. 7.

2.   *Ibid.,* p. 8.

3.   That is, a citizen of the town of Kukkus or Norgra.

4.   See note 1 above.

5.   Hattie Plum Williams, *A Social Study of the Russian-Germans* (sic), University Studies XVI, July, 1916 (University of Nebraska, Lincoln, 1916), p. 143.

6.   The long quotations from my father are from a hand-written manuscript, now of some 125 pages, that he is preparing as a legacy for his grandchildren. I describe the memoirs and the process of obtaining them in some detail at the close of this essay. With the help of Ed Carter, a Lincoln attorney, the papers are currently being prepared for submission for publication as a brief autobiography of a typical German-Russian migrant family.

7.   See note 6 above.

8.   See note 6 above.

9.   See note 6 above.

10.   Information from an interview with Albert Brehm, officer of the Society, by John Carter, February 11, 1976.

11.   Information from an interview with Ralph Giebelhaus, President of the Association, by John Carter, February 11, 1976.

12.   See note 6 above.

13.   Theodore C. Wenzlaff, *History of the Hope Reformed Church, 1908-1968* (Sutton, Nebraska: Service Press, 1968), pp. 9-10.

14.   "Die Deutschen Wolga-Flüchtlinge in Berlin," *Deutsch-Amerika: The Illustrated Weekly,* VIII: 12 (April 22, 1922), pp. 26-27.

15.   From an unpublished radio and lecture script prepared in 1974 for the National Humanities Series of the Midwestern Center for the Humanities, the University of Wisconsin, Extension Division.

16.   Information from an interview with Ruth Amen, president of the Society, by John Carter, February 10, 1976.

VI

Scandinavians: The Search for Zion

By Paul A. Olson

ACKNOWLEDGMENTS

I am indebted to the following elderly Scandinavian people for history and pictures of the past: Mr. and Mrs. Reuben C. Olson, Wahoo (my parents); Esther Lindgren; Axel Swanson; Carl Bjorkman; Hulda Landell; Samuel Dahl; Otto Hoiberg; R.L. Fredstrom; and Alvin Peterson. Nels Forde also helped. In addition, Mr. Bernie Gissler and Mrs. Geraldine Rystrom of the Stromsburg-Osceola area helped me with literature. I am indebted to Robert Turnquist, Bethphage Mission; J. Knudsen and Ernest P. Nielsen, Grandview College; and Earl Mezoff of Dana College for information and pictures. Also, the Stuhr Museum in Grand Island, Nebraska; Vesterheim, the Museum of Norwegian American Folk Art in Decorah, Iowa; and Bethany College, Lindsborg, Kansas, helped. James Bowman and Lawrence Freeman told me about Swedish Covenant tradition. Roger Rejda chose and took photos. My views of Kierkegaard were formed by O.K. Bouwsma. This essay is dedicated to my parents and to those great-grandparents of mine who were killed in the fields by merciless work.

The forks are from Norway; the shovel, immigrant. Small Scandinavian dairy farms in the Midwest still used wooden rakes in the 1930's. Tools of this sort go back to the Scandinavian Middle Ages, but were used by poor farmers in 19th century Scandinavia and the U.S. (Photo from Vesterheim Museum, Decorah, Iowa.)

Above. Altar at Harja Tyringa Church in Skane Province, Sweden. It was built in 1261 and was attended by Hulda Landell of Wausa during her childhood. Altarpiece depicts the Last Supper surrounded by angels (photo by Roger Rejda, courtesy of Hulda Landell).

Below. Lars Christensen altarpiece located in the Vesterheim Museum at Decorah, Iowa. It portrays the Last Supper, the crucifixion, birth of Christ and his presentation in the temple.

Above. N.F.S. Grundtvig, the founder of Scandinavian folkschools, seller's coops, and folk-based architecture, art and hymnology. *Below.* Søren Kierkegaard, the father of existentialism and of certain forms of Scandinavian pietism and Inner Mission work. Inspiration to Hendrik Ibsen and Ole Rölvaag.

Above. Howard Hanson, Wahoo, one of America's foremost composers and interpreters of modern music. Seen in the essay which follows as heir to the Scandinavian Populists. *Below.* Ole Rölvaag (second from left)–novelist celebrator of Giants country in northeastern Nebraska and eastern South Dakota. He was inspired by Ibsen and Kierkegaard, and also kept up the fishing ways of the old country.

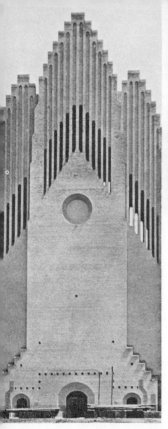

Left. P.V.J. Klint's Grundtvig's memorial church (1920's) in Copenhagen, done in the style of the medieval "step" churches in Skane, South Sweden, and in Denmark. Klint's modernistic architectural forms were inspired by Grundtvig's "back to the folk" thought. The brick work design inspired much Scandinavian modern brick work (organ motif pays tribute to Grundtvig's hymnology). *Above.* Medieval step church in Harja Toringa, Skane, Sweden, the kind of church that inspired P.V.J. Klint. *Below.* P.V.J. Klint's church at Odense, Denmark, 1921.

Above. O.J. Cervin's Zion Chapel at Bethphage Mission, Axtell, Nebraska. Notice the appropriation of medieval and Klintian style work for this "Inner Mission" institution. Dedicated, 1931. *Below.* Brick work around the main entrance to Zion Chapel. (Photos by Mr. Turnquist, president of Bethphage Mission.)

The continuation of the Grundtvig-Klint tradition in recent buildings. *Above,* the interior of Christ Lutheran Church in Minneapolis, built in 1948—the last building built by Eliel Saarinen (also a Lutheran minister)—representing a most sophisticated use of the linear design of brick so prominent in Klint's work. Trinity Lutheran Church in Lincoln is a kind of duplicate. *Below,* a jewelbox urban church in Copenhagen designed recently by Kaare Klint, P.V.J. Klint's son and inventor of Danish modern furniture. The furniture inside the church is a primary example.

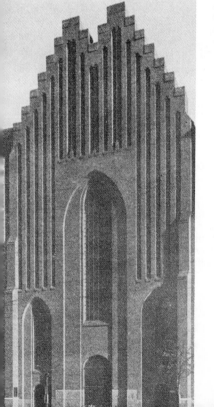

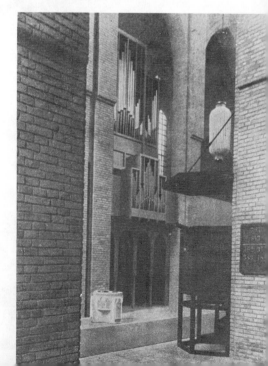

Varola Folkskola.

Many of the Scandinavian immigrants attended folkschools. *Above,* Varola folkschool in Vestergotland, Sweden—attended by Hulda Landell's husband (Mr. Landell, who lived in Wausa for many years, is now deceased). Mrs. Landell was interviewed for this chapter. *Below,* the Grundtvigian folkschool at Nysted, Nebraska. Notice the fine woodwork surrounding the door in the group picture.

Examples of Midwest Scandinavian woodcarving. *Above.* detail from the Lars Christensen altarpiece illustrated earlier. *Below right,* carved head of Swedish pioneer by Anton Pearson of Lindsborg, Kansas (photo by Richard Littleton). *Below left and insert,* carved pulpit in Danish Lutheran Church at Nysted, Nebraska with carvings of each of the four evangelists symbolizing the "living word" in the Grundtvigian tradition (the illustrated figure is Matthew). The carver was Jes Smidt, a wooden shoe carver and self taught (photos by Roger Welsch).

Above. The Lay Preacher by Herbjørn Gausta (1854-1924), a painter from Harmony, Minnesota (painting from Vesterheim—Decorah, Iowa). All of the pietistic movements in Scandinavia (Hauge, Covenant, and Beckian) depended on house meetings with lay preachers, a sort of religious underground. In the houses of the very poor, where pietism centered, folk crafts continued. *Below*, needlework and spinning wheel from Scandinavian homes in this area from the late 19th century. (Courtesy of the Stuhr Museum in Grand Island.)

Even impressionism changed radically as pietistic communities confronted the stern frontier. *Left,* "The First Bathing," etching by Anders Zorn, leading Swedish late 19th century impressionist. Notice the hedonistic treatment of the human body, wind, sea and light. *Right,* "Giant Cedars" by Zorn's student, Birger Sandzen of Lindsborg, Kansas (first half of the 20th century. Sandzen's tree forms have an almost fervile quality. In the pointment of living

VI

Scandinavians:
The Search for Zion

By Paul A. Olson

The Scandinavian immigrants to the western plains of the Midwest appear to have disappeared, scarcely any of their cultural heritage remaining. Looking at the Scandinavian cities and towns of this area—at Lindsborg, Kansas; Newman Grove, Dannebrog-Nysted, or Stromsburg, Nebraska, or Viborg, South Dakota—visitors today will find the surface of life most unlike that of the northern European countries. The Nebraska counties where Swedes settled (e.g., Saunders, Knox, Burt, Hamilton, Polk, Phelps, Fillmore, Clay, Dixon), or the Rölvaag *Giants* Norwegian counties in easter South Dakota and northeastern Nebraska now contain little that is unusual or culturally different on the surface. A few sentimental mementos, a few gingerbread Scandinavian storefronts, a word or two of the old language, a place name here and there, seem to be all that is around. And yet assimilation was very hard for the people from the northern countries.[1] I have talked to recent visitors from Scandinavia who find the Scandinavian towns of this section in some senses culturally more Scandinavian than Scandinavia itself.[2] Though the hyperbole of such statements may be more striking than their accuracy, what do remain are beliefs, patterns of life, and a few model institutions and artifacts which are reminders of why people came and what we can learn from the memory of their reasons for coming.

When the Swedes, Danes, or Norwegians came across the

Missouri in the 1860's and 70's, they found a land largely without clear political or cultural organization with which they could identify. If the old novels are correct, they were largely ignorant of Indian life; the long history of breaking Indian treaties which made the land available was unknown to them. What existed was a plains frontier 'providentially' opened for homestead settlement after the Civil War at a time when Scandinavian life was at its harshest. The familiar natural relationships were gone. Whereas Scandinavians, who, in the 1840's and 50's arrived in the midwestern states of Wisconsin, Minnesota, northeastern Iowa, and Illinois, found a landscape resembling that of the Scandinavian countries (forests, lakes, marshes, fish, and cold winters), the Scandinavians who came to western Iowa, the Dakotas, Nebraska, and Kansas came to a landscape drastically different from that of the old country. This one contained vast grasslands without trees or lakes, regions drouth-stricken and grasshopper-torn.[3] The recent immigrants were poorer than their predecessors; the old country from which they came was more strife-torn in the 60's and 70's. The culture which emerged in Scandinavian communities in the western plains *had to be* somewhat different from that in the old country or in regions further east both because it faced a different world and because, with the decline of the old feudal Scandinavian way of life, people *had to* construct new styles of community life.

The Scandinavian emigrants who wished to build a decent community had going for them when they left a set of reform-visions of what human community could be which had emerged in 19th century Scandinavia. These had seemed unlikely to be realized in Scandinavia in the 1860's-70's; its actual semi-feudal social system and moribund state church had little enough to offer community builders. The "visions" appeared, to many of the more self-conscious immigrants, to deserve a working out, and they pursued them boldly in the period 1865-1918.

To understand the roots of their efforts and the progress which they made, it will be useful to look at 19th century

Scandinavia itself. Only in the last quarter of that century did it begin to suffer its way toward reform like that which the American and French revolutions had sought a half-century to a century earlier. Because the reforms came late and in the middle of an industrialized age, the northern reform movements did not center either in freedom for the individual alone (such as Locke and Rousseau advocated) or near absolute freedom for the businessman (such as Adam Smith required and the French and American reforms had protected). Rather than seeking to protect the rights of "different individuals," the Scandinavian reformers sought to create the right to different whole communities. One stance, that of Socialism and Populism, said reforms would come from giving power to the people. Another movement, that founded by N.F.S. Grundtvig, said reform should come from exploring the folkspirit of the Scandinavian people—what that spirit uniquely said about how good communities could be build. A third movement, which originated in Kierkegaardian pietism, said that reform had to be based on what is "true for me," not what is "true in general." For it, the search for integrity was prior to the search for community. Kierkegaard was suspicious of Grundtvig's notion of the community and fellowship, and his philosophy had almost no communal content. Paradoxically it may have borne most fruit in community change.

When reform ideas came to Scandinavia, reform was desperately needed. The reform ideas came to America with every wave of immigrants who, for one reason or another, gave up on the old world.

Conditions in the Old Countries

The mid-19th century Scandinavian countries were not very open to reform. In 1840's Sweden, great land owners (8,980) and a merchant class numbering a few thousand controlled the country. Political rights hardly existed for most people. In 1840 there were 203,000 peasants, some of whom had a little land, but there were also 88,000 crofters who had virtually no land at all and 37,000 cotters who had no land except for a potato patch and who worked as the hirelings of the landlord. Beyond this, there were 28,000 hired people who depended wholly upon the landlord. There was a vast army of young coming up: about 830,000 sons and daughters of peasants, cotters, and crofters ten years of age and older who were in agricultural employment, but who were either propertyless, or who had to share property with their parents.[4] By 1870, after a very tense period of reform, there were still 1,400,000 independent farmers and 1,290,000 laborers and casual workers who were often times living close to starvation level.[5]

People who have seen the recent film "The Immigrants" will have some idea of how intolerable must have been the near-slave conditions which prevailed in much of Sweden, Norway and Denmark—particularly in the large feudal estates in the open plains of middle and southern Sweden and all of Denmark. In the more northern parts of Sweden and most of Norway, the people lived in separate small farms rather than primarily in estate villages, hacking out their existences among the rocks and making their own furniture, buildings, tools and wooden shoes.[6] The consumption of Swedish hard liquor was 50 litres a year per person.[7] Suicide was rampant and occasional revolutions of a local or provincial sort broke out. My father, Reuben C. Olson of Wahoo, describes one of these 19th century revolts, in Södermanland, in which my grandmother had a role:

> Mother was very young then. The landlord was dragged out of his place and killed. Afterward his body was placed in a trough-like container, and each man, woman and child in the village walked by the trough and used a hoe or other tool to chop into the body to show that he or she was in sympathy with the act. (The landlord *had* been a very unreasonable person.) All of the people chopped into his body, including Ma.
>
> Ma was a very peaceful person. I later asked her what she thought about that action. She said that she didn't like it at all, but that the landlord was so mean the people had to do something.[8]

Some of the sense of oppression came from dealing with hard agricultural conditions without adequate technology. Two of my great grandparents lost their lives in accidents like those portrayed in "The Immigrants," in which peasants lifting heavy rocks thrown up by the frost are torn up by their own tools.

Denmark, which was first to reform, had before—and during—the period of its alliance with Napoleonic France, developed the land reform law required to replace the feudal system with a freeholder system; but this in turn created a large landless proletariat made up of people who did not receive land or renters' rights as the medieval village system was gradually abolished. Terrible agricultural and business recessions followed. The Napoleonic reform efforts slowed, and the Danish royalty became increasingly conservative. The revolution of 1830 opened up Denmark a bit, but it still had no constitution until 1848.[9] When a constitution and a representative assembly were created then, the reforms came too late to check the discontent with agricultural conditions which were improving all too slowly and with industrial conditions which were still horrendous. Marxist strikes came to Copenhagen under Louis Pio in the 1870's and an effective Democratic Socialist Left came up in the same decade—the decade before the greatest period of Danish immigration to this section of the country.[10]

Sweden and Norway, which were under the same royal family, were even slower to adopt the reforms needed.

Though Napoleon's marshall, Bernadotte, achieved the Swedish throne in 1810, he did not do much to make the constitutional monarchy one in fact as well as in name, and he came to be increasingly absolutist until his death in 1847. Sweden's 1840's and 50's "bill of rights" liberal reforms did nothing to alter the conditions of rural poverty; the hated military tax and compulsory military service remained; and suffrage remained limited to the few.[11] Norway's reform movement, the Christian Socialist movement led by Marcus Thrane, was also snuffed out by 1851 by the jailing of Thrane, who was eventually shipped out for Chicago (1858).[12] Though cultural nationalism grew in the 50's and 60's, it was not until the 70's and 80's that any serious reform in the representational system or any serious effort to change the conditions of extreme poverty was undertaken.[13]

While the Midwest, from the perspective of land available, seemed like Eden to the immigrant Scandinavians, they very quickly learned that America also had its own forms of exploitation: speculating land companies, monopolistic railroads, the monopoly power of the "eastern banks," and the caste system which placed all non-English speaking and non-English descent people outside the "Yankee" pale of respectability.[14] Old people who remember the tales of their parents about the regime in the old country say frequently that, "It treated horses better than it treated men." But many immigrants who came to the new world found, with Rölvaag's Beret, that in the harsh natural and political conditions of the new frontier, men were again reduced to beasts. And so the old country's reform visions, modified to fit new circumstances, were applied here.

When the immigrants came to the western plains, the notion of creating a "new culture" was often stated, framed in fairly vague and hopeful religious metaphors. Two metaphors which appear frequently in sermons, folksongs, letters and other forms are the metaphors of Eden and of Exodus. The kind of community posited by the Exodus metaphor is set down well in the folksong which the Swedish immigrants sang:

> From the Northland's grieving valleys
> And Sweden's hard taxed land
> We journey to the community of free men
> In North America's land.
>
> Farewell we bid to Sweden,
> Yes, to all its inhabitants a fond farewell,
> Voices from the New World call
> And bid: welcome, every Northland thrall.

That land has the Lord surely saved
For this, our time of utmost need,
(As He in the Scriptures has made clear)
That there we shall enjoy blessedness and peace.

When the fatherland is torn by strife,
And the Monarch's tempestuous will
Spreads hate and wickedness,
We flee from this corrupting land. . . .

Ye friends, who think about the journey
But fearfully ask if Religion is there:
Yes (in America) there is no deceit or vanity,
And the Gospel's sun shines clearly there.

You who in that Egypt's bondage
Find only toil and misfortune as your legacy.
Which you cannot escape until the tomb,
Then fly like a singing sparrow. . . .

Farewell to all that Scandinavia has,
Farewell to that oppressing land.
For this band reaches up toward freedom,
Farewell to that poor land![15]

The names of many Swedish towns and churches in the high plains reflect the hopeful metaphors—names which in Swedish or English mean "Mt. Hope," "New Eden," "Zion," "Free Mount" (Freemount), "Jerusalem's Fortress" (Salemsborg), "Adullam" (one of the sites in Canaan conquered by Joshua where David found refuge from oppression), and so forth.[16] Ole Rölvaag, who worked for a time in Newcastle, Nebraska (his great trilogy beginning with *Giants in the Earth* and ending with *Their Father's God* is set in northeastern Nebraska and eastern South Dakota), speaks again and again of Norwegian settlers who regard themselves as children of Israel who have come to a formerly forbidden land to combat the evil giants of an intractable land, on the one hand, and, on the other, the American system's tendency to develop in people a lust for possession.[17] For the ordinary imagination, the Eden-regained metaphor obviously said much the same thing as the Egypt-to-Zion metaphor, but it also said that the plains would allow formerly oppressed Scandinavians who came to them to find a more favorable natural world in which to work at creating the good community.

As reality in the form of grasshoppers, drouth and railroad oppression intruded on the religious dream, the real day-to-day hopes of building a better community were given body by specific ideas from the period as to how more humane fellowship among people could be built on the wreckage of decadent traditional Scandinavian culture: Socialist or cooperative or Christian pietistic pictures of what the human village ought to be dominated. Scandinavian-American work in art and the humanities must be understood in relationship to this idea-based community-creating process conducted among very ordinary people in the last quarter of the last century and the first two decades of this, both in this country and in Scandinavia. This is not to say that common people all read the philosophers; it is to say that the philosophers who had ideas also found advocates willing to go among the people and work out with them what the institutional embodiment of rather complex ideas might be. That ideas had an effect at this time is a corollary both of the ferment which was at large and the decadence of the old institutions.

Visions of Community Building in the New Eden

Populist and Socialist Visions

Perhaps the oldest and most radical picture of a break with the old order came from the Socialists. The earliest Socialist or Marxist leaders in Denmark and Norway, Louis Pio and Marcus Thrane, were exiled from their countries for political reasons in the mid-nineteenth century and resumed their campaign for social reform through their *Den Nye Tid* newspaper published in Chicago.[18] However, despite the exiling of the early Socialist Scandinavian leaders, Marxist or mixed

Marxist-Socialist approaches to social reconstruction triumphed in Scandinavia in the late 19th and early 20th centuries with the 'collapse' of the old regime.[19] Paradoxically, strict secular Socialist ideas had little effect on Scandinavians in this country, partly because of the urban anticlerical character of much of the period's Marxism and many other forms of Socialism, and partly because of the pietistic and rural character of western plains Scandinavians.

Where reform movements parallel to Marxist movements took hold in the Scandinavian plains, they took hold under the banner of 1890's Populism.[20] As Christopher Lasch has shown, the older forms of Marxism and Populism shared a similar notion that the rich and poor were necessarily at odds, that the poor had a right to defend their interests, that public ownership of many or all of the means of production was a necessary preliminary reform.[21] Both movements were concerned with many classes of oppressed people: minorities, women, the rural poor, the industrial masses (a Wahoo Populist newspaper saluted Eugene Debs after his release from prison after the railroad strike as the "person best fitted to become the leader of the industrial classes").[22] But Populism never favored the centralization of power favored by Marxists, never said revolution was necessary (rather it sought reform in the democratic framework through income tax, primaries, initiative and referendum), and it saw wealth more as land than as labor.[23] Whereas Populism's faith in people as they are was almost boundless, "scientific Marxism" said it was necessary to change the common people to alter their consciousness of themselves and society before they could govern.

Populism had a powerful voice in many Scandinavian communities as did its successor, "Progressivism." The *Voice of Protest* shows that overwhelming sentiment among Norwegian politicians and newspapers in the late 19th and early 20th century was to support the Populist program of the break-up of monopolies, tax reform, fiscal reform, and reform of the governing process.[24] The Danes took very much the same position. The Swedish position was more complex. The might of the Augustana Lutheran Church, which organized orthodox Lutheran religious Swedes in this country in the second half of the century, was placed behind big business and the Republican party:[25] Augustana church leaders in the beginning of our period (1868) implied that "to vote anything but the Republican ticket was sin;"[26] and Carl Swenson, president of Lindsborg's Bethany College, proclaimed at the end of that century that Swedes should "Vote for McKinley and you won't have to repent."[27] When social reform was needed, the Swedish-American clergy pushed one way, the Swedish-American people another.[28] The Swedish-American intelligentsia were also divided. Whereas Carl Swenson in Lindsborg had epitomized the "establishment" end, Mr. S.M. Hill of Wahoo's Luther College (acting president in the Populist-Progressive period) epitomized the intellectual left among Swedes. Hill was a Populist-Socialist who supported the Farmers' Alliance; he opposed the imperialistic intervention of the McKinley administration in Hawaii and Cuba, developed, as he saw it, by the sugar trusts who wanted slave labor; and he admired the laboring class-oriented works of Dickens and regarded Edward Bellamy's Socialist handbook, *Looking Backward,* with respect. In the 1890's, he organized the Luther College faculty for discussion of bimetallism, workmen's insurance laws, and Socialism. He frequently lectured to his students on the theme of Christian Socialism, an activity which he continued until the eve of World War I when the growing chauvinistic atmosphere in Wahoo, Nebraska, appears to have encouraged him to leave.[29]

Whatever the positions of the intelligensia and the clergy, Populism and its offshoots triumphed in many Scandinavian communities. They used cultural expression to organize political sentiments through hoedowns, folksinging, oratorical contests, and the most widely popular adult education form which this section of the country has known—the chautauqua.[30] The folk forms, which in the Scandinavian areas of the Midwest grew out of the movement, have been badly preserved—as have most of the expressive forms which went with Populism. These forms once had a tremendous force in mobilizing people of all ages—in the same way that rock music and Woody Guthrie and Bob Dylan-type lyrics were a force in mobilizing young people in the 1960's.

As Populism was not rooted in a particular ethnic tradition, and as it was by definition "popular," it is difficult to point to specific "high" forms of culture that grow out of Scandinavian midwestern Populism. One possible member of the Populist pantheon is Howard Hanson (though he also belongs to other traditions). As head of the Eastman School of Music in Rochester, New York, Hanson has been, in the eyes of some critics, America's foremost 20th century "romantic" composer and one of its most diligent promoters of orchestral music of all types. He attended Luther College during the Hill period, and has defended his own Wahoo's "small town people's music" as the best possible training for the composer. His own view as to how music is kept alive is, to my mind, parallel to the Populist thinking about social life in general. In his University of Nebraska lectures in the 1950's, he said:

> . . . I like to think of a remark made to me by the great American poet and historian, Carl Sandburg. In speaking of his monumental work on Abraham Lincoln, Mr. Sandburg said, "When I undertake the study of a subject I must become immersed in it." This is more than a casual statement. It is an educational philosophy. To get from an act even a small fraction of its possible contribution it is necessary to become "immersed" in it—in all of it. To get the full and complete meaning of the art of music one should not only hear it but sing it, play it, and if possible write it! . . .
>
> [A]s the knowledge of the history and theory of an art should be accompanied by practical participation, so should participation wherever possible be accompanied by creation. The arts and literature are eventually an outgrowth of the desire of the human mind and spirit to create. It is possible that music may have a more genuine meaning to the man or woman who has created a simple song than to an erudite scholar who has spent his life studying musical paleography. The obscure artist who has painted a few canvases may be closer to the spirit of Raphael than the curator of a great museum who has

never attempted to hold a brush.

There is already too much evidence that we may be in the process of becoming a non-participating, non-creative race. In sports we are increasingly inclined to watch from the side-lines while eighteen hired men bat balls at each other. We set up huge athletic departments in our universities primarily for the sake—or at least so it seems—of producing a winning "team" which can be watched from the side-lines by cheering students and their slightly intellectually younger brothers, the alumni. Even in church we worship God vicariously through the sermon of the minister and the singing of a professional quartet or choir. . . .

In the highest echelon of education, the graduate school, creation is almost non-existent so far as the humanities are concerned. . . . The sciences which might be excused for being statistical are not, but are rather engaged in blazing new paths, making new discoveries, working creatively toward the unveiling of new truths. The humanities, on the other hand, are engaged in counting the number of synonyms in "Paradise Lost" but making no progress toward a paradise regained, the paradise of new beauty as well as new truth.[31]

Notice that Hanson speaks as if the humanities could produce 'paradise regained.' His is a 'popular' paradise. In the quarrel between Sinclair Lewis and Sandburg as to whether main street America in the Midwest in the early 19th century had anything to offer culturally, Hanson took his place firmly beside the Socialist-Populist Sandburg:

It always riles me a little to read the glib accounts of the main streets of the Middle West, for if that little town where I was born [Wahoo] didn't have as much appreciation of good music per square foot as some of our large eastern cities, I should be willing to eat the town, paved streets and all! People who are brought up on Handel, Mozart, Beethoven, Grieg and Lutheran chorales can hardly be musically illiterate.[32]

After the experience of Luther and Wahoo and further education outside Nebraska, Hanson at 26 became the first American composer to win the *Prix de Rome* where he wrote his first symphony, the Nordic, incorporating in the third movement (dedicated "To My Father") the Swedish folk songs which he knew in his childhood and which flourished in the Populist era.[33] His later work does not ignore either the Scandinavian backgrounds or the 'peoples' themes. The Scandinavian theme continues in his "Lament for Beowulf," the "Heroic Elegy," "Vermelande," the other pieces of "The Scandinavian Suite," and the several settings of Swedish folk songs. The 'peoples' theme continues in the "Hymn for the Pioneers," the "Symphony No. 3," the settings for Whitman's democratic poetry, and the 1960's "Song of Human Rights."[34] Hanson says of his music that it "springs from the soil of the American Midwest—music of the plains rather than of the city—reflects something of the broad promise of my native Nebraska."[35]

If this is apparent in the music, it is also apparent in the apologies for music which are full of appeals for the use of folk music, encouragements to the decentralization of power in the arts, and arguments for the development on a wide scale of the participatory, the individual creative, sense, however unspecialized the person. When Hanson attacks musical elitism, the development of music as "big business," and the substitution of records and study for performance and creation, he is actually reflecting a very basic Populist attitude.

To understand the Populist spirit, people are frequently urged to read Ignatius Donnelly and Henry Demarest Lloyd. However, if one wishes to understand the Populist spirit in art, one could do worse than to go to the sources to which Hanson went: the poems of Whitman, Scandinavian "hard times" songs, and the literature of civil rights. One could also go to Mr. Hanson's Third Symphony, his homage to the spiritual contributions made by the people from Sweden who busted sod. One could do worse than resurrect the spirit of such works as part of a Bicentennial celebration genuinely concerned with freedom.

Coops: Cooperation and Grundtvig

Now we are much more likely to associate coops with

Scandinavians than we are to associate revolutions or revolutionary fervor with them. I recall in my childhood the Saturday afternoon at the coop creamery, where the farmers brought in the cream cans, puffed corn cobs, and talked about the weather and whether they ought to keep the same butter maker next year. The scene was peaceful enough. The men knew they owned the place. Like Marxism and Populism, cultural nationalism and 'cooperation' were phenomena significant to the reform movements in all of the Scandinavian groups. The rediscovery of the Norse sagas and epics, the discovery of Norse dramatic religious systems, and the rediscovery by historians of the traditions of law and custom of the pre-Christian Norwegian and Scandinavian peoples (thought to be democratic traditions) awakened in the 19th century north countries a sense that they had a civilization having both antiquity and grandeur. Sweden's cultural nationalists, such as Atterbom, were elitists who looked to older aristocratic forms of Swedish culture. But in Norway, by contrast, Wergeland and Björnson developed a democratic cultural nationalism.[36] In Denmark, Grundtvig developed a movement not only thoroughly popular and democratic, but effective. Grundtvig's movement is the more important form of cultural nationalism for persons working to understand midwestern community building as it leads into the folk schools and coops developed here.

Grundtvig's life story is simple enough: having graduated from the University of Copenhagen, he became a chaplain there (1822) and shortly thereafter made such a fierce attack on rationalism that he was severely censured and forced to resign his position. His middle life was devoted to literary work and the expression of ideas on politics and community building —ideas which were so powerful that in his later life he became a bishop and a member of the Danish House of Parliament.[37] What is interesting about the man is not the life but the ideas: his lifelong search for an alternative to conventional rationalism which would provide him with a basis for building a new Denmark on the wreckage of the old feudal society which he knew to be going to smash. Grundtvig's search began where this essay's search began—with a question of how the pictures in men's minds determine or affect the ways in which they build a world about themselves. He was, from the beginning, interested in the ancient Norse culture and he turned to the Bible and to the old Norse sacred stories for spiritual nourishment (he translated *Beowulf* into modern Danish before it was translated into modern English). As he had a conception of *each country* as having a sacred destiny, as it were, a conception which he derived from the Old Testament picture of the sacred destiny of Israel, his first and abiding hatred was directed toward Rome: its imperialism, melting pot ideology, and worship of power. The emulation of things Roman in nineteenth century European civilization—its 'Roman' emphasis on centralized authority, military might, repressive solutions to human problems—disgusted him. Hating Roman legalistic religion which he saw continuing through the Papacy, Latin-based education, and Roman architecture, law, art and poetry, he juxtaposed against the imperial tradition, in which violence and repression created social order, his own notion of ancient Norse and Hebrew cultures—free spirited, passionate, spirit-filled, and spontaneous. He saw Norse and Hebrew culture as opposed to monopoly power in their conceptions of how land is rightfully held. He saw both cultures as dedicated to the notion of realizing the "God-kingdom" through the use of the tools of the spirit to accomplish reform—through the transforming of the human psyche from within.[38] He also saw Norse literature as embued with cooperative idealism:

> . . . The old [Norse] religion taught an outlook on religion and life in which the dieties came to the help of one another and of man in their struggle with the enemies of gods and men; the struggle between good and evil was personified in the supernatural figures of Loke and Balder; . . . fate under the name Noerne ruled the life of the individual and determined his course; and a living conception of spirit and body gave reality to conscience, dreams, and forebodings.[39]

The job of the community builder was then to liberate the

God-power or "spirit " held in check by conventional institutions, oligarchies, or repressive forms of government, worship, education and social organization. Releasing spiritual power would effect change in the total community—not simply in individuals. Thus, the totality of art was to be a popular matter and to be part of the culture construction or nation-building process. Grundtvig differed from the Populists and Socialists in rooting art and reform in the people's traditions at large in the sacred nation or community—not in a poor people's social class cut off from religious tradition.[40] Education was central to the program. The "folk school" which he first envisaged was to get rid of the academic lecture and Latin learning and of all other archaic academicism. It was to use community problems and the spontaneous desire to learn the Danish vulgar language as a tool for quickening the life sense and the will to learn in people. Universal suffrage based on education was to give expression to the spirit. And business and industrial forms such as the cooperative which every man owned were to externalize the spirit of every man.[41]

Since Grundtvigian ideology began with the hypothesis that new communities are built at the village level, it was particularly appropriate to people who moved into new rural villages in the Midwest. In Denmark and in the United States, Grundtvig's ideology is reflected in the Danish Lutheran Synod which was formed by followers of his (The Danish Evangelical Lutheran Church) and in three secular institutions which took up his ideas: the folk school, the seller's cooperative, and the "plain style" shops which turned out Scandinavian buildings or furnishings based on medieval or contemporary peasant styles. These three streams fit together.[42] Grundtvig's disciples believed that (a) new forms of education are crucial to new forms of community; (b) new economic forms, alternatives to capitalism and feudalism, would grow out of new sorts of education; and (c) new spirit-filled expressive forms would also emerge from a people awakened from Roman tyranny as their spirit disciplined itself through worship, education, and cooperation.

The cooperative is commonly traced by historians of the

movement to Robert Owens and the Rochdale pioneers in England, but the 1840's English cooperatives were retail cooperatives designed to help the consumer get around the wholesaler.[43] On the other hand, the most powerful cooperatives which have emerged in the Midwest have been sellers' cooperatives—farmers' grain elevators, cooperative creameries, and the like. The marketing cooperative, particularly the agriculture marketing cooperative, is a creation of Denmark and of the Grundtvig-Christian Kold folk schools.[44] The folk school-taught yeomanry of Denmark first developed marketing cooperatives around the schools in the 1860's and 70's because the folk schools had taught young adults the economic skills, marketing skills, the agricultural science, and the self-reliance which made coops possible. The schools did not teach cooperation directly. But as the folk schools became strong, so did the coops; the school and coop movement quickly spread to the other Scandinavian countries. In this country it was also spurred on, to a significant degree, by north country immigrants. Unfortunately in the United States, the movement did not achieve the same power. For though the western plains Scandinavian communities had both the folk school and the cooperative, they seldom had both hand in hand.

Though the Grundtvigian Danes' will to remain Danish in culture was fervent, the coops which they founded, or endeavored to found, often faced opposition from more centralized business endeavors. "Big business" often did not like the small coops. Moreover, in the later part of the life of the folk schools, a fairly strong alliance had developed between business and the public schools—at least in their methods for promoting efficient work—an alliance which worked against the integration of peculiarly Danish institutions, particularly in towns which had many cultures and ethnic groups aside from Danes. However intense the pressure against "Danishness" may have been, the Grundtvig Danes moved, in its face, and founded Danish schools for children and folk schools for adults (one located at Dannebrog, Nebraska). These were to allow the peculiar cultural ferment which had been initiated in Denmark to continue. In pushing for Danish schools, F.L. Grundtvig (the son of the founder of the movement who settled at Stanton, Iowa) saw the typical American public school with its melting pot ideology as the "most errant enemy of the Danish people and the Danish church":

> . . . It is too English, not American—its purpose is "first and last to present England as the motherland of America." . . . Much is said in the schools that may easily result in the separation of Danish parents and children and cause these children to look down upon father and mother, who come from the land of rye bread and wooden shoes. . . . [The public school] is "irreligious" and therefore "completely erroneous" because "without God all human life is absurd and spineless"; it is a "prosaic" ("spiritless") one-sided school of knowledge; [moreover], it does not develop character and tends to make the pupils dull.[46]

I believe that F.L. Grundtvig's attacks were directed primarily at—at least, they were most appropriate to—the uprooting centralized public schools in the larger towns which depended on the standardized American textbook and testing industries. As applied to those schools, as contrasted to small rural schools which "the people" did sometimes control, the critique has weight. Its examination of public school's heritage-destroying effects have been independently echoed in later generations by critics of education within almost every group which has been homogenized by those schools, most recently by blacks, Chicanos and Indians. Though the folk school at Dannebrog-Nysted survived until about five years ago, though folk schools survive elsewhere in the Midwest even today, the more important present consequence of their existence may be aspects of the community development and community school movements.

One of the earliest "community schools" in Nebraska—one of the first in the nation—was the community school at Mullen developed by the people of Mullen, working with Walt Beggs and others, with Otto Hoiberg as a consultant.[47] Mr. Hoiberg, himself a product of the folk schools, was also a prime developer of the "community development" movement in this state, and both movements have a distinctly Grundtvigian twist. The important connecting link is Mr. Hoiberg, who until recently held rank at the University of Nebraska in extension and sociology. His father, the Reverend Karl P. Højbjerg, was the president of three Grundtvigian institutions (Nysted Folk School at Dannebrog, Nebraska; Grandview College in Des Moines, Iowa; and Danebod Folk School at Tyler, Minnesota), and he taught his son much that was valuable both in the folk school and in the "community school" and "community development" movements.

As Mr. Hoiberg puts it:

> We ran a curriculum that was not unlike the folk schools of Denmark. There would be a winter term for men or coeducational. During the summer months, there would be a term for girls. The curriculum there ran along sociological lines— economics and politics—and my dad was a great one for history and biography. . . . There are no such things as examinations or credits or diplomas or things of that nature. And there was nothing compulsory, although we assumed that people would come to what went on. . . . Whatever they really did was on a voluntary basis. . . . We were interested not so much in the actual factual knowledge but in whether we were able to give them a stimulus to further investigation and reading or discussion. . . .
>
> The folk schools did not teach cooperation as such; it was not a propaganda agency for coops or anything like that. It was a matter of working with the young men and young women of Denmark and Danish extraction. . . . After a term or two at a folk school, something happened to them in an inner sense. They became alert to the good life—the abundant life spiritually, intellectually. And when they got back home to the communities, they began to see some things that needed to be done. One of the things they hit upon as a way of raising the Danish farmer was the coop movement—also there was a certain fellowship involved . . . I heard about a little episode at the Tyler, Minnesota, folk school last summer. A young

fellow came into a folk school and asked the head of the folk school, "Can you teach me to make good butter?" And the leader said, "No, we can't teach you to make good butter; but I'll tell you one thing: when you leave here, you'll never want to make bad butter again." Now that's the pitch.

In looking back at the whole thing, Grundtvig placed a great deal of emphasis on the fellowship in the congregation— not so much on the individual—Kierkegaard would be along that line. I have drawn a great deal of strength from that concept here in my work with Nebraska communities. This feeling of fellowship, of standing on common ground, having common goals—in other words, the feeling of community— *that* has been central to my work here in Nebraska through the years. There is a direct relationship between what Grundtvig stood for in the religious context and things I have been trying to do here in the community. Let me illustrate with three projects:

First, the one [project] with Walt Beggs and Mullen [Nebraska, the community school project] was conducted at Teachers College, and I dipped into that as a resource.

Second, so far as our community development in university extension, we attempted to make the resources of the intellect available to the communities along the lines of community studies, community planning, community research and so on in any way that the communities needed it: problems of community organization; planning commissions; recreation boards; the setting of goals through discussion and study, etc.

Third, in the last twelve years, much effort has been put into a joint project with the State Department of Economic Development called the Nebraska Community Improvement Program. There are a couple of hundred Nebraska communities involved in that: new sewer systems, cleanup campaigns, programs in the cultural arts. . . .

Each of these has a connection to Grundtvig's educational philosophy. One of the keynotes of the folk school has been the "living word" which can be interpreted as the influence of a teacher on students or other people, a teacher who is really influential to them and helps them gain new insights and motivation to walk on their own. That has been part of my objective in my work with communities. . . . I have been inter-

ested in results along the academic lines or results in terms of
concrete happenings after working with the community. Far
more than that, I have an interest in 'turning on' whomever I
worked with as an educator—getting people to move on their
own steam with their own projects and towards their own
goals. . . . That really is akin to what the folk schools were
about. . . . As time has gone on there has been less emphasis
in Denmark in the folk schools on the lecture system—more
upon study groups, discussion groups, dialogue, personal contact between faculty and students and sometimes trying to
come to some conclusions—get into an action program. I see a
connection between the philosophy of community development and Grundtvig's philosophy of education: you are not
out in the communities of Nebraska telling them what to do or
doing things for them. You are sharing procedures, possibilities, insights. In other words, it is a teaching situation, albeit a
very informal type of thing completely outside the classroom.
The job of the teacher is to lend a hand. . . . The notion is as
relevant to urban centers as to rural: the neighborhood programs developing in Lincoln. You really have the same thing
there . . . people in Belmont or whatever banding together to
improve the economic and cultural life of the neighborhood.

The happiness in the Grundtvigian tradition is a joy of
living; *it's a joy of living!*—and there's nothing wrong in the
Grundtvigian tradition with genuine joy. You need to have a
good time and share things that really make you joyous and
so on. . . . For Grundtvig, man is at his best in the fellowship
of a congregation and in the very nature of the case there is a
strong joyous element.[48]

The "community improvement" programs functioning in
two hundred communities and developed partly by Hoiberg on
the basis of Grundtvig's kind of ideology are obviously influenc-
ing the whole face of Nebraska now. The community school
movement is equally alive—the one in Alliance, Nebraska, in its
second year, has 2,600 adults in its evening classes. In addition,
Emerson, Crete, York and Plattsmouth have programs. In
endeavoring to meet real community need, York recently had a
short course which dealt with coping with death and dying. Yet,

even in our time the community school and community development movements could perhaps profit from some investigation of the spiritual, motivational, and linguistic bases of the educational philosophy of Grundtvig—an investigation which would be useful not only to community development and community school people, but to advocates of alternative economic and cultural forms for community development and alternative forms of education: open classrooms (which are now fairly widely diffused in Nebraska) and culture-based schools, whether those schools begin with the culture of Scandinavians or of other groups.[49]

Unfortunately, as we have mentioned, the folk school and the cooperative did not go hand in hand in this country to the degree that they should have. The Nebraska Grain Dealers Association was perhaps the earliest American grain monopoly to be challenged (1899); the Farmers Elevator movement originated in Nebraska and Iowa, apparently at least partly in Scandinavian areas; and the beef, grain, cream and egg marketing cooperatives which existed in considerable strength in the Midwest and western plains between 1900 and 1940 were concentrated in the states having sizable Scandinavian populations. In many cases, perhaps in most cases, Scandinavian people took leadership roles in forming the early cooperatives, perhaps partly because they had had training in an old country folk school, but mainly because they were able to use coop models which they had experienced in late 19th century Sweden, Norway and Denmark where the cooperative movement was spreading like wildfire and rectifying some of the earlier conditions of economic oppression.[50]

The increasingly centralized American public schools, even those located in fairly small towns, did not function as the folk school did in Scandinavia—as a community, adult education center which fostered the habit of cooperation. This is not surprising. The modern consolidated multi-roomed school, as anthropologists see it, fosters a highly competitive ethos; if it is not surrounded by a community school component and by a phalanx of projects centering in community needs, it very easily becomes a channel for many young people out of the community and its culture and on into large-scale organizations—universities, bureaucracies, larger industries and offices. Similarly, the old small town cooperative, which was a local community institution centered in the processing, storing and wholesale marketing of food and grains, is for the most part gone.[51] Large agribusiness enterprises and corporate cooperatives, such as Associated Milk Producers and Farmland Industries, have been formed, and only recently has there come a major return to the development of small cooperatives.

The return to the small cooperative is founded on reasons similar to those which led to the development of the original small coops. In the inner city, poor people have created cooperatives to feed themselves and to share garden produce; in urban areas, young people have developed coops to get food at cheaper prices, to share community-raised produce, and to assure the quality of the food they purchase. In some rural areas, family farmers concerned with stopping the apparently unstoppable tide of agribusiness have turned again to the sellers' coop as a basis for controlling their own economic destiny. One may hope that this second trial of community educational institutions and of coops will lead to a more complete integration of the alternative institutions to each other, for lacking the sense of nationhood which created the first, the institutions may be fragile in the extreme.

Grundtvig's program for the arts bore fruit. In Denmark, the most prominent buildings inspired by Grundtvig's notions were the Copenhagen Town Hall built by Martin Nyrop and the Grundtvig Memorial Church designed by Jensen Klint.[52] Klint reflects the old bishop's ideology by using admirably the rural folk medieval architecture of Skane in South Sweden and the Danish northern provinces in his later buildings: the step roof, the light or white color, the upward linear sweep, the plain lines of the medieval parish churches are all there. At the same time, the starkness and harmony of Klint's folk-based 1900-1920's buildings suggest the architecture of more recent northern European architects familiar to our time, such as Eliel

Saarinen and Aalto. Anyone looking at Jensen Klint's late 19th century and early 20th century work and the parallel work done in the 1920's by Olaf J. Cervin at Bethphage Mission at Axtell, Nebraska, cannot but perceive the similarity of styles and conceptions. Cervin was influenced by the same medieval architecture of South Sweden and Denmark which had influenced Jensen Klint and appears to have been influenced by Klint himself. He studied the folk country architecture of South Sweden and Denmark, was aware of what was going on in those countries during the period when Jensen Klint was the most powerful architectural voice in the region, and it is hard to believe the similarities between the two architects are an accident.[53] Folk-country church architecture from South Sweden and Denmark and the work of the Grundtvig-Klint school appear also to be reflected in other important Scandinavian buildings in this area: in the old buildings such as Old Main at Luther College (recently burned), Old Main at Dana College, Bethany Church in Lindsborg, Kansas; and in the new buildings, particularly in the buildings lying just outside this area, such as Eliel Saarinen's Christ Lutheran Church in Minneapolis and the Des Moines Art Center, and in a fair number of less distinguished recent buildings in this part of the country which appear to be inspired by Klintian and post-Klintian romantic-modernist Scandinavian notions.

As if by way of footnote, the last, and perhaps the most fashionable surge of Grundtvigian ideology appears with the invention of Danish modern furniture by Kaare Klint, Jensen Klint's son and student—another off-shoot of Scandinavian country culture and of the use of plain things advocated by Grundtvig's folk movement.[54] Though midwestern homes, Scandinavian and non-Scandinavian alike, are full of Danish modern furniture or imitations of it, nothing comparable to Danish modern design has developed in this area so far as I know. In the relatively woodless western plains it is perhaps to be expected that the handling of wood should be relatively undistinguished. An Anton Pierson or a Jes Schmidt becomes an excellent wood sculptor; some fine, early peasant furniture remains, but little enough, perhaps an emblem of the extent to which the different natural environment of this area has pushed people to different artistic and craft tasks.

The Religious Quest: Kierkegaard and the Inner Mission:

Though the plain folk-based style, the folk-based institutions and the communal joy which grew out of the development of Grundtvig style institutions are a real part of Scandinavian —particularly Danish—tradition in this section of the country, there is another side to the Scandinavian presence—the stubborn pietistic side, brooding, melancholy, given over at its most intense to what is sometimes called religious madness. The main fountain of nineteenth century pietistic thinking in Scandinavian countries was perhaps Kierkegaard, through his influence on Wilhelm Beck and the Scandinavian "Inner Mission." Kierkegaard's rejection of the life of pleasure, his refusal of marriage, and his later attack on the enjoyment of sex (sex to him is fallen egoism) foreshadow the demands for temperance and asceticism of the Beck people in Denmark and later of pietists all over Scandinavia: the Hauge people in Norway and the 'Covenanters' in Sweden.[55] All three movements were, like Kierkegaard's life, active against complacent official religion. And all, like Kierkegaard, gave great prominence to the laity. When Kierkegaard was dying, he refused the sacrament from the official clergymen, representatives of a world of hypocrisy and pretense which he hated. He said he would accept such rites only from a lay preacher, and when he was denied these, he died 'unblessed.'[56] However, twenty years after his 1855 death, the frontiers of Sweden, Norway and Denmark were full of lay preachers—democratic men who were performing all sorts of rites of the official church without its official sanction.[57]

The same pietists who brought a mission of teaching and asceticism and mild social reform to the 'wretched of the earth' in Scandinavia also brought some of Kierkegaard's concern for the love of neighbor to their 'charitable' work. Both he and the

later pietists, with their brooding sense of sin and of a direct
relationship with God, had some difficulty articulating a community vision. As one critic of Kierkegaard has put it, a man
alone with God finds it hard to be with anyone else. Kierkegaard's only explanations of community come in his explanations of neighbor love:

> In the love of neighbor, I no longer treat him as a distant
> third party or as a means to my own happiness but as a fellow
> person . . . to whom I must respond with all that is most
> intimate and personal in me, [substituting] the egotistic and
> ruthless 'mine and thing' for a 'mine and thine' based upon
> common sharing and helping.[58]

This conception of 'sharing and helping' was most easily expressed through the reformed human services institutions
developed by the Inner Mission under the influence of Kierkegaard's disciple, Beck.[59]

Actually, the Inner Mission at first grew up outside Scandinavia. First headed and really developed as an international
movement by Germans in the first half of the 19th century, it
grew to maturity in a Germany which had experienced the
massive hopes which grew up with the Napoleonic exportation
of the French Revolution and the frustration of those hopes in
the continuation of industrial oppression in cities such as
Hamburg. Its German program, more activist than anything
Kierkegaard envisaged, was a two-stepped one: first, it wished
to stop the immediate suffering of the poor, the starving, the
sick, etc. and to organize them into model Christian communities; second, it wished to attack the problems inherent in the
industrial institutions which caused the suffering among the
wretched of the earth. The disaffected were to be attracted to
the new Christian culture through teaching and through the
unselfish care which was extended to them whether they were
railroad workers, prostitutes, seamen, immigrants, journeymen,
alcoholics, or whatever. One of the most notable of the institutions was that for epileptics founded at Bielefeld by Franz
von Bodelschwingh, the second head of the Inner Mission in

Germany. As the "outcasts of the world" were organized into model Christian communities, they were to start the ferment which would move in the direction of a new Christian society. The second stage of the Inner Mission was to have been a restructuring of society at large. (Unfortunately, the second stage, the mobilization of people to create a new society, was too easy to put off and was put off until World War II when 'demonic' Nazism with its euthanasia plans threatened to disrupt the very institutions Inner Mission had created. After World War II—too late—the Inner Mission turned to social reform.)

The Inner Mission came to be a powerful force in Denmark, Sweden and Norway, where it fell under Kierkegaardian influence. It is possible to trace the history of a number of significant institutions in the western plains in relation to the Scandinavian Inner Mission movement—Dana College, the pietistic wing of the Danish Church, part of the Swedish Covenant Church, the Haugian Norwegian Church, and Bethphage Mission.[61] Clearly the Inner Mission, as it came to Scandinavia and was affected by the theology of Kierkegaard and Beck, became a more inward-looking movement—one more concerned with Kierkegaardian "works of love" and one all too at ease with the injustices of the old order. Of the Inner Mission communities built in this part of the country, Bethphage Mission, founded by William Dahl as a place for epileptics in Axtell, Nebraska, is perhaps the most interesting in that it illustrates how Scandinavian and German "Inner Mission" ideology was used to build good human service communities.

Dahl, the founder, was the pattern pietist. He was, in the words of his son, "something of a rebel in his early life," having left Sweden to get away from the draft. As a youth, he had little interest in religion until he heard some Swedish hymn singing in an eastern city, which "called him to God." Shortly thereafter he experienced the pattern "conversion." He went to the seminary and came to hold a position in Omaha in the early 1900's where he worked with people who were put in the Omaha jail. Among those placed in the jail were epileptics imprisoned as common criminals. Dahl, having been influenced by Scandinavian Inner Mission ideology, saw the epileptics in the same light which European Inner Mission people had seen them—not as criminals, but as human beings having a potential for dignity and for creating their own sort of self-respecting community. He determined to do something about them. After studying the writings of von Bodelschwingh (which he translated from English into Swedish for Nebraska audiences), he visited the colonies for the epileptics which Bodelschwingh had founded at Bielefeld, and upon his return to the United States, he founded Bethphage Mission as a community for the epileptics organized along Bodelschwinghian Inner Mission lines.[62] At Bielefeld's Bethel Colony, Dahl saw a new mode of treating epileptics which accorded them dignity and a modicum of self-sufficiency:

> By far the largest and most successful effort in behalf of epileptics is Bethel, near Bielefeld, Westphalia, fitly termed "A Colony of Mercy." . . . The good pastor von Bodelschwingh, at the beginning of the work, seeking for some means to provide for epileptics, issued an appeal to the mothers of Germany for a thank-offering for each perfect child born to them. The pennies came showering in, and among them two from a sorrowing mother, who gave thanks for two infants gathered safely in the arms of "Him who loveth children." . . .
>
> Begun in the autumn of 1867 with 3 patients, at the close of its seventh year it [Bethel] report[ed] a list of 144; having received in that time 450 patients. Adding house to house and land to land, enlarging operations as experience and necessity indicated, it stands today a model village which, with its outlying farm and park-lands, provides every convenience for its large population. . . .
>
> . . . [It] provid[ed] for the homeless a home, for the sick hospitals—from which also remedies are sent all over the world, benefiting it is estimated over 50,000 persons—and for the hopeless and despondent that greatest of all panaceas, work, more than 20 different trades and avocations being pursued, exclusive of those of the household; 6 pastors and 12 physicians are in charge.[63] *(From an early 20th Century account.)*

Dahl developed the Bielefeld model at Bethphage; the new way asked that the epileptic learn a craft, be to a maximum degree self-supporting, and enter into the local community to the degree possible. The products of the community were sold through a sort of cooperative.

The difference between Bielefeld and the Bethphage Mission and the normal practice of incarcerating epileptics is as great as the difference between a community psychology center with out-patient placement and a snake pit. Indeed, it seems probable that the 19th century community treatment of epileptics is one of the main sources for modern community psychology ideas. Dahl took the Bielefeld concept and like concepts developed by the Scandinavian Inner Mission and, using his own intense energy and ingenuity, created an interesting architectural complex and a rehabilitation community supported by a farm, crafts and industry.

Oldtimers today can remember vividly how Dahl went from house to house, parish to parish, to raise the money to make concrete his vision of a community for epileptics. But Dahl's attitudes have not been extended further among plains Scandinavians. We have not reached out to apply, to the imprisoned, the poor, the unemployed, the concept that to live with dignity, men and women must live in communities and have available both the skills and the material resources requisite to supporting themselves and taking pride in their craft. We also have not begun the Inner Mission State II, the reform of the conditions which create poverty—perhaps partly because we have been so heavily under the influence of Kierkegaard's sort of vision of the religious quest as a lonely private quest in which the sense of the social either does not exist at all or is made by God.

Kierkegaard and the Subjective Visioning in this Country

In fact, Kierkegaard and his tradition are the hardest to handle in any account of Scandinavian community building.

His type are the kind that tear communities apart in the name of some distant "Truth" which they claim to possess, some inner voice absolute for them and madness for the rest of us. And, yet, it is hard to believe that the thinker who exercised a crucial influence on Ibsen, Sartre, Auden, Updike, Tillich and Barth—on reformers and literary men of all stripes—had nothing to say which found an echo in how Scandinavians of his century built or took apart their communities here.[64] Certain it is that the pietists tore many communities apart both in the old country and on the frontier.[65] But the "vision" at whose behest they tore things apart is best approached through the literature of the "individual" as over against the community set down by three Scandinavians who had important reading audiences with people who knew the Scandinavian languages: Kierkegaard himself, and his "disciplies," Ibsen and Rölvaag.

Kierkegaard is known to philosophy as the thinker who more perfectly than anyone before or since described urban villageless man's isolation and made that isolation, even the religious madness which may go with it, a final reality. By rejecting all speculative thought and focussing only on such "thinking" as is felt in the private self and acted out totally by the inner and outer person, Kierkegaard became the model of "existentialist commitment" or "radical isolation." His vision of man as finally, a creature alone, living in a world radically separated from God, shipwrecked in a fallen creation which made worship seem either like madness or the sublimest sanity, left no room for a social vision beyond the "works of love" such as Grundtvig possessed. Even survival or the wish to survive might be sin: "Flesh and blood and spirit are opposites; [what 'spirit' means] is being free to will that which flesh and blood must shrink from . . . from dying, and most of all from the death throes."

This sense of radical isolation, of a willingness—perhaps a necessity—to die or to sacrifice one's own for one's inner voice is dramatized in Kierkegaard's Abraham. Of him, Kierkegaard writes that from the perspective of conventional ethics, when he takes Isaac, the sticks and the knife to the hill, he is "about to murder Isaac" but from the perspective of religion, he is "about to sacrifice Isaac." Humanly speaking, Abraham "is mad and cannot make himself intelligible to anyone."[67] Indeed, virtually all of Kierkegaard's "Knights of Faith" are madmen when seen from time and "saints" when seen from eternity.

This extreme reliance on what the private self, which may echo "God" or "Truth," tells one, comes up over and over in the writing of Henrik Ibsen, one of Kierkegaard's best students.[68] Over and over in Ibsen's plays, the central figure is some intense, self-conscious person who has an inner voice and who sets himself over against the community in the name of his voice until he tears himself and the community apart. The first, and perhaps the best, of these Ibsenian heroes is Brand, who first has to subdue himself to working in a humble setting rather than trying to bring the world to his revival meeting. Once having adopted the ascetic discipline of the rural preacher, he, like Abraham, offers up his miserly mother for her miserliness, his child to his love of his congregation, his wife to his ascetic will to forego mourning, and all other natural longing. As a pastor, he does not build a church which he had wanted to build because he knows that the edifice will satisfy "flesh" rather than "spirit." He tries to make his flock see his vision, but it cannot. When he sees it fully by himself, all he sees is a troll's "Ice Kirk" in which his dead wife tells him to forget his vision, a troll girl sees him as crucified and calls him savior, and he sees himself as having selfishly constructed himself as a god for himself and others. At the end, he calls on God as love and is forgiven; the church melts and destroys him. To survive, for Brand, is to live in such impurity of action as denies the spirit of his vision; to die is to be wholly alive.

Patriarchs and saints, Abrahams and Brands, seem to have little to do with Swedes or Norwegians or Danes in our Nebraska (except that all had a reputation for being stubborn and many suffered "religious melancholy"). However, Ole Rölvaag was powerfully under the influence of Ibsen's Brand throughout his life.[69] He took from Kierkegaard his notions of the central place in the work of great writers of a capacity to set down the detail of subjective insight.[70] From both Kierkegaard and Ibsen he took, I think, the notions of the conflict between the demands of survival and community, on the one hand, and the demands of an intense subjective vision of Truth or God, on the other. In Beret Holm, he creates another Brand or another Kierkegaard's Abraham. The usual reading of Beret's role in *Giants in the Earth, Peder Victorious,* and *Their Father's God* is that she is a madwoman driven so by the hardships of frontier life—one who, on the recovery of her sanity, gradually accommodates to the new life on the frontier so long as she has a church around. But it is also possible to see her as like the "knights of faith" in Ibsen or Kierkegaard. She comes to the new world having been told that it will be the holy land—Canaan, the land of milk and honey.[71] She comes carrying with her a Kierkegaardian pietism and a reverence for old world beliefs which to her are absolute and to others are mere conveniences for understanding a world—to be cast aside when that world is left behind. Her husband's resetting the boundary posts reveals to her, in a little concrete deed, the intense survival instincts and the communal willingness to violate what custom and her inner voice tell her are right which the frontier arouses in men.[72] Then, the natural plagues come as if to reveal that these survival instincts may not be blessed, that the new land may not be Zion, but the very Egypt which people thought they had left. She retreats to a religious center where she is alone with her God, and at the voice of that God she sacrifices her husband, her own sexuality, her relationship to her son and daughter-in-law, and finally her "official religion" (by performing a lay baptism).[73] Even her husband's survival and her own appear to mean little to her. From one perspective, she is a mad and repressive old woman. From another she is the only person in the novel who is a "knight of faith," the only Abraham for whom the journey can, in Kierkegaardian terms, be seen as a journey urged by *Their Father's God.*[74]

Toward the end of *Their Father's God,* Reverend Kaldahl speaks a speech which might, but for a few phrases, be the merest Rotarian rhetoric: "What do we want today? . . . we cast on the scrap heap the noblest traditions of our race. We set higher value on apeing strange manners and customs than on guarding our God-given heritage. . . . God's command to his people of old means nothing to us."[7][5] Beret Holm is moved by the speech. The difference between Rölvaag's Beret Holm and the rest of the immigrants in the novel is that the land itself, material conquest, Canaan as a rich place, mean nothing to her. Canaan is only Canaan to her, as to Abraham, if it is made so by a "God-given command" which she personally has heard. Therein lies her madness, her difference from Peder and Per Hansa who are more the Grundtvigians, interested in survival, community, and "God-given" joys here. Therein lies the basis for her antagonism to the melting pot public school and the rest of the modern world, and her similitude to Abraham. She sees in the intractable plains and the new world social phenomena, the emblem of a world radically separated from God, a fallen creation in which she and those about her are shipwrecked.

Rölvaag does not say she is right in holding to her vision. He suggests that she *may* be right. The *Giants in the Earth* of the title of the first novel are clearly the trolls of misdirection of purpose and natural disaster which threaten to undo the Scandinavian exodus, and these trolls are identified with the "giants in the earth" of Genesis, 6:4, giants which are traditionally figures for greed and the useless quest for power in Scandinavian lore from *Beowulf* on down.[7][6] Neither Peder nor Per Hansa are greedy or gross men, and yet, from Beret's perspective, their very quest for survival raises the specter that the quest is false. Thus Rölvaag raises the possibility that our whole hundred-year-and-more journey to Canaan may have led us further into Egypt.

These then are the ideologies which we have: Populism, cooperation and pietism, and with them their expressive forms and their artists. All are the efforts of poor men to make some meaning, perhaps to assert some control, over their lives. Each meant a good bit to a large number of ordinary people when we first came. Each died or drastically changed its content, perhaps most noticeably in the period of the massive mobilization of chauvinism and melting pot sentiment during World Wars I and II.

Summary

It would have been possible to have made this chapter a different sort of chapter. One could have concentrated on how European traditions of high culture, developed in the romantic period, were transmitted by Scandinavians to this country through emigrant artists—how Zorn's sort of Swedish hedonistic impressionism was transformed by Sandzen and his school at Lindsborg to a more ascetic solid style; how Milles worked here and in Sweden and founded a school of American sculpture; how Hanson picked up on Grieg and Carl Nielsen.[77] But that would have made the chapter one in the history of style. One could also have made the chapter an undifferentiated chapter in the history of folk art and celebration—the festivals at Stromsburg and Osceola, the Norwegian folk art developed at Decorah, Iowa, the woodcarvers at Lindsborg and Wahoo, and elsewhere, the painted Dalecarlian horses which grace many a midwestern house, the heritage of fine food which had to be modified in the almost fishless plains—lutefisk and potato sausage, lingenberries and ostkaka. But to have recited this heritage would have been to have recited a heritage which had little to do with the unique things that Scandinavians in Europe and in this country did as they sought to create new model communities with the dissolution of the old regime. It would not have touched on what we can learn from them.

The Scandinavians who came to this country came as their countries were being touched—barely touched—by the liberal revolutions, the French and the American. The ideology of freedom as it developed in those countries was not predominantly Lockian or individualistic. The Scandinavian ideologies, apart from the Kierkegaardian, generally sought reform or change which had some communal, some corporate, expression: the folk school, the Inner Mission, the Farmer's Alliance, the Populist chapter, the congregation. The Scandinavians who came were stubborn plain people, and they created stubborn plain corporate institutions which gave rise to people's art which went with that spirit: the hymn, the folk song, Howard Hanson's Populist music; the plain brick work and wood of the plains Grundtvigian architects and their present day successors; the hard lines of Sandzen's painting and Milles' sculpture; Scandinavian modern furniture and plain folk furniture; the brooding pietistic stubbornness of an Ole Rölvaag refusing to assimilate and calling on his people "to serve their Father's God." The early Scandinavians provided for twentieth century persons, through the cooperative and folk school especially, developed models of ordinary people's communities where self-sufficiency and interdependency both were possible. Unfortunately, the small institutions so created were too soon swallowed up in bigger institutions seemingly required by the 'maximum growth' of the economy in the last forty years.[78] Education was separated from economic institutions, and the identification with poverty and social change of the early Scandinavian immigrants was lost, particularly during World War I as the Scandinavian languages were wiped out as public languages and a unique culture came unravelled.

In the over fifty years since the first world war, the sons and daughters of people who came to this section of the country seeking Salem have come to be, like Matthew Arnold's Socrates, "Terribly at ease in Zion." A group of visions was lost as our sleep came on. They were good visions. The Scandinavians who hoped to leave behind the harsher aspects of urban 19th century industrial capitalism and rural feudalism, who hated compulsory military service and a hierarchical society, soon grew to be comfortable with each of those institutions here. Third generation Scandinavians in this country have produced no explorers of the anguish of the soul in compromise, the folly of selling out, comparable to Ibsen and Kierkegaard in the old country or Rölvaag in this. We have ourselves become the compromisers, insensitive to the reasons for which our ancestors came and casting whatever Exodus treasures we had on the scrap heap. The vision which formed a few good institutions is still possible to us—the visions behind the small coop, the folk school, the Inner Mission rehabilitative community, and the Populist units. Plain furniture, the plain line in architecture, plain good faith and plain talk may still be possible to most of us even if the wildness of Beret's or Brand's or Kierkegaard's leaps into full existence is not.

FOOTNOTES

1. Dorothy Burton Skårdal, *The Divided Heart* (Lincoln: The University of Nebraska Press, 1974), pp. 87-107, 147-86, 187-222, 334-35: "Some [immigrants] felt it [the immigration experience] a challenge; . . . some felt permanently scarred or crippled by their experience; most fell somewhere in between," p. 335.

2. Interview with Mona Pers, University of Uppsala, 1974. Ms. Pers was completing her doctorate on Willa Cather and visited Scandinavian communities in Nebraska while doing this. One evidence of "continuity" among the immigrants, particularly among the Swedes, is the persistence of Lutheranism among a very high proportion of third-generation Scandinavians. Sweden, on the other hand, has the least proportion of "believers in God" of any western European country (about 40 percent according to a recent poll).

3. Cf. Skårdal, pp. 82-83.

4. Karl A. Olsson, *By One Spirit* (Chicago: The Covenant Press, 1962), p. 36.

5. Ingvar Andersson, *A History of Sweden,* trans. by Carolyn Hannay (New York: Praeger, 1956), p. 364.

6. Skårdal, pp. 53-57.

7. In the 1830's and 40's, "the staple drink was *brännvin,* a fiery liquor distilled from grain and potatoes and of high alcoholic proof. The per capita consumption of *brännvin* soared to 50 liters per year. . . . It was . . . given as a pacifier to infants." Olsson, p. 40. Cf. Ernst Newman, *Nordskanska Vackelserorelser under 1800-talet* (Lund, 1925), p. 133.

8. Interview with Reuben C. Olson, February, 1976.

9. Stewart Oakley, *A Short History of Denmark* (New York: Praeger, 1972), pp. 152-79.

10. Oakley, p. 196.

11. Andersson, pp. 296-337, esp. pp. 330-34; cf. pp. 357-58. Sweden created the first written constitution in Europe in 1809; however, this had limited effect.

12. T. K. Derry, *A Short History of Norway* (London: Allen and Unwin, 1968), pp. 164-66, 175-76, 232. Thrane formed something like "cooperatives" during the short period (1848 to 1851) when his group caught the imagination of the poor in Oslo and throughout Norway.

13. Derry, pp. 173-93.

14. Skårdal, pp. 187-223. Cf. James Iverne Dowie, *Prairie Grass Dividing* (Rock Island: Augustana Historical Society, 1959), pp. 1-23, 131-78; see also John R. Kleinschmidt, "The Political Behavior of the Bohemian and Swedish Ethnic Groups in Nebraska, 1884-1900" (unpublished Master's Thesis, University of Nebraska, 1968), *passim.* The distinction between "Yankees" and "Scandinavians" was a common distinction in mixed towns (cf. Skårdal, *passim*); my grandfather, Andrew Olson, even perceived mixed Indian-white families living in Bancroft, Nebraska, as "Yankees" and part of the ruling caste. This phrase "it treated horses better than it treated men" was used by Andrew Olson of Wausa, Nebraska, but I have also heard it from other old timers.

15. Robert L. Wright, *Swedish Emigrant Ballads* (Lincoln: University of Nebraska Press, 1965), pp. 45-48.

16. Most of these names are taken from Charles F. Sandahl's *The Nebraska Conference* (Rock Island: Augustana Book Concern, 1931), *passim,* and Ruth Bergin Bildt and others, *The Smoky Valley in After Years* (Lindsborg, 1919).

17. The best discussions of Rölvaag's use of the Egyptian and Canaan metaphors are to be found in Paul Reigstad, *Rölvaag: His Life and Art* (Lincoln: University of Nebraska Press, 1972), p. 122, and in Theodore Jorgenson and Norma O. Solum, *Ole Edvart Rölvaag* (New York: Harper and Brothers, 1939), pp. 265-66, 413-25. For Rölvaag's connections to Nebraska, see Jorgenson and Solum, pp. 65-81, 145-46; Carlton Qualey, *Norwegian Settlements in the United States* (New York: Arno, 1970), put all north Nebraska Missouri River Norwegian settlements in *Giants* country.

18. One of the best accounts of *Den Nye Tid* and of the activities of Louis Pio and Marcus Thrane in Chicago and across the Midwest is found in Leola Marjorie Bergmann, *Americans from Norway* (Philadelphia: Lippincott, 1950), pp. 189-94.

19. Andersson, pp. 391 ff; Oakley, pp. 196, 238 and *passim;* Derry, p. 165, 190, 191, 229-35; and Olsson, *passim.* Olsson traces out the degree to which pietists in Scandinavia initiated the move toward democratization but were not able to support the industrial masses in strikes or other drastic moves and so lost the initiative with them to secular Socialism (Olsson, *passim,* but see especially pp. 504, 505 and 764.)

20. Cf. Kleinschmidt, *passim;* cf. David Trask, "The Nebraska Populist Party" (unpublished Ph.D. Dissertation, University of Nebraska, 1971), *passim.* Trask demonstrates that ethnicity was not a crucial feature for all Scandinavians. Some predominantly Scandinavian communities

remained Republican through the Populist and Progressive years. Esther Lindgren, whose parents were Republican, remembers the Populist years well. She says that, while numerous Swedish farmers in the Malmo, Nebraska, area became Populists, her father only remarked that "empty barrels make the most noise."

21. Christopher Lasch, *The Agony of the American Left* (New York: Random House, 1966), pp. 1-31.

22. Norman Pollack, *The Populist Mind* (New York: Bobbs-Merrill, 1967), p. 456. Peter H. Argersinger traces the systematic efforts of establishment groups to eliminate Socialist doctrine from Populist platforms and to force it into the racist posture of the other parties, *Populism and Politics* (Lexington: University of Kentucky Press, 1974).

23. Lasch, pp. 6-8.

24. Jon Wefald, *A Voice of Protest* (Northfield: The Norwegian American Historical Association, 1971), *passim*, esp. pp. 18-72.

25. Cf. Kleinschmidt, *passim;* cf. Dowie, pp. 172 ff.

26. Dowie, p. 172.

27. Dowie, p. 172.

28. Cf. Kleinschmidt, *passim.*

29. Dowie, pp. 165-78. Esther Lindgren, who knew Hill, told me that she thought that Hill's interest in redistributing the wealth came out of his incredibly poverty-stricken childhood.

30. The best account of the Populist educational programs which I have seen does not concern a Scandinavian county; cf. Annabel Beal, "The Populist Party in Custer County" (unpublished Ph.D. Dissertation, University of Nebraska, 1965), *passim.*

31. Howard Hanson, *Music in Contemporary Civilization* (Lincoln: University of Nebraska Press, 1951), pp. 43-44.

32. Joseph Machlis, *American Composers of Our Time* (New York: Thomas Y. Crowell, 1963), p. 64.

33. Cf. Machlis, p. 67, for Hanson's indebtedness to Scandinavian tradition; see Milton Cross, *Encyclopedia of the Great Composers* (New York: Doubleday, 1969), I, p. 448.

34. All of Howard Hanson's compositions until 1940 are listed in Martha Alter, "Howard Hanson," *Modern Music* (New York: The League of Composers, 1940), pp. 84 ff. For other discussions of Hanson's music, see Machlis, pp. 63 ff. Carl Nielsen (1863-1931) is the modern Scandinavian composer most like Hanson; cf. John Hy. Yoell, *The Nordic Sound: Explorations into The Music of Denmark, Norway, and Sweden* (Boston: Crescendo Publishing Co., 1974). For Hanson's *Song of Human Rights*

(UN-HRO cantata), first performed December 10, 1963, see N. Slonimsky, *Music Since 1900* (New York: Scribners, 1971), p. 1172.

35.   Milton Cross, *Encyclopedia of Great Composers* (New York: Doubleday, 1953), pp. 349-50.

36.   For Atterbon, see Andersson, pp. 325 ff; for Wergeland and Björnson, see Elias Bredsdorff *et al.*, *An Introduction to Scandinavian Literature* (Westport: Greenwood Press, 1970), pp. 128-44. Wergeland's daughter was also a poet, historian, and persecuted feminist who taught at the University of Wyoming in her mature years. For an account of Björnson's 1880 visit to the Midwest and the anger which his unorthodox religious notions awakened in Norwegian clergy, read Bergmann, pp. 191 ff and throughout.

37.   The most interesting accounts of Grundtvig which I have found are Ernest D. Nielsen, *N.F.S. Grundtvig: An American Study* (Rock Island: Augustana Book Concern, 1955); Anders Norgaard, *Grundtvigianismen* (Copenhagen: Kirkeligt Sanfunds Forlag, 1936), 3 vols.; and Kaj Thaning, *N.F.S. Grundtvig*, trans. by David Hohnen (New York: Det Danske Selskob, 1972). I have also profited from conversations with Otto Hoiberg and correspondence with Ernest Nielsen and Johs. Knudsen. Both are translating Grundtvig at Grandview College in Des Moines. Nielsen writes: "Whether the majority of the immigrants were conscious of any community-building ideology, strictly Danish, is, in my opinion, a very mute question. It is correct to say that those who were influenced in their youth by attending the folk schools either in Denmark or the U.S.A. were definitely historically oriented. And their teachers—at least the brightest among them—saw the relevancy of history to the contemporary scene." Thaning is particularly useful for his comparisons between Grundtvig and Marx, Kierkegaard, and the conventional nineteenth century liberals.

38.   Nielsen, pp. 13-63.

39.   Nielsen, p. 16.

40.   Thaning, pp. 72-73, and both Thaning and Nielsen, *passim.* For the contrast with Marxist thought, see Thaning, pp. 117-19, 135-38, 160-76.

41.   Thaning, pp. 160-76.

42.   Thaning, pp. 160-76.

43.   Ewell P. Roy, *Cooperatives Today and Tomorrow* (Danville: Interstate, 1964), p. 71; Owen's scheme was more communal or socialistic than was that of the Rochdale Pioneers.

44.   The most useful account which I have found of the Grundtvig-

Christian Kold style cooperatives which grew up around the folk schools is found in Peter Manniche, *Denmark: A Social Laboratory* (Oxford: Oxford University Press, 1939), pp. 70-73, 74-135.

45. Raymond Callahan, *Education and the Cult of Efficiency* (Chicago: University of Chicago Press, 1962), *passim,* traces out the process whereby business and the public schools formed an alliance based on trying to create efficient all-alike workers. The resistance to this homogenization in the Scandinavian communities is described by Rölvaag in *Peder Victorious,* a resistance somewhat like that found in the Boston Irish [cf. Michael Katz, *Class, Bureaucracy and Schools* (New York: Praeger, 1971)].

46. Paul Nyholm, *The Americanization of the Danish Lutheran Churches in America* (Minneapolis: Institute for Danish Church History, 1963), pp. 233-34.

47. For a brief discussion of the community school at Mullen and related later Nebraska community-based experimental work in education, see Mal Provus, *The Grand Experiment: A Life and Death of the TTT Project* (Berkeley: McCutchan, 1975), pp. 85-122.

48. Interview with Mr. Hoiberg, February, 1976.

49. A listing of efforts to create community culture-based institutions in Nebraska was prepared by this author for the Alternatives for Small Communities Conference held in October, 1975 (available from the author of this article).

50. H. Clyde Filley, *Cooperation in Agriculture* (London: John Wiley, 1929), pp. 45-66; Joseph Knapp, "From the Ground Up," *Farmers in Business* (Washington: AIC, 1963), pp. 205-09. Several of the histories of cooperation observe that producer cooperatives emerged first and most strongly in the states settled heavily by Scandinavians: Wisconsin, Minnesota, North Dakota, South Dakota and Nebraska. Cooperation grew up where the Farmers Alliance was strong, which tended to be the Scandinavian sections [cf. Joseph G. Knapp, *The Rise of American Corporate Enterprise* (Danville: Interstate, 1969), I, pp. 4-68]. The Land O'Lakes Coops show a high proportion of Scandinavian directors [Kenneth Ruble, *Men to Remember* (Chicago: Lakeside, 1947), pp. 309-15]. Cattle breeding coops were originated in Denmark and imitated here; revolving fund coops have the same history [Louis P.F. Smith, *The Evolution of Agricultural Cooperation* (Oxford: Blackwell, 1961), pp. 465, 154-55]. Interestingly, Danish cooperation was also influenced by American coop work in the 19th century (Knapp, I, p. 460). This is not to say that so multifaceted a movement as the cooperation does not have many sources in

many lands.

51. For a hostile account of centralization in agriculture, including the coops, see Grant McConnell, *The Decline of Agrarian Democracy* (Berkeley: University of California Press, 1953). Some critics have argued, however, that some coops cannot survive in a 'big corporation' milieu.

52. For Grundtvig's influence on the expressive and planning arts, see Thaning, pp. 160-76, esp. 164-66; Carl Laurin, *et al. Scandinavian Art* (New York: Scandinavian-American Foundation, 1922), pp. 429-34; Thomas Paulsson, *Scandinavian Architecture* (Newton: Branford, 1959), pp. 203-04. The artistic credo of the Klint school and many of its buildings are illustrated in Kay Fisker, *et al., Modern Danish Architecture* (London: Benn, 1927), esp. pp. 5-IX.

53. For Olaf Cervin, Arthur A. Christenson, *Miracle of the Prairies* (Axtell: Bethphage Press, 1944), p. 26. That Cervin had studied Grundtvigian architecture carefully is evident from his essay on Martin Nyrop's Copenhagen City Hall ["The City Hall at Copenhagen," *Architectural Record*, XVIII (1905), pp. 283-99]. He also studied the Norwegian slave churches (*Architectural Record*, XX, pp. 93-102) and those in Sweden (*American Architecture and Building News*, LXXXVIII, pp. 91-95).

54. For Kaare Klint, see Tobias Faber, *New Danish Architecture* (New York: Praeger, 1968), pp. 12, 176; Esbjørn Hiort, *Nyere Dansk Bygningkunst* (Copenhagen: Gjellerups Forlag, 1949), pp. 14-18.

55. Joseph Thompson, *Kierkegaard* (New York: Knopf, 1973), p. 210. "As the nerve filaments be under the nail, so human egoism is concentrated in the sexual relation, the propagation of the species, the giving of life. . . . The Fall is the satisfaction of this egoism—and this is where the history of temporality properly begins. . . ."

56. Thompson, pp. 231-34.

57. Cf. Olsson, *By One Spirit, passim.*

58. Cf. James Collins, *The Mind of Kierkegaard* (Chicago: Regnery: 1953), p. 199. For Kierkegaard's opinion of Grundtvig (he regarded him as sort of a facile humanist), see *The Present Age*, trans. by Dru and Lowrie (New York: Oxford University Press, 1940), pp. 32-33, and *The Point of View*, trans. by Walter Lowrie (New York: Oxford University Press, 1939), p. 88.

59. For a useful introduction to Beck, see Christian Sørensen, *Vilhelm Beck* (Copenhagen: O. Lohse, 1913).

60. The accounts of the origins of the Inner Mission and of Bodelschwingh are from J.B. Paton, *The Inner Mission;* John Henry Wichern (1808-81) originated the two stage program and was Bodelschwingh's

predecessor.

61.   A good account of Dana College's relationship to the Inner Mission is contained in William E. Christensen, *Saga of the Tower* (Blair, Nebraska: Lutheran Publishing House, 1959). For the Covenants, see Olsson, *op. cit.*

62.   Interview with William G. Dahl's son, Professor Samuel Dahl of Nebraska Wesleyan University, 1975.

63.   Martin W. Barr, *Mental Defectives: Their History, Treatment, and Training* (Philadelphia: P. Blakiston's Son, 1904), p. 47.

64.   E.g. for Sartre on Kierkegaard, see "The Singular Universal" in *Between Existentialism and Marxism* (London: NLB, 1974); W.H. Auden, "A Preface to Kierkegaard," *New Republic*, CX (1944), pp. 683-86; John Updike, "The Fork," *The New Yorker* (February 26, 1966), pp. 115-34; Paul Tillich, "Existential Philosophy," *Journal of the History of Ideas*, V (1944), pp. 44-70.

65.   Esther Lindgren remarked that the hardest days in the frontier Swedish communities were not the days of grasshoppers or drouth but the days when the pietists came through "and turned people around" and divided the community. My father tells the story of the relation between pietists and Lutherans in one town; the pietist pastor is said to have said, "The devil stands on the very threshold of the Lutheran church;" the Lutheran to have said, "I would rather see my daughter dead than attending the Lutheran church."

66.   Kierkegaard's papers, quoted in Josiah Thompson, *Kierkegaard*, p. 212. Again Kierkegaard wrote, "The purpose of life is to be brought to the highest degree of disgust with life." Thompson, p. 215.

67.   Soren Kierkegaard, *Fear and Trembling,* trans. by Walter Lowrie (Princeton: Princeton University Press, 1968), preface by "Johannes de Silentio."

68.   The extent of Kierkegaard's influence on Ibsen has been disputed since Ibsen sometimes denied it (Ibsen was notorious for denying "debts"). The clergyman, Lammers, after whom the character "Brand" is modelled was a Kierkegaardian [M.C. Bradbrook, *Ibsen the Norwegian* (London: Chatto and Windus, 1948), p. 43; cf. pp. 43-53]. Many of Ibsen's friends in Bergen and on the continent were Kierkegaardian (Magdalene Thoreson to priest Christopher Bruun, etc.) and Ibsen frequently uses language and characters identical with Kierkegaard's. Cf. Michael Meyer, *Ibsen—A Biography* (New York: Doubleday, 1971), pp. 175-77.

69.   For Rölvaag's interest in Brand, see Paul Reigstad, *Rölvaag: His Life and Art* (Lincoln: University of Nebraska Press, 1972), pp. 33,

35. Cf. Theodore Jorgenson and Nora O. Solum, *Ole Edvart Rölvaag: A Biography* (New York: Harper, 1934), pp. 271-73.

70. For Rölvaag's interest in Kierkegaard, see Jorgenson and Solum, pp. 312-13. For Rölvaagian parallels to Kierkegaard, see Jorgenson and Solum, pp. 147 ff, 199, 205.

71. Ole E. Rölvaag, *Giants in the Earth* (New York: Harper, 1927), p. 39.

72. Cf. Rölvaag, *Giants*, pp. 119, 124, 254, 341-49, 372. Beret sees America as a country in which "man lives by bread alone," p. 226. The paradox of the West as a possible "Beulah-land" and as actually plague sticken occurs to Beret's mind first, p. 227; cf. pp. 330-32, 350.

73. Ole Rölvaag, *Their Father's God* (New York: Harper, 1931), pp. 257-58.

74. The notion that Beret may, somewhat like Abraham, be willing to "sacrifice" her child at the voice of her mother occurs to Per Hansa and the pastor; *Giants*, p. 388.

75. *Their Father's God*, p. 208. Kaldahl also says, "We are ashamed of the age old speech of our forefathers," p. 208. Esther Lindgren also remarked to me that she saw the main declines in our culture to be the giving up of Swedish and of good novels (e.g. Dickens). Kaldahl's speech is, in some ways, a Grundtvigian speech; he emphasizes the ancient "democratic" traditions of the Norsemen and their likeness to Israel. Beret, however, understands the speech in a Kierkegaardian way, as the command of God; at the end, she says, "Now lettest thou thy servant depart in peace," echoing the Song of Simeon.

76. Cf. D.W. Robertson, "The Doctrine of Charity in Medieval Literary Gardens," *Speculum*, XXVI (1951), pp. 32-34; Bernard F. Huppe, *Doctrine and Poetry* (New York: University Pub., 1959), pp. 153-68; 231-33. The "giants in the earth" phrase is identified with Genesis 6:4 in both Reigstad and Jorgenson and Solum. It may be that Rölvaag conceptualized the troll "Plains" as like the mountains in *Brand* where the "troll's kirk" poses the last survival-temptation to Brand before he achieves the God-vision.

77. See the works cited above under the discussion of Hanson for Hanson's relation to Carl Nielsen (also to Grieg and Sibelius). For Zorn, see the discussion of Zorn in Laurin, *Scandinavian Art*, pp. 188-95. There are also useful discussions of Zorn in the books titled *Anders Zorn* by Malcolm Salaman, and by Axel Romdahl. Sandzen is best understood by viewing him at the Sandzen Museum, Lindsborg, Kansas. The most useful book on Milles is Meyric R. Rogers, *Carl Milles: An Interpretation*

of His Work (New Haven: Yale, 1940), which illustrates triton fountains like that found in Lindsborg, The Meeting of the Waters (St. Louis), the Diana Fountain (Chicago), and the Peace Monument (St. Paul). It does not include post-1940 Milles work in this section of the country.

78. The possibility that the development of maximum growth and centralized institutions has been a disaster to the race is posed by a number of very serious books on the relationship between fossil fuels, population, pollution and survival: Edward Goldsmith and others, *Blueprint for Survival* (Boston: Houghton Mifflin, 1972), *passim;* Donella H. Meadows and others, *The Limits to Growth* (New York: Universe Books, 1972), and E.F. Schumacher, *Small is Beautiful* (London: Blond and Briggs, 1973).

CATALOGUE

HOW TO FIND OUT ABOUT SCANDINA VIANS IN THIS AREA

Communities

Western plains Scandinavians did not much depend on lodges or "Scandinavian-American organizations" for their strength. The Scandinavians who came earlier and settled further east did more of that. Those Scandinavian lodges and fraternal organizations which were founded are, save for the Norden clubs, almost without cultural identity now. The old traditions are alive more in the rural Scandinavian Lutheran and Covenant churches and in the predominantly Scandinavian rural communities. Moving westward, the Swedish communities of interest (and date of Swedish arrival) are:

Nebraska:	Omaha—1855
	Swedeburg, Wahoo, Mead—1867
	Stromsburg, Osceola, Swedehome—early 1870's.
	Bertrand, Holdrege, Axtell—1870's
	Saronville, Shickley, Ong—early 1870's
North Nebraska:	Oakland, Bancroft—1860's
	Wausa, Wakefield—1880's
	Bristow, Rosedale—1890's
Kansas:	Lindsborg, Marquette—1860's

Stromsburg, Lindsborg, and Wausa have Swedish festivals still (Stromsburg on Midsummer Day, Lindsborg in October, and Wausa in the fall). The communities settled later, such as Wausa, are likely to still have first generation immigrants who speak the old language and remember 19th century Scandinavia. Lindsborg, Kansas, which was visited this year by King Carl Gustav of Sweden, is an older community which works at preserving Swedish tradition (Bethany Church, Lindsborg, Kansas, is a notable piece of 19th century folk architecture in the Skane step style).

Almost all of the towns have fine Swedish style churches from the late 19th and early 20th century, many of them built by S.P. Wahlstrom, a contractor from Wahoo (perhaps the finest of the Wahlstrom churches is that at Wausa). These communities still retain a fair number of coops, Swedish cooking at holiday time, and Swedish craft work. The best description of traditional Swedish culture in the Holdrege-Axtell area is to be found in the novels of Willa Cather, particularly *Song of the Lark* and *My Antonia.*

The Danish and Norwegian community is much smaller in Nebraska than is the Swedish, but both are very important for a history of the intellectual evolution of this area. Some of the important Danish communities are to be found in Des Moines, Iowa (around Grandview College, the Grundtvigian college, founded in 1894; the Reverend Ernest D. Nielsen, who was the former president of the college, is one of America's chief interpreters of Grundtvig). Further west, there is Blair, Nebraska, which began in the 60's, but which took its importance as a Danish intellectual center from the foundation of Trinity Seminary there in 1884 and the foundation of Dana College in 1899, both of which became significant centers for the continuation of the Kierkegaard-Wilhelm Beck tradition. Further west are Dannebrog and Nysted, Nebraska, including some "Inner Mission" and some Grundtvigian colonies (Nysted was also the location of the Nysted Folk School).

The major Norwegian colonies in Nebraska have been located along the Missouri and near Newcastle and Newman Grove, Nebraska. The Norwegian colonies in Nebraska are best regarded as extensions of Rölvaag *Giants* country in South Dakota and should be approached through his works.

Architecture and Related Matters

The way to get to know the older Scandinavian-American architecture, as well as the design of the cemeteries and the character of the cabinet making and woodcraft tradition, is to visit the towns listed above. A sample of more notable pieces of Scandinavian or pseudo-Scandinavian architecture in the region along with those listed in the essay (or obviously visible in the communities listed) might include the following:

Des Moines Art Center—Eliel Saarinen, architect (1940's).
Trinity Lutheran Church, Lincoln, Nebraska, copied from Christ Lutheran Church, Minneapolis (1950's).
Scandinavian style house, located in the 1800 block on South 22nd Street in Lincoln, Nebraska, once featured in a prominent national architecture magazine.

First Lutheran Church, Lincoln, Nebraska, South 70th Street, built
by a formerly predominantly Swedish congregation on the
model of medieval Norwegian Stave churches (1960's).

Pioneer Hall, Dana College, Blair, Nebraska (1941); "the design is an
adaptation of contemporary Scandinavian architecture, ac-
centuated by such features as the tower, the irregularity of
line, and the brick frieze of the Administration section."
William Ingemann was the architect.

Buckley Park Pavillion, Stromsburg, Nebraska, an elegant little
building just completed and part of a "cooperative" community development program.

Many Nebraskans have picked up on Scandinavian motifs, and such architects as Eliel Saarinen are so international as to have influenced architects
almost everywhere. This listing, therefore, is generally confined to buildings which have some relation to the collective cultural experience of
Scandinavian peoples in this area.

Painting and Sculpture

Scandinavian-American painting and sculpture is primarily folk work
having its origin in a deep peasant past or work which takes off from late
19th century romantic impressionism in Paris and Stockholm. Both sorts
of work have tended to center in Lindsborg, Kansas, though other towns
in the area have fine craftsmen, too. Folk art in Lindsborg is represented
by the harsh Swedish portrait heads of Anton Pearson and the tough concrete sculptures and stylized snow scenes of Oscar Gunnarson. More
recent metal sculpture by Malcolm Esping may be seen as part of this
same tradition. One of Gunnarson's concrete statues is a folk-rendering
of a pauper's funeral—the old man on the slab, the organist, the preacher,
and but two "mourners" looking none too sad.

Other fine folk statuary is still to be seen: J. Schmidt of Christians-
feld, Denmark, and West Denmark, Wisconsin, a carver of wooden shoes,
has carved beautiful oak pulpits for Danish Lutheran churches in Nysted,
Nebraska; Viborg, South Dakota; and Clinton, Iowa. Vesterheim, the
Museum of Norwegian Folk Art in Decorah, Iowa, includes other samples
of fine woodcarving—as does the American Institute of Swedish Arts,
Literature and Science, in Minneapolis, Minnesota. Gutzon Borglum,
Scandinavian by descent, spent part of his childhood in Fremont, Nebraska, and obviously did some of his best known work at Mount Rush-

more, South Dakota; but it is hard to find in Borglum's work anything Scandinavian. He works on the basis of Rodin and popular conceptions of the American tradition.

Lindsborg is a conservative pietistic community. When Birger Sandzen came to Lindsborg in the late 19th century, straight from the impressionistic studios of Paris and from work with Anders Zorn in Stockholm, he modified Zorn's soft light and hedonistic feeling, turned largely away from the human figure (save for a few portraits), and painted the rough rocks of Colorado and the Smoky Hill River Valley. His final product is as austere as Zorn's is hedonistic. In his great period, the early part of this century, Sandzen's work—while remaining impressionistic—comes to be a bit reminescent of Japanese prints, on the one hand, and of Cezanne, on the other, in its search for large outlines and a feeling of rocky solidarity.

Sandzen once told me that he deliberately chose the American Midwest and Rocky Mountain Region as his subject because he thought the Midwest was the best place to capture the epic of the prairies. To him, the stern rocks, rivers, and barren country best symbolized what that immigration epic was about. Sandzen's followers in the impressionistic mode in Lindsborg include Margaret Greenough, Charles Rogers, and perhaps Lester Raymer. Other Swedes around Lindsborg do macrame, goldsmithing, and a variety of other fine craft processes, a tradition which reflects the late 19th century emphasis on the refinement of folk craft tradition developing out of the folk school tradition. Many Nebraska landscape painters imitate Sandzen's style (e.g., Thomas B. Johnson, whose work hangs in the Historical Society Museum in Lincoln).

Sandzen's friend, Carl Milles, was an occasional visitor to Lindsborg. His style is much more eclectic than Sandzen's—sometimes impressionistic, sometimes neo-classic, sometimes entirely abstract. Lindsborg has Milles' Triton Fountain; Milles also has statues at the Des Moines Art Center and in most other urban centers in the Midwest, though none in Nebraska to my knowledge.

Literature

In general, most of the present Scandinavian communities appear to have lost touch with Scandinavian literature, past or present. The literary figures who carried a meaningful Scandinavian tradition into this country in the late 19th and early 20th century almost all wrote inspired by two or three Scandinavian giants: Ibsen, Kierkegaard, Björnsen, and perhaps

Tegner. Grundtvig was not particularly a literary inspiration (his works are finally being translated into English at Grandview College). Unfortunately Ibsen is seldom performed in the Midwest anymore; Kierkegaard is taught, but largely as an existentialist, and apart both from his cultural context and the ways in which he came into the cultural life of this section of the country. The rest of the great Scandinavian literary men of the 19th and 20th century, with the exception of Dag Hammarskjöld (who is read for his connection with the UN), and Ingmar Bergmann (whose plays are read because they're the basis of great films), are not to be found much on the stage or in the bookstores. The great left-wing American-Scandinavians who organized in the old country but settled in Chicago, Louis Pio and Marcus Thrane *(The Old Wisconsin Bible)*, are not studied either as literary or historical figures.

The dominant mode of the Scandinavian writers from the western plains is a fusion of romantic mysticism with a realistic, even a naturalistic surface, a feature which runs through the works of Kierkegaard, the later Ibsen, Rölvaag, Strindberg, and the later Bergmann among Scandinavian writers, and appears in the works of American-Scandinavian writers such as Rölvaag and David Edstrom *(Son of Caliban)*. This work ought properly to be contrasted with the work of Scandinavian reformist or Socialist writers who tended to write in a satiric or polemical vein: e.g. Thrane or Sandburg and with Scandinavian people's poetry (see Robert L. Wright, *Swedish Emigrant Ballads,* University of Nebraska Press, 1965). The following people are also worthy of attention:

> *Magnus Henrik Elmblad* (1848-88): Lived at Kearney, Nebraska for a time, translated Ibsen's *Brand* into Swedish; wrote the novel *Azilla* in which he portrays Indian anger at the white seizure of Indian land.

> *Carl Adolph Lönnquist* (1869-1937): Stylist in Swedish; wrote three books of Swedish poetry while resident as a pastor at Bethphage Mission, Axtell, Nebraska. Sam Dahl of Lincoln, who knew Lönnquist, says that he sat out under the trees at Axtell to meditate and write poetry.

> *K.G. William Dahl* (1883-1917): "Inner Mission" founder of Bethphage Mission who also wrote prairie vignettes in Swedish which deserve to be translated. Mr. Dahl's diary, in the possession of Samuel Dahl of Lincoln, deserves to be translated from the Swedish and published.

> *Oscar Leonard Stromberg:* Wrote about 40 novels in Swedish

while living in Nebraska; popular religious fiction having no quality.

    Carl Sandburg: Sandburg was born August Johnson; like Howard Hanson, Sandburg was a Populist in the generic sense and inspired by Whitman. He was an assistant to the Socialist mayor of Milwaukee early in the century; while he spent little enough time in Nebraska, he wrote one notable tribute to Nebraska's Chicago in the form of the poem "Omaha."

    Agnes Mathilde Wergeland (1857-1914): Historian and stylist, cousin of Henrik Wergeland, the famous Norwegian 19th century poet; wrote two volumes of fine poetry in Norwegian, then entered into intensive research concerning the history of Norse and Icelandic law. Wrote the eloquent *Slavery in Germanic Society in the Middle Ages.* Eventually head of the history department at the University of Wyoming, Ms. Wergeland was intensely persecuted as a woman intellectual and deserves a good feminist biography and republication.

    David Edstrom, The Testament of Caliban: Edstrom was also a sculptor; he was one of the few American-Scandinavian writers aside from Rolvaag who wrote using a Kierkegaardian mode.

    [Some critics also consider Wallace Stegner from Minnesota to be a writer in the Scandinavian tradition, but the novels are pretty much mainstream works.]

Music

The musical tradition of Scandinavians in this part of the country has been dominated by two contrastive movements which both had force for the Scandinavian people when they came: the hymn-chorale tradition which centers in Bach and Scandinavian Lutheran composers, and the "romantic" 19th century tradition associated with the liberal revolution in Europe at that time. Howard Hanson (cf. essay above), is the foremost Scandinavian representative of the romantic tradition. The "Bach chorale" tradition is often associated with Kierkegaardian communities.

The most notable Scandinavian composers who are from this section of the country who reflect Bach and pietist tradition are Hagbard Brase and F. Melius Christiansen. Neither is very closely linked to this region. Hagbard Brase was for many years the organist at Bethany College, Lindsborg, Kansas, and wrote several chorales for organ and choruses and works for organ and orchestra. Brase was an exceedingly modest man and published few of his works (his "Arietta" was published by A.G. Ogren,

but somebody needs to edit and publish the remaining work, particularly
that for organ). [Lindsborg is obviously well known for its Bach and
Handel performances initiated under Samuel Thorstenberg, also head of
the Jamestown Conservatory and an ardent advocate of Swedish music.]

F. Melius Christiansen was not from the western plains area (he was
located at St. Olaf's College in Minnesota); but he exercised a tremendous
influence in the area by virtue of the fact that his St. Olaf's choir travelled
through this section frequently and shaped the conception of what perfec-
tion in church music might be. Christiansen also arranged—for choirs—
versions of the fiftieth psalm, the crusaders, hymns and Norwegian folk
and pious songs. Unfortunately, Christiansen's compositions are not in
print in collected editions.

Intellectual Centers

Perhaps the most active center of intellectual activity focusing on
Scandinavian culture and life in the immediate area is Dana College
presently. Dana College's history is well recorded in *Saga of the Tower* by
William E. Christiansen (1959). One of the foremost intellectuals at the
school in the early days, the heir of Kierkegaard and Wilhelm Beck, was
P.S. Vig, whose numerous writings need to be collected, edited and translated. Dana College now reserves a center for Danish musical performances, folk dancing, and the teaching of Scandinavian languages and
literature. The Danish royalty will visit Dana this year out of respect for
its work. Bethany College, Lindsborg, Kansas, is a central college for the
study of Swedish intellectual tradition (as are the Grundtvigians at Grandview mentioned elsewhere). Norwegian intellectual centers exist further
away, at St. Olaf College in Minnesota, or Lutheran College in Decorah,
Iowa. Wahoo's Luther College, which for years was a source of the cultural
leaders mentioned in the essay above, was closed in the 1960's. Bethphage
Mission in Axtell, Nebraska, still continues some innovative medical work
though the Bielefeld paradigm has been pushed away from its original
intention somewhat by outside bureaucratic and other pressures.

Museums

So far as I can tell, no separate museums of Scandinavian life exist
in Nebraska. We have mentioned the Sandzen Gallery in Lindsborg; the
Swedish Pavilion from an early World's Fair is also located in Lindsborg
and includes a fairly ample collection of Swedish crafts. Some fine Scandi-

navian folk art is to be found at the Stuhr Museum in Grand Island, Nebraska. The American Institute of Swedish Art, Literature and Science in Minneapolis has collected a good quantity of Swedish paintings, sculpture, glass, folk art, and writing—as have the American Swedish Natural Museum in Philadelphia and Vesteheim in Decorah, Iowa.

Libraries

The most interesting libraries bearing on material touched on in this catalogue are those at St. Olaf College (the Rölvaag collection casts a good deal of light on Norwegian life in northeastern Nebraska and eastern South Dakota); the Norwegian collection at Luther College, Decorah, Iowa; the library and Sandzen Museum of Bethany College will assist with the artistic history of Swedes in that area; so will the archives of the Nebraska Synod of the Lutheran Church in America and the Central Conference of the American Lutheran Church. The public libraries and archives in the Scandinavian towns will help, as will the collections of the Nebraska State Historical Society Museum. The University of Nebraska Library has some Scandinavian books, but not much in the way of Scandinavian archives yet. For Danes in this area, the really significant libraries and archives are to be found at Grandview College in Des Moines and at Dana College, Blair.

Resource People

The greatest resources are the old people themselves. The people I have talked to are (among others) the following:

For Swedish Tradition:
Reuben C. Olson and Bessie Olson, Wahoo, Nebraska; my parents have been the best sources across forty years.
Esther Lindgren, in her 90's, Tabitha Home, Lincoln, Nebraska.
Axel Swanson, in his 90's, Wausa, Nebraska.
Hulda Landell, Wausa, Nebraska.
Samuel Dahl, Lincoln, Nebraska.
Carl Bjorkman, in his 90's, Wausa, Nebraska.
R.L. Fredstrom, Lincoln, Nebraska.
For Danish Tradition:
Otto Hoiberg, Lincoln, Nebraska; source on Dannebrog-Nysted.

   Alvin Petersen, Lincoln, Nebraska; source on Dana and Danish
tradition.

I have used Nels Forde and a few other Norwegians as guides to Norwegian
tradition in the area; and I have consulted Osceola and Stromsburg town
and family histories. For people willing to walk this trail in their family or
town, I can only suggest that one find the old timers (over 70 years—
preferably over 90); that one read enough so that one can ask good questions; and that one listen carefully to the powerful stories which come.

VII

Jews: The Exodus People

By Betty Levitov

ACKNOWLEDGMENTS

I wish to express my gratitude to Carol Gendler for her advice and criticisms and for her willingness to share her file cabinets of information about the first Jews in Omaha. The library staff at the Nebraska State Historical Society, especially Dave Hoober, were generous with their time and assistance. I owe special thanks to Phyllis Bernt for her contributions and insights, to Bob Kaiser for his help with the catalogue segments, and to Peter Levitov for his editorial suggestions.

Above. Julius Meyer (1851-1909) of Omaha, an Indian trader in the 1870's, with some of his Indian friends.

Below. While very few Jewish immigrants to the Midwest settled on farms, this sod farmhouse was part of a Jewish agricultural colony, around 1885.

VII

Jews: The Exodus People

By Betty Levitov

The Jew has nearly always been an immigrant and a problem. Nowhere is he accepted as indigenous; neither in Russia, where he has lived for centuries, nor in New York, where he will soon represent the bulk of the population. He is as much a stranger on his home soil in Palestine as upon the rawest bit of ground staked into a city, in Wyoming or the Dakotas.[1]

Jewish immigrants in America were related in that they shared the chief elements of an ancient faith; they had no homeland, no geography in common. Determined as any other immigrant group to settle in this country, they came from many countries; before 1900, the largest numbers came from Germany and Bohemia, and after 1900, from Russia; but they also came from Roumania, Poland, Galicia, Turkey, Hungary, etc. Most of them spoke Yiddish in addition to the language of their native country, but they spoke various dialects of Yiddish; the Jew from the Near East did not usually know Yiddish but spoke Greek, Ladino, Turkish or Arabic.[2] In their religious ritual they were orthodox or reform.[3] There were Chassidic Jews— pietistic and mystical—and, at the other extreme, the "free thinkers." Consequently, the differences and mutual prejudices among groups of Jews were at times as great as those between members of different religions, and these inner divisions affected the whole nature of their history in the United States, their religious and institutional life, their personal relations, their politics, their efforts at community-building.

While the Jews, like most other immigrant groups, tended to remain where they disembarked from their ships in the eastern seaport cities, their history of settlement in Nebraska dates back to 1855, one year after Congress authorized the new territory. Three local "histories" have been written. Two early manuscripts are largely personal reminiscences with sporadic documentation; the first appeared as an article in a special issue of *Reform Advocate* in 1908; the second was an unpublished manuscript, "Jewish Settlement in Nebraska," by Ella Fleishman Auerbach in 1927. The primary source used in this chapter and the one considered the best general research paper on Nebraska Jewish history is a master's thesis written by Carol Gendler in 1968, "The Jews of Omaha: the First Sixty years."

The first Jews in Nebraska were chiefly of German, Austrian or Bohemian origin, refugees from political and economic conditions in Europe. Nevertheless, usually having spent one or more years in one of the larger eastern cities where Jewish colonies were sizeable, they considered themselves not immigrants so much as pioneers.[4] Gendler relates the following description quoted from Anita Labeson:

> From Florida to New England, from the Atlantic to the Pacific, there were Jewish builders and pioneers who wove the pattern of their lives into the picturesque design of American history. Stooping under the heavy burden of his pack, or walking erect behind an ox-team, the Jew marched into the wilderness beside the Christian pioneer. He too dreamed of the prairies, awakened, and the forests and rivers quickened to life by the coming of new settlers. He gave of his best energies, of his tireless labor that the new communities might survive. And if he prospered—others prospered too. It was a common cause with Jew and Gentile—this building of a new land.[5]

There is some truth to be weeded out of this heroic scenario. While it is unlikely that any of these early Jews resembled a

young John Wayne, it is likely that most of the pioneers were
male, young and single. They were adventurers, entrepreneurs,
who left families to seek out their fortunes. Early on, they saw
Omaha's untapped resources and its potential as a boom town.
Most of this chapter deals with Omaha Jewry, for reasons of
sheer numbers of settlers and available source materials. Other
early settlements were started in Lincoln, Nebraska City, Fremont, Grand Island, and Hastings (see pp. 326-28 for a brief
accounting).

Understandably, there is some difference of opinion about
who the first Nebraska Jew was, but documentation can be
found to describe a few of these people. For example, we can
imagine the existence of Leopold May, an early merchant.
When May came to Omaha from Council Bluffs in 1855 where
he had opened a retail clothing store, the population was probably about 300.[6] Eventually, May opened a store in Omaha but
still lived in Council Bluffs and ferried across the Missouri to
work. In the first issue of *Rocky Mountain News,* dated April
23, 1859, the following advertisement appeared for May and
Weil of Omaha and Council Bluffs which offered "ready made
clothing, boots and shoes, hats and caps, India rubber goods,
blankets, buffalo robes and overshirts, revolvers and knives."[7]

In the mid-nineteenth century, Omaha's prosperity can be
gauged by reference to real estate values. Gendler cites the
Omaha City Times of June 11, 1857 as reporting that prime
building lots were selling for $100 in 1855, but by June, 1857,
similar lots were assessed at $4,000.[8] Another Jew attracted
by this flourishing economy was Meyer Hellman. Born in
Germany in 1834, he emigrated to the States in 1850 and
settled in Cincinnati where there was a colony of German Jews.
After working as a traveling salesman for several years, he chose
Omaha as a promising place to undertake his own business.
He eventually brought his wife, her brother, Aaron Cahn (who
had immigrated from Germany in 1898), and Cahn's wife to
Nebraska. They comprised the first known Jewish family group
in the state. The brothers-in-law opened M. Hellman and Com-
pany, a clothing business, at the corner of 13th and Farnam. In

a Sunday *Omaha World-Herald* series entitled "The People Who Make Up Omaha," Hellman and Cahn were credited with bringing the first prefabricated house to Nebraska.[9] The headline read, "Jew Brought First 'Pre-Fab' House in Year 1856." Business was accelerating for Hellman and Cahn but adequate building materials and construction workers were lacking. The young businessmen decided to have a building framed in Cincinnati and transported board by board to Omaha. It was a simple 20-by-80-foot frame structure, and was easily designed and cut to specifications in Cleveland. The job of erecting the building was largely a matter of nailing the pieces together. This experiment apparently worked well enough so that sometime later the brothers had their Cincinnati house dismantled and transferred to Omaha. Hellman and Cahn built up one of the largest mercantile establishments of their time. Their customers included Mormons, settlers headed out on the Oregon Trail, returning Civil War veterans, railroad construction workers and Indians.[10] On one occasion Cahn made a sales trip west by stage coach to Goldfield and Canon City in Nevada. He sold men's clothing in exchange for gold nuggets. Auerbach reports that on Cahn's return to Omaha, a $5,000 sack of gold was lost off the rear end of his stage coach—"it was scarcely counted a loss."[11]

One of the most prominent nineteenth century public figures, and perhaps the only Jew whose name regularly appears in Nebraska histories, was Edward Rosewater. His political life was stormy, his publishing career controversial, and his place in the Jewish community debated by Gendler and Auerbach. Born in Bohemia in 1841, he came to Omaha as local manager of the Pacific Telegraph Company. He previously was a telegrapher, first in Cincinnati and then during the Civil War in Alabama, Nashville, and finally Washington, D.C. as part of the United States Telegraph Corps. He did, in fact, operate the keyboard in Washington when President Abraham Lincoln's historic Emancipation Proclamation was communicated to Union commanders in the field.[12] Rosewater's association with telegraph operations brought him in direct contact with the sources of the news and he became press agent and telegraph correspondent for several eastern daily newspapers. His interest in the educational system of the new state of Nebraska prompted him to issue a small paper called *Punchinello,* which he distributed free of charge. In this publication he outlined his views on the school system, supported a campaign for the establishment of a Board of Education, and exposed two local newspapers which he thought were hampering the progress of education.

Rosewater gave up telegraphy to devote his full time to the publication of his newspaper, which he renamed the *Omaha Bee.* For more than thirty years, Rosewater was a powerful personality in western politics. He was a member of the Nebraska legislature and of the Republican National Committee. As a member of the legislature, he initiated impeachment proceedings against Governor David Butler, conducted an investigation of state institutions, and was instrumental in securing passage of bills pertaining to the postal telegraph system, the regulation of the private practice of medicine, the creation of the Omaha Board of Education, and the institute for the deaf and dumb.[13]

Rosewater's relationship with William Jennings Bryan and his on-again, off-again support for the Populists is well-documented. One Nebraska archivist considers Rosewater a good subject for a "psychological profile." An analysis of Rosewater and his vitriolic personality leads Auerbach and Gendler to differing views as to his position among the early Jews of Nebraska. Auerbach promotes him to heroic stature (she worked for Victor, Edward's son, for a number of years). She has hailed his coming to Nebraska as one of the most important events in the state's history, if Rosewater's "service to posterity" is taken into proper account.[14] Gendler, on the other hand, reflects in Rosewater a diminished sense of affiliation with the Jews of Omaha. She finds no evidence whatsoever, either in the diaries, letters, news articles, public addresses or contributions, that Rosewater identified with the Jewish people.[15] Gendler cites the following reference to Rosewater as it appeared in the *Daily Republican,* May 22, 1883, indicating his controversial reputation and ambiguous relation to the Omaha Jewish community:

> . . . it is noticeable that Mr. Rosewater's devotion consists solely of an attempt to stir that race of people into indignation against *The Republican*. In other ways he fights very shy of them. He has never been remarkable for upholding the Jewish faith or Jewish customs, nor has he ever said anything in his paper favorable to his race. . . . His associates have never been Jews, and in no way has he ever appeared to hold any sort of communion with the people whom he affects with such indignation to defend whenever he is alluded to as one of them.
>
> The Jewish people need no defense at the hands of Mr. Rosewater, first because *The Republican* has never attacked them, secondly because Mr. Rosewater has no authority to speak for them, and thirdly, because he is about the worst thing that ever happened to them.[16]

Another young pioneer, Julius Meyer, of Germany, arrived at the frontier of Omaha on January 2, 1866, where he joined his three older brothers and began trading with the Indians. His brothers supplied him with trinkets and cigars which he exchanged for furs, beads, moccasins, wampum pouches, and other articles from the Indians. The hazards of this trade almost cost him his life, and only through the intervention of Pawnee Chief Standing Bear was he saved from being scalped.[17] This led to a lifelong friendship with Standing Bear. He learned to speak at least six Pawnee dialects and served as government interpreter. The Pawnee tribe adopted him and named him "Box-ka-re-sha-hash-ta-ka," which means "curly haired white chief with one tongue."[18]

Meyer opened a curio shop in Omaha, known as the "Indian Wigwam," which became the headquarters for his Indian friends. After the completion of the Union Pacific Railway in 1869, it assumed the character of a local museum, attracting wide tourist attention. Historians are in debt to Meyer for his part in preserving on film the likenesses of various

Indian leaders, including Chiefs Swift Bear, Red Cloud, Standing Bear and Spotted Tail. To allay some of their fears of the camera, Meyer posed with them. Before Buffalo Bill employed Indians in his Wild West Show, Meyer thought of taking Indians to Europe for public appearances.[19]

Interested in culture as well as trade, Meyer organized the Omaha Musical Union in 1871. Together with Rosewater, he was instrumental in bringing famous musical entertainers to Omaha. In 1885, Julius and his brother Max established the first opera house in Omaha. Meyer was active in Jewish circles as a member of Temple Israel and as one of the organizers of the Hebrew Benevolent Society.

James Olson describes the 1880's in Nebraska as a period of accelerated growth, both in population and business. Between 1880-1890, Nebraska's population more than doubled; Omaha grew from 30,000 to 140,000 in the same ten years, almost quintupling in size.[20] Meat packing accounted for a large part of the business boom; smelting, linseed oil, soap, brickyards, clothing factories, food processing, and distilleries were other growing industries.[21] During this period the Jewish community likewise was growing.

With growth came a degree of cohesion in the community. An announcement in the Omaha *Daily Herald* of September 29, 1867, is the first record of a Jewish service:[22]

> Israelites' New Year's Day comes on Monday, September 30 (tomorrow). There will be prayer by Mr. Rosenthal at his house at 10 A.M. and 6 P.M. All brothers are earnestly solicited to take part in this festival and help the organization of a synagogue in Omaha.

Congregation B'ni Israel, a local charitable organization, a fraternal and social club and a burial society developed along with the forging of community links. The institutional setting became the pervasive means for shaping the lives of the immigrants and holding them together. The influx of more diverse immigrant groups, beginning with the migrations from Russia, both splintered and solidified community structure. The task of absorbing the new refugees complicated and taxed the lives of a few people who had finally achieved a modicum of economic security and social acceptance; yet, the newcomers strengthened religious interest which had been on the decline. This process introduced an expanded notion of democracy and reform within institutional structures which characterized Nebraska Jews in the formative years of their community.

The Great Migration and Settlement in America

> America was in everybody's mouth. Businessmen talked of it over their accounts; the market women made up their quarrels that they might discuss it from stall to stall; people who had relatives in the famous land went around reading letters for the enlightenment of fortunate folks; the one-letter-carrier informed the public how many letters arrived from America, and who were the recipients; children played at emigrating . . . all talked of it, but scarcely anybody knew one true fact about this magic land.[23]

The quality of Jewish life in Russia began to deteriorate rapidly after 1880. Poverty and oppression made demands on the populace which could not be met. It became a choice of starvation, imprisonment or flight. "Each time the Romanov autocracy tightened the vise on Russian Jewry, the tempo of exodus was accelerated and, after the May Laws and the pogroms of 1881, the flight burst through all restraints."[24] Between 1800 and 1881, the total emigration from eastern to western Europe and the United States was approximately 250,000, about 3,000 a year. From 1881 to 1889, the number of Jewish emigrants rose to 450,000, about 23,000 a year.[25]

There was a degree of resistance in western Europe and America against the influx of Russian Jews. In fact, the older established German-Jewish immigrants were caught in a critical dilemma. As decent, well-meaning human beings, they sympathized with the plight of the refugees. On the other hand, "they had labored for many decades to achieve and maintain their status as westernized nationals and were convinced that they would jeopardize that status, and would lend credence to the emergent anti-Semitic propaganda, by identifying themselves with the bearded, Yiddish-speaking, frequently exotic-looking 'alien people' from eastern Europe."[26] In addition, they were simply psychologically and technically unprepared to organize the kind of major relief demanded by the hundreds of thousands of new immigrants.

One of three areas of conflict arising from the settlement of the Russian immigrants, as reported by the American Jewish press, was the increase in religious orthodoxy. The immigration of the Russian Jews, able to worship without harassment in this country, generated a flourishing development of synagogue life. By the end of the 1880's, "shuls" had sprung up in practically all of the large cities. To the "fashionable uptown Jews" of New York, for example, already grown accustomed to limiting their synagogue activity to perfunctory attendance at services several times a year, the feverish activity of the Russian Jews, not only in building synagogues but in frequenting them, was a source of amazement.[27] Religion forbade working on Holy Days and the Sabbath, an additional irritation for the predominantly German garment businessmen who employed hundreds of refugees in their sweatshops.

In addition to the orthodoxy in religious life, the Russian immigrants were unwilling to abandon their ethnic and cultural inheritance. Huddled in crowded tenements, the refugees lived a life of old-world flavor, attracting much attention from outsiders and causing the established Jews a good deal of embarrassment.[28]

The third . . . and perhaps the most serious . . . irritant was the means of economic and political integration adopted by the Russian Jews. Many of these people brought with them an austere social conscience and an enduring devotion to the ideals of industrial democracy and the resultant socialism. They formed unions, held strikes, and, in spite of their unfamiliarity with the political processes, had a continuing and significant effect on electoral and revolutionary activity. Much of this activity was interpreted by the older Jews as ungratefulness and rejection of the recipient/host community.

Socialism seemed to bolster the immigrants' faith in themselves, to offer the worker in the sweatshop the prospects of dignity and respect.[29] The influence of Russian-Jewish involvement in Eugene Deb's Socialist Party, while based largely in New York City, spread to other large cities and lent a good deal of support to a rapidly growing movement.

While Nebraska was far removed from the political arenas in the East, both Auerbach and Gendler note the impact the immigrants had on Omaha Jewry. Gendler cites Auerbach and the Omaha *Daily Herald,* July 16, 1882, as follows:

> On July 14, 1882, the Jewish population of Omaha was considerably augmented by the arrival of 161 refugees. Included were some 40 families, a number of single men and women, some of whom bore the scars of the ill-treatment they had received at the hands of the authorities in their native land. Many of these refugees came from Kiev.[30]

The influx of Russian Jews to Nebraska caused a great deal of agony for the more established Jews. Interestingly enough, however, these intense, energetic, resourceful people significantly enlivened and strengthened the Jewish community. Gendler writes:

> In general, it (the orthodox community) was splintered, disorganized, financially insecure, and lacking in strong leadership, both lay and professional. But the most important effect of the settlement of orthodox Jews in Omaha was the development of a considerably more complex, changing, and assuredly stronger Jewish community.[31]

There is evidence that Nebraska Jewry took an avid interest in politics. Reproduced on the next page is the only extant copy of the English version of a bilingual (Yiddish-English) political circular issued in Omaha in 1900. It is an interesting commentary on the attempt on the part of some Jews to control the "Jewish" vote. It is also interesting to note the jobs held by some of the Jewish residents in the city's administration.

Omaha, Nebraska, March 5th, 1900

Dear Sir.—Every good American citizen regardless of political affiliations is now studying over the position he should take tomorrow at the ballot box. By too hasty a stroke of the pencil in the election booth he might make a blunder and vote for a man who is entirely unfit to become our representative for the next three years.

In order to cope with the great problem of municipal ownership of the waterworks, which means a great deal of saving to the taxpayers, we have to be very careful in our selection and try to elect a municipal ticket composed of good, honest and clean men. Especially must we deliberate, whom we should support by our vote and influence for mayor. Now we have before us two candidates, who are aspiring for the office of municipal executive. One is Frank E. Moores who was re-nominated by the republican party, and the other is William S. Poppleton, the fusion candidate for the same office. The question arises, which one of them is worthy of our confidence, vote and support. While some of us may not be property owners, and therefore lack the interest of others in regard to the municipal ownership of the water works, but as loyal American citizens we all desire to have a man for mayor whose heart beats in sympathy with his fellow men and who treats all citizens alike without partiality.

From the experience we had of Frank E. Moores as mayor, we fail to see why we should support him again. You all remember the promises he made us three years ago, how good and generous he would be to the Jewish people, if they would only tender him their support for election. Has he adhered to his pledges and fulfilled his promises? What has he done for any of us to entitle him to our vote and influence for re-election? Whenever we came to him asking a favor for some unfortunate one among us, he gave us a deaf ear. We had S.L. Morris, a bright and honorable young man, on the police force and Mayor Moores had him discharged without cause. We had H. Brown, an unfortunate poor man of a large family, who was trying to gain a livelihood for himself and starving children by getting a position on the city force as a street sweeper, then he was fired.

If the Jewish people are so low in the estimation of Mayor Moores as not to entitle them even to the honor of handling a broom on the public streets under his administration, why, then, not drop the party lines and support W.S. Poppleton, who is a good, clean and honest business man.

Mr. Poppleton has always been a friend of the Jewish people and if elected for mayor will show his appreciation by giving us a good and clean municipal administration. Let us all use our united efforts and help to elect him.

Yours respectfully,

H. Rubin,
John Simon,
Sol. Prince,
J.D. Nathanson.

The following chart is Ella Auerbach's summary of Jewish involvement in the political life of Nebraska from 1863-1922.[33]

Mayors
H.B. Zimman, Omaha
Dr. Alexander Baehr, Norfolk
Carl Kramer, Columbus
Frederick Sonnenschein and Bennett Goldsmith, West Point
Joseph Sarbach, Fairbury
Joseph Einstein, Arapahoe
R. Brody and H.D. Horwitz, Winnebago

State Legislature

Aaron Cahn	1863
Edward Rosewater	1870-72
Dr. Alexander Baehr	lower house, 1875-79, Senate, 1879-85
S.N. Wolbach	lower house, 1885; Senate, 1887-89
Bennet Goldsmith	1892
Martin Sugarman	1912-13
Edward Simon	1912-13
Jacob Klein	1912-13

Assistant Attorney General.
By appointment, O.S. Spillman
Harry Silverman, appointed 1923

Deputy County Attorney
Arthur Rosenblum, 1919 to April 15, 1921
Irvin S. Stalmaster, 1922
Jack L. Marer, Sept. 1, 1927

City Council (Omaha when not otherwise identified):
Sol Prince	1892
Albert Cahn	1894-95
H.B. Zimman	1900
	1918-22 (acting mayor Febr. 1906-09)

School Board
Simeon Bloom	1878-81
Andrew Rosewater	
Charles S. Elgutter	1891
Morris Levy	

Chief of Detectives
Ben Danbaum

County Treasurer
Emanuel Steinau, Hastings,
1881-82

City Engineer
Andrew Rosewater
Charles Logasa *Department*
David Grodinsky *Employees*
Michael Chaisen

Board of Public Welfare
Rabbi Frederick Cohn
Henry Monsky

**Nebraska-Iowa Boundary
Commission**
H.H. Lapidus

Justice of the Peace
Jacob Levy   1892-1916
William Altstadt

Veteran Fire Association
Sol Prince   Charles Schlank, Asst. Fire Chief
Meyer Hellman   Aaron Cahn
Carl Brandeis   Joseph Rothholz

Chief Clerk to Governors
Holcomb and Poynter,
Henry Blum, of Lincoln

City Meat Inspector
Rev. Esau Fleishman, 1909

City Bacteriologist
Dr. Millard Langfeld

Park Board
Jonas L. Brandeis

Juvenile Court Officer
Mogy Bernstein

Republican National Committee
Edward Rosewater, Nebraska committeeman, 1892, advisory board,
1896, 1900 and 1904
Victor Rosewater, delegate, 1908, on committee 1908-1912,
chairman, 1912.

The task of accommodating the thousands of new immigrants in Nebraska and across the country stimulated the development of a complex network of institutions formed *ad hoc,* for that very purpose. A scheme of various specialized agencies evolved to implement the process. Many of the new immigrants, directed from the ports of entry and transported to the Midwest, were met in Omaha by volunteers from the Hebrew Benevolent Society, who located temporary living quarters. A subcommittee of the Benevolent Society was established to raise funds, collect food and clothes, and find jobs for the many who arrived penniless.[34] Another committee was formed in Omaha to raise money for the purchase of land outside the city where the Russians might establish a farming community. This was done in part on the assumption that many of the immigrants had been farmers, but primarily to reduce the numbers of those peddling in the streets. The agricultural experiment proved unsuccessful. Most of the immigrants had no farming experience and they felt uncomfortably isolated away from the urban community life.[35] The Industrial Removal Office, created in 1901 under the auspices of the Industrial Aid Society, administered the Galveston plan, whereby a port of entry in the South was designated to allow for settlement in the interior of the country, thus curtailing the heavy stream of Jewish settlements in the eastern seaboard cities. Gendler reports that more than 5,000 immigrants passed through Galveston by 1912.[36] Immigrants were directed towards those cities where their particular skills were in demand: thus butchers were sent to Kansas City, Fort Worth, and Omaha; carpenters to Grand Rapids; and tanners to Milwaukee. The IRO was responsible for the removal and settlement of more than 100,000 refugees in over 1,000 cities in central and southern United States.[37] There was a good amount of fear and insecurity among the Jews who were transported to midwestern cities where the Jewish colonies were small and where there were no friends and relatives from the old country.

An Agricultural Experiment Fails

Closely allied with the work of the Industrial Removal Office was a back-to-the-soil movement sponsored by the Jewish Agricultural Society. In Nebraska, this movement took the form of a settlement of some fourteen families in Cherry County; the farmers were of Russian origin, very young (only one over 30) and inexperienced. Auerbach quotes from a report made in 1911 by Gabriel Davidson, general manager of the Jewish Agricultural Society, after a visit to the colony.[38]

> In 1906 the Government opened up for settlement under the so-called "Kinkaid Act," land in the western part of Nebraska, giving each settler the right to file 640 acres of land. In 1908 and 1909 fourteen Jewish immigrant families, all of whom, with one exception, came either from Milwaukee or Omaha, took up homesteads under this Act. The settlers were young, intelligent and industrious people, who operated their farms understandingly, and during off seasons worked out so as to maintain their families without getting into debt. The settlement was located between two railroads, 45 miles from the Town of Gordon on the Northwestern, and 25 miles from the Town of Hyannis on the Burlington. This was a great hardship. It took a farmer two days to get to town and back, while with a freight team four days would be consumed in travelling to and fro. Therefore general farming could not be engaged in profitably. It was too hard to haul the produce to market. The Jewish farmers therefore engaged largely in stock raising.
>
> In 1908, the Jewish Agricultural Society made them loans for various farm purposes. But it was plain to the Society that the settlement would only be of temporary duration.
>
> In 1913, at the end of the minimum period required to get title, the families commenced to move out. Three left that year, one the following year, and the rest in 1915 and 1916.
>
> We have lost track of most of these farmers. The only ones of whom we now have information are two families that are on farms in Michigan.

The report also included a table which listed names, size

of family, occupations and period of time on the farm as
follows:

Name	Size of Family	Occupation	Date of Settlement On Homestead	Date of Leaving
Jacob Levine	4	Machinist	1908	1913
Louis Offengenden	2	Tinsmith	1910	1915
Harry Rosenbaum	4	Tailor	1909	1915
Israel Miller	1	Shoemaker	1909	1915
Mendel Bernstein	3	Carpenter	1908	1916
Samuel Roteman	10	Tailor	1908	1915
Joseph Gold	5	Tailor	1909	1915
Louis Gellman	1	Tailor	1908	1913
Harry Cohen	4	Carpenter	1908	1915
Morris Mearsen	5	Machinist	1908	1915
Hyman Schwartz	1	Shoemaker	1908	1914
David Singer	5	Carpenter	1908	1916
Sam Zabow	1	Tailor	1908	1913

As the new immigrants became well-established Omaha
citizens, they had a marked influence on not only the practice
of Judaism, but the whole nature of the Jewish neighborhood;
they were responsible for Omaha's first kosher butcher shop,
the city's first "mohel" (a paramedical person who circumcizes
Jewish boys in accordance with traditional custom), and a
number of congregations.[39] An interesting picture of the
ethnic neighborhood is Howard Chudacoff's chart listing names,
addresses, and occupations on North 24th Street:[40]

	1912	1916	1920
1102	Jacob Finkenstein	Jacob Finkenstein	Harry Slutzky
1104	Jacob Kaplan	Abraham Stoler	Abraham Stoler
1111	Anshe Sholom Synagogue	Anshe Sholom Synagogue	Anshe Sholom Synagogue
1114	Samuel Krasne, grocer	Simon Krasne	Simon Krasne

	1912	**1916**	**1920**
1114			Samuel Cohn
1115	Irene Reber	F.L. Bickford	F.L. Johnson
1117	J.E. Hartman	John Baird	H.C. Orron
1201	Ella Bentley (c)	Wesley Horn (c)	Harvey Williams
1202	Fruma London, grocer	Fruma London, grocer	Fruma London, grocer
1204	Max Fogel, meats	Daniel Hirsch, meats	Daniel Hirsch, meats
			Margaret Egan
1205	Sam Spiegal, junk	Sam Spiegal, junk	Sam Spiegal, junk
1206	Max Hertzberg, baker	Benjamin Blend, baker	C.C. Nerness
1208	Samuel Cohn	Samuel Cohn	Vacant
1210	Max Hertzberg	Everett Brown	J. Ewing
			J.R. Smith
1302		Joseph Margolis, grocer	Joseph Gotsdiner, grocer
1304	Sophia Howard	Max Krasne, shoemaker	Bernie Gault
1304½	Isadore Hurwitz, photographer	Vacant	Thomas Hutchison, billiards
1306	Boyd Burrows, printer	Joseph Bemrose, confectioner	Joseph Bemrose, confectioner
1307	T.H. Weirich, fixtures	T.H. Weirich, fixtures	Vacant
1308	Christian Anderson	Doherty & Mortenson, plumbers	J.W. Wright
1310	E.P. Trumble, coffee house	Samuel Krizelman, hardware	William Mays
1312	Emanuel Thomsen, saloon	Arendt Jensen	J.W. Wright, barber
1314	Louis Pinkovitz, blacksmith	Vacant	C.H. Warden, billiards
1316	Isaac Abramson, feed	Isaac Abramson, feed	Isaac Abramson, feed
1322	T.V. Allison, grocer	Vacant	Belle Christian
1401	Edwin Walker, restaurant	General Scott (c) restaurant	General Scott, restaurant
1402	Joel Bloom, saloon	Joel Bloom, saloon	Sam Flax, grocer
1404	C.J. Olsen	J.C. Carlson, cigars	Mary Glass, restaurant
1405	Hersch Friedman, shoemaker	Isaac Zarinsky, shoemaker	Isaac Zarinsky, shoemaker
	Herman Theodore, tailor	P.H. Miller, upholsterer	
1406			Harry Siref, clothes
1408		Isaac Brooks, shoes	Isaac Brooks, shoes
1410		Samuel Meyer, ladies' clothes	
1412		Jacob Kaplan, second hand goods	
1414	G.A. Walker	Max Rosenbloom	R.H. Robins, grocer
1415	Frank Kellerman		Sarah Shotz
	A.J. Lamb, confectioner	Mushkin & Epstein, meats	Mushkin & Epstein, meats
1417	L.H. Adams (c), barber	Omaha Fish Co.	Max Resick, grocer
	J.L. Kolec, pool	Abraham Goldstein	Eureka Furniture
1419	David Spector, tailor	Paul Eisenmann, baker	R.H. Blend, baker
1421	Jacob Berkowitz	Vacant	S.W. Mills, furniture

1912	1916	1920
1421 Benjamin Cohn, men's clothes		
1422 Hersch Friedman	Harry Adelstein	Harry Adelstein
1423 Samuel Babior, meats	Moses Silver, tailor	Herman Gilinsky, second hand goods
Methodist Episcopal Church		
1424 C.G. Krasne	C.G. Krasne	Max Kalmonson
1425 Solomon Garmel, grocer	Solomon Garmel, grocer	Kemp Bros, grocers

In Omaha, the new century was characterized by the development of a strong community spirit, the birth of new organizations and building enterprises; among these undertakings were new synagogues, the Wise Memorial Hospital and the formation of the Associated Jewish Charities. In 1914 all Jewish activities were merged into one Jewish Welfare Federation, which Auerbach describes as "the first and most complete federation in the country and the pattern for the present-day Community Chest."[41] Many organizations for men, women, and young people joined the federation, which served the entire Jewish community with departments in relief, free loans, legal aid, employment, education, transportation, immigration, hospital, desertion and naturalization. The scope of community involvement is reflected in the list of those organizations within the new federation.

> Associated Jewish Charities, *Annual Report,* 1914:
> Organizations represented: Congregation B'nai Israel, Nebraska State Lodge No. 144 Order Brith Abraham, Modern Woodmen Hebrew Camp No. 4944, Beth Hamedrosh Hagodol, Temple Israel, Omaha Hebrew Club, Hungarian Society, Wise Hospital, Temple Israel Sisterhood, Wm. McKinley Lodge No. 521 Independent Order B'nai Brith, Nebraska Lodge No. 354 B'nai Brith, Daughters of Israel Aid Society, Ladies Auxiliary of Wm. McKinley Lodge, B'nai Jacob Anshe Shalom, Jewish Ladies' Relief Society, and Ladies Auxiliary of Beth Hamedrosh Hagodol.[42]

The act of federation was described as "the concentration of an entire community in an organized effort for the general for charitable and philanthropic endeavor for the general good and benefit of all, doing away with duplication and waste, and bringing to the beneficiary of charity the full measure of the community's support."[43]

The synagogue augmented the social welfare agencies, providing for everything from religious worship to social and physical well-being. As social centers, the synagogues took on the color and shape of the old country lifestyles . . . the Russian, Roumanian, Hungarian and Lithuanian. The "Litvische shul," for example, was a religious, cultural and social center for Omaha Lithuanian Jews.

Jewish immigration to Nebraska and the United States generally trailed off after the first decade of the twentieth century. As the communities stabilized, American Jews began their upwardly mobile climb. After World War I, most Jews were no longer in the sweatshops or engaged in other types of physical labor; many now owned factories as well as retail establishments. As financial situations improved, Jews acquired greater access to education. Soon American Jews entered the professions in great numbers in proportion to their population. With the luxury and security of a more stable economic base, Jews sought out the dignity and distinction and challenges associated with the arts, medicine, law. There was a tremendous upsurge of intellectual activity in the humanistic as well as the practical fields.

An Experiment in Community—New York City

One of the more creative and comprehensive attempts at self-sufficiency and autonomy in community organization was what the Polish Jewry called *Kahal,* an all-inclusive community authority.

> Kahal (kehilla)—Hebrew term meaning "community," applied to the administrative body of Jewish communities

which in recent history has been known as the *Kehilla.* . . .

During the Middle Ages and especially beginning with the 18th century, the *Kahal* became an important authoritative Jewish organization, officially recognized by the government. . . .

One of the chief functions of the *kahal* . . . was the collection of taxes for the government from members of the Jewish community. Other important functions of the *Kahal* were: the organization and supervision of Jewish religious education; the administration of all types of charitable institutions; the supervision of *kashrut* (dietary laws); the placement of community functionaries; the erection and maintenance of Jewish law courts; and in general, supervision over the welfare, religious, educational economic and other social problems.[44]

The *kahal* embraced nearly every phase of Jewish public life: religion, education, law, hygiene, social welfare. As long as the taxes were paid, the Polish had no reason to interfere with this secular group. The *Kehilla,* surprisingly, served as a model for a more contemporary American Jewish community organization.

At the beginning of this century, after the principal immigrant groups had been settled, Jewish community organizations began to falter and disintegrate. The fact that old community agencies were no longer adequate to control the moral life of a vast population troubled the Jewish leadership. It took an ugly incident to inspire action. In 1908, the police commissioner of New York City published an article in which he voiced current anti-immigrant prejudices by saying that half the city's criminals were Jews.[45] The incident emphasized the importance for the Jews to unite in defense of their common interests. Judah L. Magnes, at that time rabbi for the reform Temple Emanu-El, organized necessary support and in February, 1909, the New York *Kehilla* came into existence. The *Kehilla* also proposed to institute supervision of the *kashrut,* to improve Jewish education, to gather statistics in various areas, to strengthen and democratize philanthropy . . . to create an entire internal unification of the Jewish community.[46] Another *Kehilla* was started in Philadelphia and there was hope of forming similar organizations in other cities across the country. Unfortunately, differences that would not be resolved led to the demise of the New York *Kehilla,* and it was only because of Magnes himself that the organization functioned as a unit for about ten years. Antagonism between the economically distinct portions of the Jewish community and resentment toward the attempts at supervision, were part of the problem. Above all, however, World War I divided interests and outraged Magnes, who was a staunch pacifist.

The Legacy of Community

The *Kehilla* movement of the early twentieth century left a legacy in the form of several institutions that continued to exert a strong influence on Jewish life. The Jewish Community Councils, an adaptation of the *kehilla,* have increased in importance in the past twenty years. Through this council, representatives of Jewish organizations across the country can present the points of view of their own communities. Activities in the council embrace fields of philanthropy, community relations, education, and internal Jewish affairs. The Council speaks for the community and also serves as liaison with the general public.[47]

The "Third Wave"—The Remnants of a People

During the post-World War II years, between 1945-1955, the consciousness of two things dominated Jewish life: the disappearance of Jewish communities in the European diaspora and the rise of the Jewish state in Israel. The second was, to a large degree, the creative response to the first. The following table, if only approximate, is the best picture of what happened to the Jews in Europe:[48]

	Jewish Population in 1939 or 1940	Jewish Population in 1945 or 1946	Losses
Germany	150,000	20,000	130,000
Austria	190,000	4,000	185,000
Italy	45,000	35,000	10,000
Poland	3,250,000	45,000	3,205,000
Roumania	750,000	425,000	325,000
Hungary	725,000	143,000	582,000
Czechoslovakia	360,000	100,000	260,000
Bulgaria	48,000	28,000	20,000
Yugoslavia	75,000	15,000	60,000
Greece	75,000	10,000	65,000
France	250,000	130,000	120,000
The Netherlands	140,000	35,000	105,000
Belgium	75,000	20,000	55,000
Luxembourg	5,000	1,200	3,800
Denmark	2,500	1,500	1,000
Norway	1,300	700	600

Not all the losses were a result of extermination, since thousands of Jews were able to emigrate to Russia and the United States, but historians agree on 6,000,000 as closest to the true figure. The end of the war was not the end of the tragedy for the Jews remaining in Europe. Some of those in exile in Russia had the choice of returning to their former homes, often to find no trace of family or friends. Many fled to the displaced persons' camps controlled by the Americans and British.

After Israel had been declared a state in 1948, and the mass migrations from the displaced persons' camps began, there was no need for the United States to continue its restrictive immigration laws. It was, in fact, more practical to close down the camps which had been maintained at great expense and allow more Jews into the country. The personality of this so-called "third wave" was so dramatically different from any other influxes, being neither made up of pioneers nor refugees, but of political fugitives, exiles, leftovers from concentration camps, displaced persons' camps—the remnants of a people. These people had no hope or idealism regarding their future in America, no expectation of a new, creative life. What had happened in Europe deadened their imaginations, extinguished their optimism, and drained their strength.

The following is an account of one family that came to America toward the tail end of the wave of immigration which followed the Second World War. The family consisted of two parents, a teenager, and a two year old who, after talking at length with the other members of the family 25 years later, recounts their experiences and reactions.

Because I grew up taking American history and government classes and saying the pledge of allegiance every school day, I always thought we had come to this country in search of liberty, equality, and other high-sounding idealistic words. But after talking to my parents, I discovered that we didn't come here with any idealistic hopes of political freedom or illusions of wealth and opportunity. We came to America because there wasn't any place else to go. Our relatives were gone; our possessions were destroyed—there was no reason to stay in Europe.

The American-run displaced persons camp in southern Germany had been pleasant enough. There was enough to eat and warm clothing to wear. My mother always talks about the D.P. camps as the best time of her life because everyone was poor and Jewish and could speak Yiddish. But the Americans were disbanding the camps and trying to help people resettle. We had to find a permanent home, but we knew of no surviving close relatives anywhere and Israel was in turmoil. America was the only place to go.

The only cities my parents had heard of were New York and Chicago, but those were the cities everyone had heard of and wanted to settle in. The American officials, however, wanted to spread the D.P.'s out over the country so that we could be more easily absorbed economically and, hopefully, socially. Each family was assigned a city where the local Jewish Federation had pledged to help them settle and find work. We were assigned to Omaha. We had never heard of the place; as a matter of fact, the nice Jewish lady from New York City who worked as a translator for the American Consulate and who had befriended my mother was aghast when she heard of our assignment. She pulled out a map, looked for a long time before she found Omaha on it, and commiserated with my mother—who was getting frantic—about being sent out into the middle of nowhere. But frantic or not, in the summer of 1951 we found ourselves in Omaha with some clothing and housewares and about $26.

None of us had had any lessons in reading or speaking English. We were totally dependent on the Jewish Federation who provided us with the bottom half of an old one-family dwelling (another immigrant family lived upstairs), furniture, groceries, and shortly thereafter, jobs for my father. My father had been a shoemaker by trade, a self-employed businessman who liked his work and was successful at it. He'd lost everything because of the war—even his work. The American officials hadn't been able to settle people by occupational opportunity. There was little chance for a shoemaker with no capital in Omaha. The jobs the Jewish Federation found my father were heavy labor jobs. The economy wasn't very good in 1951, and jobs for a man in his late 40's who spoke no English were hard to find.

The Jewish Federation organized English classes, but they were in the evenings, and since my father either worked nights or was exhausted when he got home after work, he never took advantage of them. My mother was too shy and intimidated to go. My sister learned English in school; my parents picked up what English they know from watching television, talking with neighbors, and, for my father, dealing with his co-workers. They didn't pick it up from their children; we never spoke English at home. My parents insisted on speaking nothing but Yiddish to us so that we'd preserve some sense of Jewish identity in a country that in many ways scared and bewildered them. My folks were often amazed at living in a country where knowing Russian, Polish, and Yiddish didn't get them anywhere, while not knowing English marked them as uneducated and different.

Twenty-five years after coming here, my parents haven't exactly fulfilled the American Dream. Most of the people who came here when we did learned English, adopted an American life-style, modified their religion, and tried hard to be financially successful. My father was always a poor laborer; today he

is a poor retired laborer. Both my parents have clung to their
language, their religion, and their memories and have avoided
becoming Americanized. My father thinks it's because he was
too old to change when he came. My mother claims it's
because she just doesn't understand how things are done here.
For her the tempo is too fast; families aren't close enough;
people are too caught up in their own affairs and don't care
enough for other people.

Are they sorry they came to America? My father says he
isn't. His children got an education; he has a place to live and
food to eat; no one bothers him. He hasn't fulfilled any great
dreams or ambitions, but ask him if he's satisfied and he
answers, "Why not? We're alive."

Sachar summarizes some of the salient characteristics of
the American Jewish community at the mid-twentieth century:

The Jews remained an urban people: not merely urban,
indeed, but metropolitan. Sixty-five percent of America's
5,200,000 Jews were still to be found in New York, Chicago,
Los Angeles, Philadelphia, Boston and Miami Beach. This was
a higher percentage of urbanization . . . than could be found
among any other ethnic groups in the United States. Most of
the remaining 35 percent were located in cities of intermediate
size. The "small-town" Jews, perhaps 150,000 in 1950, were
disappearing rapidly, moving into—or being absorbed by—
larger urban areas.

But while the demographic patterns were not changing,
the economic patterns were. If the preoccupation with political and economic liberalism was one basic concern of Jewish
life in the New World, the unremitting struggle for economic
security was another. It was the driving passion of every Jewish immigrant family to rise above proletarian levels, to afford
a more fashionable neighborhood, to belong to a socially
"more acceptable" synagogue, to marry children into a better
economic and social stratum.[49]

"By 1957, perhaps the most characteristic feature of the
economic pyramid was the narrowness of its base: the paucity
of Jewish unskilled workers or farmers. Conversely, some

20 percent of America's 9,000 millionaires were Jews."[50]

Aside from Omaha, where the present Jewish population numbers around 10,000, Lincoln is the only other community where a sizeable community still exists. Yet there were early settlements in other areas of the state. Ella Fleishman Auerbach's history reports communities in the following Nebraska towns: Alliance, Arapahoe, Beatrice, Columbus, Fairbury, Falls City, Fremont, Gothenburg, Grafton, Grand Island, Hastings, Humboldt, Madison, Nebraska City, Neligh, Norfolk, North Platte, Oakland, Plattsmouth, Sargent, Sidney, Tecumseh, Walthill, and West Point. Towns in which there were only one or two Jewish residents were: Albion, Ashland, Elgin, Friend, Gering, Gretna, Harvard, Loup City, Lyons, Pender, Schuyler, Scottsbluff, Silver Creek, and Winnebago.[51]

Whereas the scope of this chapter does not allow for descriptions of the settlements listed above, three communities—Lincoln, Hastings, and Grand Island—are presented in summary form as examples of some of the first colonies.

Lincoln:

The first Jews settled in Lincoln in the late 1860's.[52] In 1885, when the legislature donated city lots for the erecting of houses of worship, a group of Jews went before the state legislature and for $50 were given the deeds to two lots. These were held until 1893 when Congregation B'nai Jeshurun (actually established nine years before) reached 28 in membership and enough money was raised to begin construction. The new Temple was dedicated for Rosh Hashonah (the Jewish New Year) but was unable to support its own rabbi until 1906. An orthodox congregation, now synagogue Tifereth Israel, was organized in 1886; in 1913 funds were collected for a building.

Although the Jewish population numbered only a few hundred, several organizations were established. A Lincoln chapter of B'nai Brith was started in 1886-87, and the Hebrew Relief Society was organized in 1906. A Jewish Ladies Aid Society was also begun.

The Lincoln Jewish community has grown considerably and has been able not only to maintain two synagogues, but also to support several service, educational, charitable and social organizations. As the capital city prospered, many Jewish merchants from Omaha, and around the state, were inspired to begin businesses in Lincoln. Today the population nears 1,000. Jewish names can be found in business and civic groups, university circles and in political and educational areas. (See the catalogue which follows this chapter for a present accounting of Jewish community life in Lincoln.)

Grand Island

The leading Jewish citizen of Grand Island was Samuel N. Wolbach who settled in 1874 and for whom Wolbach, Nebraska, is named. He established a business, Wolbach and Sons, and became active in local politics. He was a member of the lower house of the legislature in 1885, and a member of the state senate in 1887 and 1889. He was an unsuccessful candidate for lieutenant governor of Nebraska in 1892, on the ticket with J. Sterling Morton. Wolbach was one of the organizers of the First National Bank of Grand Island and several other financial institutions in this area of the state.[53]

Hastings

Auerbach lists Emanuel Steinau, later county treasurer, as the first Jewish settler in Hastings. He came in 1873 and worked in the real estate and insurance business.[54] Several Jews were involved in fur buying and trapping in the Adams County area in the 1860's; these people came from Omaha and Kansas City. Apparently these merchants, who operated out of wagons and packs, formed a small community which still endures.

In 1886 a religious congregation was formed called Mt. Sinai Hebrew Congregation of Hastings, Nebraska. At the same time the Mt. Sinai Cemetery Association was organized. Membership in both the cemetery association and the congregation came from many Nebraska communities, including Hastings, Harvard, Sutton, Holdrege, McCook, Central City, Aurora, Blue Hill, Red Cloud, and Ainsworth.

Between 1880 and 1890 it was estimated that some one hundred Jews lived in Adams County. During the first war, a few Jewish businessmen came to Adams County to establish scrap yards, prompted by the government's urgent need for metal.

Over the years, religious services were held in homes and rented halls. In 1931, as a result of the depression and diminished Jewish population, the sacred books were moved to Tifereth Israel Synagogue in Lincoln. In recent years, with easy access to modern transportation, most Jews in the Adams County area are members of Lincoln or Omaha synagoges, where they come for Bar Mitzvah training or confirmation. In 1946, the Jewish women of Hastings, Grand Island, and Kearney started their own chapter of Hadassah, a national women's service organization, and in 1949 the men organized to form a lodge of B'nai Brith.[55]

FOOTNOTES

1. Edward A. Steiner, *The Immigrant Tide: It's Ebb and Flow* (New York: Fleming H. Revell Company, 1919), p. 276.

2. Carol Gendler, correspondence, March, 1976. "Some, especially from Russia, Poland, Galicia, didn't even speak the language of the country in which they lived. Many of the Jewish communities in Europe existed quite apart from and independent of the national state in which they were located. The *kehilla* provided the governmental structure and the tax-collecting process, and the government wanted as little as possible to do with these Jewish communities."

3. Carol Gendler, correspondence, March, 1976."Most came as orthodox Jews. Some German Jews brought reform Judaism with them in the mid-nineteenth century. Conservative Judaism is largely an American invention and was designed to provide a road between orthodoxy and reform for formerly orthodox Americanized Jews as they became assimilated and successful."

4. Carol Gendler, interview, October, 1975.

5. Anita Labeson, *Jewish Pioneers in America 1492-1848* (New York: Brentano's, 1931), pp. 310-11.

6. Carol Gendler, "The Jews of Omaha: the First Sixty Years." (Master's Thesis, University of Omaha, March, 1968), p. 6.

7. *Ibid.*, p. 7.

8. *Ibid.*, p. 8.

9. Robert McMorris, "The People Who Make Up Omaha," *Omaha World-Herald* (December 10, 1961), p. B1.

10. *Ibid.*, p. B5.

11. Ella Fleishman Auerbach, "The Jewish Settlement in Nebraska." (Unpublished typescript, State Historical Society, 1927), p. 11.

12. Albert Woldman, "First Broadcast of Emancipation Proclamation," *The Jewish Digest,* vol. viii, no. 5 (February, 1963), p. 13.

13. Gendler, "The Jews of Omaha," p. 64.

14. McMorris, *op. cit.,* p. B5. Auerbach, *op. cit.,* summary, p. 3.

15. Carol Gendler, interview, October 23, 1975.

16. Gendler, "The Jews of Omaha," p. 69.

17. "Trail Blazers of the Trans-Mississippi West," *American Jewish Archives,* vol. viii, no. 2 (October, 1956), p. 120.

18. *Ibid.*

19. McMorris, *op. cit.,* p. B5.

20.   James C. Olson, *History of Nebraska* (Lincoln: University of Nebraska Press, 1955), pp. 209-10.

21.   *Ibid.*

22.   Gendler, "The Jews of Omaha," p. 31.

23.   Mary Antin, *From Polotzk to Boston* in Howard Morley Sachar, *The Course of Modern Jewish History* (New York: Dell Publishing Company, Inc., 1963), p. 306.

24.   Sachar, *Ibid.*

25.   *Ibid.*

26.   *Ibid.*, p. 309.

27.   Irving Aaron Mandel, "The Attitude of the American Jewish Community Toward East-European Immigration as Reflected in the Anglo-Jewish Press," *American Jewish Archives,* vol. iii, no. 1 (June, 1950), pp. 30-32.

28.   *Ibid.*

29.   Sachar, *op. cit.*, p. 323.

30.   Gendler, "The Jews of Omaha," p. 75.

31.   *Ibid.*, p. 99.

32.   "Trail Blazers," *op. cit.*, pp. 120-21.

33.   Auerbach, *op. cit.*, p. 114.

34.   Gendler, "The Jews of Omaha," p. 76.

35.   *Ibid.*, p. 80.

36.   *Ibid.*, p. 81.

37.   *Ibid.*

38.   Auerbach, *op. cit.*, pp. 67-69 (report and chart).

39.   Gendler, "The Jews of Omaha," p. 77.

40.   Howard P. Chudacoff, "A New Look at Ethnic Neighborhoods: Residential Dispersion and the Concept of Visibility in a Medium-Sized City," *Journal of American History,* vol. Lx, no. 1 (June, 1973), p. 88.

41.   Auerbach, *op. cit.*, p. 70.

42.   *Annual Report,* Associated Jewish Charities, 1914 (in Gendler, "The Jews of Omaha," p. 112).

43.   *Ibid.*

44.   David Bridger, ed., *The New Jewish Encyclopedia,* (New York: Behrman House, Inc., 1962), p. 260.

45.   Robert E. Park and Herbert A. Miller, *Old World Traits Transplanted* (New York: Harper and Brothers Publishers, 1921), pp. 210-11.

46.   Sachar, *op. cit.*, p. 71.

47.   Cecil Roth and Geoffrey Wigoder, eds., *The New Standard*

Jewish Encyclopedia (Garden City, New York: Doubleday and Company, Inc., 1970), p. 471.

48.　Solomon Grayzel, *A History of Contemporary Jews from 1900 to the Present* (New York: Harper and Row Publishers, 1960), p. 125.

49.　Sachar, *op. cit.*, p. 343.

50.　*Ibid.*, p. 346.

51.　Auerbach, *op. cit.*, pp. 125-64. (See these pages for details, names of settlers, etc.)

52.　*Ibid.*, pp. 125-36.

53.　*Ibid.*, pp. 145-46.

54.　*Ibid.*, pp. 147-49.

55.　Max D. Prostok and David Rosenberg, "History of the Jewish People in Adams County and City of Hastings, Nebraska." (Unpublished paper prepared for the Adams County Historical Society, November 30, 1970.)

CATALOGUE

HOW TO FIND OUT ABOUT NEBRASKA JEWS

Lincoln

The Jewish community of Lincoln, Nebraska numbers approximately one thousand, a figure which has remained surprisingly constant through the century. The vast preponderance of the Jewish community (probably 90 percent) belongs to the two congregations: Tifereth Israel (with a membership of about 180 families) and B'nai Jeshurun (with a membership of 90 families). The two congregations reflect the spectrum of contemporary Jewish belief and practice. Tifereth Israel is a conservative congregation with traditional tendencies (perhaps 10 percent of its families keep kosher) while B'nai Jeshurun is a reform congregation with classical reform tendencies.

While differing in standards of Jewish belief and practice, the congregations in recent years have been moving toward the development of joint goals. In addition to the traditional combined annual Federation service which initiates each year's fund raising appeal, the congregations have united to protest certain matters of combined interest such as jointly condemning at a unified service the recent United Nations anti-Zionist resolution. This past year, the congregations, under the auspices of the Lincoln Jewish Welfare Federation, sponsored an educational workshop featuring a leading thinker on the contemporary Jewish scene. Also, the congregations have experimented successfully in conducting combined adult education classes.

Organizations and Community Services

Lincoln Jewish Welfare Federation is a voluntary association of contributers, agencies, and organizations that seeks to serve the needs of the Jewish community. Its funds are derived primarily from the Jewish Philanthropies, Israel Emergency Funds and private contributions, which are then allocated to the local, national and overseas beneficiaries.

Herb Gaba, President
Louis Finkelstein, Treasurer

Congregation B'nai Jeshurun

Sheldon Stick, President

Congregation Tifereth Israel
> Sheldon Kushner, President

Hadassah
> Cece Hill, President

South Street Temple (B'nai Jeshurun) Sisterhood
> Mrs. Max Ellinger, President

Tifereth Israel Sisterhood
> Elaine Evnen, President

B'nai Brith
> Robert Pitlor, President

South Street Temple Youth Group
> Steve Dworsky, President

United Synagogue Youth
> Paul Chandler, Tom Segal
> Co-Presidents

B'nai Brith Youth
> Dan Nieden, President

Other Resources

Rabbi Mark Bisman, of Tifereth Israel, and Rabbi Bob Kaiser, B'nai Jeshurun (South Street Temple) are excellent resource people for an on-going accounting of Jewish life in Lincoln. Written resource materials are extremely sparce; the only history was compiled by Ella Fleishman Auerbach in 1927, an unpublished typescript entitled "The Jewish Settlement in Nebraska." Mostly a listing of names of early settlers in Lincoln, this manuscript is useful for tracing family histories and is available at the Lincoln State Historical Society library. Perhaps the best resource on Jewish history in the state is Carol Gendler of Omaha, who for the past ten years has amassed file cabinets of data with the intention of publishing a book on the subject (see Omaha Jewish History Project, this catalogue, for more information.)

Some Written Materials

The poet and critic Karl Shapiro, who spent about eight years in Lincoln as editor of *Prairie Schooner,* reflects on the nature of Judaism in his introduction to *Poems of a Jew:*

> No one has been able to define *Jew,* and in essence this
> defiance of definition is the central meaning of Jewish con-
> sciousness. For to be a Jew is to be in a certain state of con-
> sciousness which is inescapable. As everyone knows, a Jew
> who becomes an atheist remains a Jew. A Jew who becomes a
> Catholic remains a Jew. Being a Jew is the consciousness of
> being a Jew, and the Jewish identity, with or without religion,
> with or without history, is the significant fact. The Jew is
> unique among mankind, once he accepts this identity, and the
> word *Jew* retains its eternal shock, a shock that has nothing to
> do with Christ or the Crucifixion. The shock has to do with
> the Covenant, the intimacy of Jew and God. This intimacy is
> not sentimental; on the contrary, it is unfriendly. And it is the
> kind of intimacy that precludes religion itself—for Judaism is
> the minimum religion—and, secondarily, art itself. The unbe-
> lievable survival of the Jews must be seen against a background
> of Nothing, a people outside art or literature, a people in dread
> of the graven image, a people outside a Heaven and Hell,
> whose very sanctum sanctorum is an empty chamber. Yet this
> background of Nothing does not signify asceticism but the
> opposite, the sense of worldliness. The Jew is absolutely com-
> mitted to the world. This people beyond philosophy, beyond
> art, virtually beyond religion, a stranger even to mysticism,
> finds itself at the very center of the divine manifestation—man.
> The Jew represents the primitive ego of the human race; he is
> its first exponent, the first, as it were, to accept the mission of
> the ego. This mission of the ego has proved all but suicidal,
> and yet the Jew cannot be erased from human consciousness,
> even by force.

Mordecai Marcus, local poet and member of the English staff at the
University of Nebraska, reflects his Jewish background in his writing. The
following are examples of Marcus' poetry where Jewish themes are central:

THE SADNESS OF APOSTASY
Reprinted from *Shaman*

> I do not go
> any longer
> to the synagogue.
> Have not in truth gone

these thirty-one years.
I remember sitting
over breakfast
readied for school
while my father
readied himself
for the Yom Kippur.
His eyes
more shy than pained
evaded mine,
and I was unsure
in my defiance.
Longer ago,
at the roots of childhood,
I went with him
to the old ash-gray synagogue
on Victory Boulevard,
sat out my pointless hours,
saw my father nodding
over the prayer books,
approving me—
good little Jewish boy.
But such acts
hardened to cruelty
in the years I sat
forced to sound out
the Hebrew symbols
that were blank
to my understanding.

I do not go
any longer
to the synagogue
because something
twists in me
at the naming
of Adonai.
Because I would not
be greeted
by an aura
of fellowship
recalling
the ashy nourishment
of my childhood

where the sound of love
was another
blankness of humming.
Forever churchless,
I will have men
for my brothers
by a harsher choosing,
with the pains
of candor
and the anguish
of my own exclusions.

I do not go
any longer
to the synagogue,
for the poem
of its form
is dead to me,
though now
for a flickering moment
I think of you,
Ancient of Days,
in the agonized gap
between meaningless matter
and the forms
of truth and beauty.
It's a strange
shape you take—
twisted ropes
of anger and love
woven into a knowing cloud
on all horizons.
Ancient of Days,
all that precedes you
is rooted in dark places
that need our light.

LONG-DISTANCE
Reprinted from *Shenandoah*

It is my father's voice
from fifteen-hundred miles,
at the end of eighty-six knots
on the rope of years.
He says he is dangling
over hell. He wants divinity,
not librium. He can't stand
my sister dismantling his nerves.
He is holed up in a boardwalk hotel
with his Hebrew Bible
and his bottomless sack
of betrayals that
nobody understands.
He tells me that I
don't know what it's like.
And will I please send
him back some of his money.

Dad, when I listened to you
all those years
banging a pot on the kitchen floor
so I would come and
help you to the bed of pity,
all I had was a closed fist
and a gaping heart.
Now I am full of gifts
that will bring you even less.

As for the money you gave me,
I will send either all
or none of it back to you.
I won't supply you slowly
with stakes for the love-hate game
you play with my sister.
You drink away at her angry words
as at a bubbling fountain—
only to boast
that the slather on your lips
is the final poison.

Here is another rope.
It is the long hurt of loneliness
drawn taut. You never saw
how its tangled strands
choked our lives,
nor did you know
that hand over fist
with the candor of quiet pain
a man can swing up.

WHAT'S IN A NAME?
Reprinted from *Pebble*

When the Mirkens unshipped
on shores they could not trust,
they tossed aside those
nice syllables and called
themselves after the
predominant judge (in America
a Jew goes far), Marcus.

When Manglenamed Mournit
was asked if he wanted
the name Marvin still, or
would he prefer that
they use only his
anglicized Yiddisha moniker
for a daily tag,
he was bullied to make
the wrong choice
and so he became—
in the word's mouth—
Mordecai Marcus.

When Mornisgray Marquest
opened his eyes to various
dawns, he could not find
the clear window
all are entitled to.
He fumbled at the world
they told him was true,
sickening for want
of the real one
they always denied.

When Makeplaceforme Meltwit
took the bit between his teeth,
it took a score of years
to close the spaces
between himself and
a realer world, but
seeing the work was to be
chiefly his own, at last
(he was then past forty)
he became in fact
Mordecai Marcus,
hesitant but hopeful to be
before scholar and poet
at least a man,
and to look constantly
out of his own window.

Of General Interest

Irving Howe, *World of Our Fathers*
Abraham Cahan, *The Rise of David Levinsky*
Oscar Handlin, *The Uprooted*
Hutchins Hapgood, *Spirit of the Ghetto*
Karl Shapiro, *Poems of a Jew, The Bourgeois Poet*
Film: "Hester Street"

Omaha

In the one hundred years since the first formal synagogue was organized, the Omaha Jewish community has developed a large variety of community groups to meet religious, educational, social service, recreational and philanthropy needs. Major responsibility for the dispensation of charity and social service within the Jewish community was assumed by the Associated Jewish Charities upon its formation in 1903. By 1914, most of the religious, fraternal and charitable organizations within the community and affiliated with the Associated Jewish Charities joined to form the Jewish Welfare Federation. Since that time, a well-knit pattern of services has developed, each contributing to the community welfare and each providing valuable benefits to the lives of Omaha's Jewish people.

Community Services

Jewish Federation of Omaha
    333 South 132nd Street 334-8200
    Executive Director. . . . . Lou Solomon

Is a voluntary association of contributors, agencies, and organizations that
seeks to serve the needs of the Jewish community. Its funds are derived primarily from the Jewish Philanthropies and Israel Emergency Funds, which are
then allocated to the local, national and overseas beneficiaries. Among its
many functions and departments are community planning, internal relations,
services. It maintains a community calendar to clear dates.

Jewish Community Library
    333 South 132nd Street 334-8200
    Librarian . . . . Mrs. Martin Wolf

Contains a comprehensive collection of books of all Jewish subjects, recordings of Jewish interest, a film library, library of filmstrips, extensive reference
files of materials and helps for Jewish club programs and activities and a
children's judaica department.

Jewish Press
    333 South 132nd Street 334-8200
    Editor . . . . Rich Pearl

Is issued weekly and serves as the medium of Jewish news of local, regional,
national, and world-wide interest, and for Jewish education through its articles
and news columns.

Jewish Philanthropies
    333 South 132nd Street 334-8200
    Campaign Associate . . . . .Samuel Lauber

Is the fund raising department of the Federation, which conducts the annual
over-all campaign for funds to meet Jewish needs in Omaha, nationally, overseas, and Israel. This campaign eliminates duplication in fund raising by conducting one drive for all agencies and institutions. Separate divisions being:
Men, Women, High School and College.

Federation of Jewish Women's Organizations
    333 South 132nd Street 334-8200

Cooperates with the Jewish Federation of Omaha in carrying out its commu-
nity-wide functions. Participates as a unit in city-wide civic causes, and serves
the Armed Forces.

Dr. Philip Sher Jewish Home for the Aged
　　4801 North 52nd Street 451-7220
　　Director. . . . . Ben Laub
　　Mikvah

Provides a Jewish home atmosphere, which includes boarding, nursing and
convalescent care for Jewish aged, as well as a program of occupational and
recreational therapy for its residents. Cooperation organizations: Bikur Cholim
and National Council of Jewish Women, Omaha section.

Jewish Family Service
　　333 South 132nd Street 334-8200

Conducts a program of family counseling for the purpose of strengthening
Jewish family life in the community. It concerns itself with helping families
enjoy productive and to rehabilitate disturbed families. It offers counseling in
marital problems, physical and mental illness and handicaps, vocational adjustment, adoption and drug related problems. It processes scholarship applica-
tions for Camp Esther K. Newman and college. Counseling on all Israeli programs is also available. Limited funds are available for financial assistance.

Community Relations Committee
　　537 Securities Building. 341-3575
　　Director. . . . . Howard Weinstein

Conducts a community relations program, coordinating Jewish civic-protective
activities in Omaha, establishing and maintaining good relations in matters
affecting the Jewish and general community, and promoting better understanding among all groups in the community.

Bureau of Jewish Education
　　333 South 132nd Street 334-8200
　　Chairman. . . . . Rabbi Daniel Breslauer

Promotes Jewish education in the community, sets standards, coordinates and
provides financial assistance to Jewish religious schools in the community.

Jewish Community Center
　　333 South 132nd Street 334-8200
　　Director. . . . . Hy Tabachnick

Serves the leisure time need for the Jewish Community of all ages, through
recreational, cultural, social, educational, athletic and character-building programs and facilities. It promotes the American way of life as well as intensifies
Jewish culture and traditions. It is the "Town Hall" of the Jewish community.

Esther K. Newman Camp

333 South 132nd Street 334-8200

Director. . . . . Robert Litvak

A co-educational camp for children which provides outdoor vacation, and opportunities for personality development with emphasis on meeting spiritual needs of Jewish children.

Nursery School

333 South 132nd Street 334-8200

Director. . . . . Robert Litvak

The nursery school facilities consist of three spacious and cheerful rooms opening onto a large outdoor play area designed especially for young children. Children use many of the facilities of the new JCC, including the gym, the swimming pool, the library, the dance studio, the crafts studios, and the theatre. The nursery school has been designed with its own entrance, office, and isolation room in case of illness. One-way observation windows permit classrooms to be observed without distracting the children.

Jewish Cultural & Performing Art Department

333 South 132nd Street 334-8200

Director. . . . . Mark Zalkin

Omaha's Jewish cultural activities are planned and coordinated by the Jewish Cultural Arts Council which serves as the advisory arm to the Cultural Arts Department. The Arts Council is responsible for the following programs: Adult Jewish Studies, Jewish Forum Lecture Series, classes and activities in Music, Drama, Art and Dance, JCC Center Stage Series, JCC Film classes series, and performing arts special events. The Arts Council has representatives from all of Omaha's major synagogues, major organizations and the Jewish Community Center.

Older Adults

333 South 132nd Street 334-8200

Director. . . . . Molly Delman

Holds regular Monday Luncheon and activities sessions, Wednesday and Thursday morning lounge activity, gala monthly dinner meetings and special programs, special study circles, crafts activities, movies, trips and tours, and swimming programs. Older Adults are active and interested in engaging in purposeful recreational, educational and cultural pursuits. An Older Adult Advisory Committee will be formed so that participants can share in planning of the programs.

Jewish Youth Council
     333 South 132nd Street 334-8200
     Director. . . . . Jeff Lowe

> Is a Federation of all teenage clubs that aims to bring about unity among Jewish youth and through which they act together on common problems, and carry on joint activities. It aids groups in the development of their programs, youth education and leadership development.

Omaha Jewish Day School
     126th & Pacific Street 333-1919
     Consulting Coordinator . . . . .Rabbi Jack Zelasko

> The Jewish Day School of Omaha operates for grades Kindergarten through 4th with one full-time teacher and one part-time teacher. One teaches the general studies program and the other teaches the secular studies programs. The school formally opened in September, 1972, and hopes to expand into the upper grades in future years. The school is not affiliated with any National Day School Association, but is a community supported school receiving financial assistance from the Jewish Federation of Omaha, but operating as an independent organization. It is approved by the State of Nebraska.

Synagogues and Temples

Orthodox

B'nai Jacob
3028 Cumings. 342-2737

> Services only.

Beth Israel
1502 North 52nd Street 556-6288
Rabbi Isaac Nadoff

> Daily Minyon Services, Hebrew School, Religious School, Sisterhood, Men's Club, Youth Group (SYO), Nursery School, and Services.

Conservative

Beth El
210 South 49th Street 553-3221
Rabbi Kenneth Bromberg

> Daily Minyon Services, Hebrew School, Religious School, Sisterhood, Men's Club, Youth Group (USY), and Services.

Reform

Temple Israel
7023 Cass Street 556-6536
Rabbi Sidney Brooks

> Hebrew School, Religious School, Men's Club, Sisterhood, Youth Group
> (NIFTY).

A Proposal: Omaha Jewish History Project

Carol Gendler, an Omaha historian, has been working for the past
ten years gathering data on Jewish history in Nebraska. Her work began in
the form of a master's thesis submitted to the department of history of the
University of Nebraska at Omaha in 1968 and is entitled "The Jews of
Omaha: The First Sixty Years." Gendler is presently seeking funds to
launch an Omaha Jewish History Project, an effort to document the lives,
activities, experiences, and contributions of the Jews of Omaha, and to
collate and publish in narrative form the data collected.

Excerpts from Gendler's proposal reflect the scope of the project:

> Local Jewish histories are being published throughout
> the United States. They represent an attempt to increase our
> understanding of the national Jewish experience, and of the
> contribution of Jews to American life, as well as the processes
> through which Jews have become a part of the mainstream of
> American historical development. A comprehensive history of
> Jews in America can be undertaken only after local experi-
> ences are recorded. We must discover the local similarities and
> differences in regard to such areas as religious observance,
> community institutions, the interaction of Jews with each
> other and with the community at large, and the particular
> characteristics of the local Jewish community vis a vis the gen-
> eral community. More than one hundred local Jewish histories
> have now been published, including those of such nearby com-
> munities as Sioux City, Des Moines, Milwaukee, and the Jews
> of Colorado.
>
> Similarly, ethnic history is an important and necessary
> part of general local history. Little work has been done on the
> history of Omaha; in fact, the last published work is now more
> than fifty years old. The history of the Jews of Omaha will
> one day become part of a larger work—a history of the city of
> Omaha.

The published work which will result from this long-range study will cover genealogy, local history, ethnic history, business and economic and social history, and documentation of the religious life and the contributions of Jews to city, state, and country. Omaha Jewish history dates from 1855, the very beginning of this community.

PROGRAM: There must be a concerted effort to gather together all of the source materials available in the community: institutional records, private manuscripts, business records, family histories, photographs, films—in short, whatever can be found. This will require cooperation from a great many people. The project historian has already succeeded in acquiring a large number of primary materials. They have been found in attics, basements, private homes, and synagogues, as well as at the Jewish Community Center. Many more documents should be available somewhere in the community. Much has probably been lost. We should ensure that the records of all of the organizations and institutions of the community are preserved and properly cared for. In this regard, a community archival collection should be organized, preferably in space provided at the Jewish Community Center. Synagogues and Jewish organizations should be encouraged to collect and preserve their archival material.

Another aspect of the program is oral history. The project historian is presently engaged in discussions with the Omaha Section, National Council of Jewish Women, in hopes that NCJW will undertake an oral history project. The information collected from this oral history project would then become part of the raw material of the final product. . . .

ADDITIONAL INFORMATION: The project historian would solicit cooperation from the Omaha Jewish Federation and other local organizations in terms of helping to locate materials and documents, and in terms of establishing a community archival program. The Jewish Community Center has indicated willingness to cooperate in this effort by providing some space and equipment for the community archives.

PROFILE OF PROJECT HISTORIAN: Carol Gendler holds a B.A. degree in political science from Wellesley College and an M.A. degree in history from the University of Nebraska at Omaha. She is a member of the boards of directors of the Omaha Public Library and the Douglas County Historical Society, has been a contributor to *Nebraska History* (journal of the Nebraska State Historical Society), the *Western States*

Jewish Historical Quarterly, and writes a weekly column, "In Retrospect," for the *Jewish Press.* She is director of the Omaha High School of Jewish Studies.

The author of this chapter would like to see Gendler's proposal expanded to include the history of Jews in the whole state. Anyone interested in supporting this project should contact Betty Levitov, Department of English, University of Nebraska, Lincoln, 68588—or Carol Gendler, 9820 Spring Street, Omaha, 98124.

VIII

Italians: La Famiglia

By Betty Levitov

ACKNOWLEDGMENTS

I wish to thank the library staff of the Nebraska State Historical Society, especially Dave Hoober, for all their help. The assistance of Anthony Troia of the Sons of Italy in compiling the resource section, and the editorial assistance of Peter Levitov is also greatly appreciated.

Above. The wine industry employed Italian immigrants in the 30's, in the factories and warehouses. *Below.* Italians continued to prosper in shoe repair businesses, barber shops and restaurants.

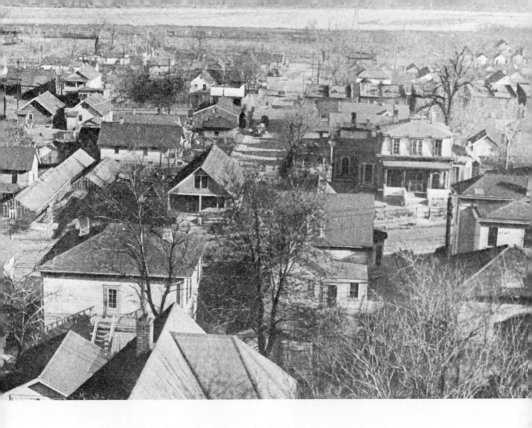

This cluster of houses in the vicinity of lower Pierce Street is a view of Omaha's "Little Italy," around 1930. The Missouri River at the top of the photograph forms the east boundary.

Above. Italian immigrants arriving after 1880 for the most part joined general construction crews and railroad maintenance gangs across the state *(directly below).* *Bottom.* Workers in a macaroni factory in Omaha.

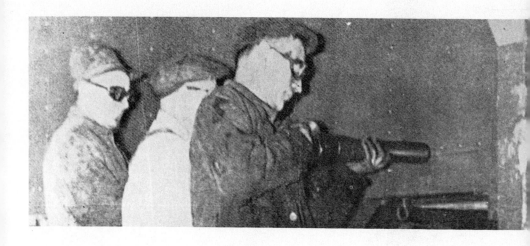

Saint Francis Cabrini Church in Omaha, Nebraska.

This statue of Santa Lucia was brought to Nebraska from Italy to be used in the annual Santa Lucia festival and is permanently displayed in the Saint Francis Cabrini Church in Omaha. (Courtesy of the Santa Lucia Society.)

SANTA LUCIA V. e M.
PAT. DI CARLENTINI MCMXXV

VIII

Italians: La Famiglia

By Betty Levitov

Before the organized immigration of the late 19th and 20th centuries, the Midwest was largely populated by adventurers, explorers, traders, and missionaries who more or less traveled back and forth across the Missouri without any intentions of settling. Italian names can be found among journals and letters as early as 1820.[1] The most well-known early missionary explorer in the Midwest, the Belgian Jean DeSmet, for example, mentions Italian lay brothers and priests who served in various Catholic missions. Notable among them were Brother Andrew Mazzella who served as carpenter, shoemaker, tailor, laborer, farmer, cook, sacristan and doctor for two years at the Pottawattamie village (Council Bluffs) and Father Gregorio Mengarini who volunteered to serve the Flathead Indian Mission in Montana.

By 1860 the United States Census listed 18 foreign-born Italians in Nebraska Territory, which then included parts of Montana, Wyoming, Colorado, North and South Dakota. Two men who were among these Italian pioneers are usually considered Nebraska's first permanent Italian settlers. John Godola, a shoe merchant who had come from Genoa, was listed as a leading businessman in Omaha in 1857. George Ciacomini left for America at the age of 18 in search of freedom and opportunity. He first found work in a restaurant in St. Louis and later earned enough there to become a restaurant manager in Leavenworth,

Kansas. In just two years he was able to save enough to open his own business and he chose Omaha as a promising location. In 1863 he opened the Nebraska Bar and Restaurant at the corner of Thirteenth and Douglas Streets.[2] He eventually was able to buy the building in which his restaurant was located and added a barber shop and baths. In 1868 he sent to Lombardy for his brothers, Antonio and Pietro, and employed them in the business.

The Nebraska census for 1870 lists only 44 Italians.[3] For the most part they were from the North, and were either established tradesmen looking for a more prosperous market, or adventurers seeking excitement and chance in the new world. They were a scattered group, differing widely in social, business and occupational interests and often speaking different dialects ("Piemontesi," "Calabresi," "Siciliani"). Among them were Omaha's first fruit and vegetable vendors and street musicians; there were shoemakers, tailors, cooks, barbers, laborers, railroad workers, masons, and scissors and knife grinders (complete with clanging bell and grindstone outfit). With few resident Italians able to patronize their countrymen, conditions were not conducive to the success of Italians in the professions. Except for musicians, where language presented no problem, few early settlers rose to prominence in the professional/cultural arena.

Two trends were apparent in the early settlement. The immigrants who came without families and without intentions to remain any longer than it would take to save some money put up in cheap boarding houses. These houses, located in an area between Jackson and Leavenworth Streets and from Thirteenth to Sixteenth Streets, had provided residence for earlier immigrant groups. While these settlements were regarded as locales for Italians, the population was so transient that they were not identified as communities, as such.

As opposed to this rather unstable settlement, there were newcomers—mostly from Calabria and Basilicata—who either brought families or married soon after arrival. These people tended to establish homes, more often flimsy shacks than anything else, but they had a sense of permanent commitment to Omaha and each other.[4]

An amusing, but unlikely, legend concerns the establishment of Omaha's Calabresi colony, later called "Dago Hill."
A newspaper account read as follows:

> The story has it that a number of early-day Calabresi
> immigrants built temporary houses in a low-lying area at
> Twentieth Streets and Poppleton Avenue. Heavy rains came.
> Police moved the residents to higher ground four blocks to the
> east. One of the rescuers ordered the flood victims: "Stay
> here!" They did. Permanently.[5]

The flow of Italian immigration into the United States
between 1881-1890 was nearly six times as great as the previous
decade; the flow for the following decade was still greater, with
a total of 651,893 arrivals. And between 1901-1910 the wave of
Italian immigration reached 2,045,877,[6] a magnitude never
again equalled. Of this last number, Omaha received 2,477
immigrants, an increase of 444 percent over the last decade.[7]

The new Italian immigrant was a male and usually came to
this country alone, with a brother, or perhaps with a male
friend. He was likely to be from the peasant or "contadini"
class and from the South.[8] The four strata in the Southern
Italian social system were:

(1) galantuomini (upper class)—large landowners, profes-
    sionals such as doctors, lawyers, teachers, bureaucrats.
(2) artigiani-mercanti (artisans and merchants)—dependent
    on both upper class and peasant.
(3) contadini (peasants)—usually owned small land plots and
    modest houses in town, animals and some tools.
(4) giornalieri (day laborers)—propertyless, agricultural day
    laborers, lowest stratum.[9]

To pay for his passage, he may have borrowed money, worked
aboard ship, been subsidized by friends or relatives, or was
advanced funds by a "padrone." Life in steerage—as has been
replayed for Americans in countless films—was grim, several
weeks long, crowded and uncomfortable. Italians have been

pictured with knapsacks of cheese and salami to supplement the soup doled out to passengers. Lice, scurvy and seasickness added to the general misery. Once finally on land, the immigrants were subjected to demeaning literacy tests and physical examinations. A few were met by family or "padroni," but many others, with name tags pinned to their clothing, were victimized by boarding-house swindlers or loan sharks.

The Padrone System Shields and Exploits

The "padrone" system grew up out of the seventeenth century indentured servant tradition, in which a "padrone" or boss made a contract for labor with an individual. The "padrone" in the U.S. was one who spoke the language of the immigrant and who acted as a middleman between the American employer and the worker. Guidance by the "padrone" had the advantage of "shielding the laborer against the excesses of employers"[10] and provided the security of job, food, bed, and often the company of compatriots (in the labor gangs). The disadvantages soon became apparent. A self-serving "padrone," in collusion with contractors, could easily exploit the guillible immigrant, binding him from one to seven years in a low-paying contract.

There were also honest "padroni" in this country who saw it as their mission to take over some of the old-world family functions. Secchi de Casali was one such "padroni" who recognized the importance of relieving those countrymen crowded in the ghettos and directing them towards rural districts. In 1874 Casali and an American landowner, Charles Landis, developed tracts of land in Vineland, New Jersey, for an Italian colony. The men worked in factories and women and children picked berries on farms, earning the money to buy uncleared land for $20-$25 an acre. By 1908 over 950 families owned land. Vineland was one example of how Italians could manage without "padroni" as the colony eventually became self-supporting.[11]

Conditions deteriorated to such an extent that at the turn of the century the Society for the Protection of Italian Immigrants was formed to help newcomers at dockside.[12] The Society's first secretary, Gino C. Speranza, with the aid of the Italian government, amassed volunteers to help the immigrants find family, friends, housing and employment. The organization put pressure on landlords to improve substandard housing and investigated the wretched conditions of labor camps.

In spite of the poverty of the Italian immigrants, the 1904 Bureau of Immigration records reveal that they were not high on pauper lists nor did they dominate welfare rolls or charitable institutions. Of foreign-born indigents, the following percentages were recorded in 1904:[13]

Irish	30 %
Germans	19 %
English	8.5%
Italians	8 %
Hebrews	8 %

In New York City alone there were 258 Italian mutual aid societies, mostly weak, unstructured organizations supported by nickel-dime contributions, but reflective of an awakening sense of community among Italians in American cities, and the emergence of "Little Italys."[14]

The Italians constituted a significant segment of the swarms of southern Europeans crowding into Ellis Island at the turn of the century. Social, economic and political conditions in the home country best account for the numbers who left Italy for America. Italy was beset with problems. Periodic famines, harshened by an increasing population, accounted for the poverty of the village and farm people in the South. Poor rainfall, depleted soil and diseases made life for the "contadini" an unending struggle. (In 1887 more than 21,000 people died of malaria.)[15] In the North a revival of industry was favored by protective tariffs, while at the same time disproportionate burdens of taxation contributed further to the weakening of the economy of the South. In 1870 Italy became united, but the average Italian was not able to cultivate a national set of perspectives.

During 1900, an estimated one million workers spent up to
two months a year working away from their own village.[16]
The land distribution promised by Garibaldi never materialized
so that the wealthy "galantuomo" maintained exclusive property rights. The peasant population were relegated to minimal
plots of substandard land, paying high rents as well as a sizeable
portion of the crops to the nobles. While the government was
collectively regarded as the "enemy," there were little or no
cooperative efforts towards change.

Finally, the Italian government began to adopt a positive
policy towards emigration. While other immigrant groups left
their homelands as political refugees, the Italian left with a
sense of pride, as if emigration were an act of patriotism. Luigi
Bodio, head of the Italian Immigration Bureau, 1894-95,
praised emigration as a step towards bettering and equalizing
conditions for Italians. He asserted that emigration was a
safety valve, or security, against envy and class hatred, and an
"efficacious instrument in the equalization of human forces;
that emigration was not only desirable but necessary for Italy,
that with the present industrial and agricultural conditions, with
so little capital to dispose of, thousands of Italians might go
forth to find work."[17]

Pascal d'Angelo, an immigrant who was called the "Pick
and Shovel Poet," recorded in 1910 why he left Italy:

> Our people have to emigrate. It is a matter of too much
> boundless life and too little space. . . . Every bit of cultivatable
> soil is owned by those fortunate few who lord over us. Before
> spring comes over the valley all the obtainable land is rented
> out or given to the peasants for a season under usurious condi-
> tions, namely for three-fourths, one-half, or one-fourth of the
> crops. . . . But now there was escape from the rich landowners,
> from the terrors of drought, from the spectre of starvation, in
> the boundless America out of which people returned with
> fabulous tales of thousands of lira—riches unheard of before,
> among the peasants.[18]

Several other factors stimulated emigration. One was the fear of
eventual restrictive immigration laws by the American govern-

ment—physical examinations, literacy tests, quotas. Letters
from the United States telling of jobs and money were highly
effective inducements. The Commissioner General of Immigration in 1907 described the process:

> . . . after a few months of employment here he has been able
> to save from $150-$200, a small fortune to the immigrant
> peasant. He pictures in homely but glowing terms the oppor-
> tunities in this country for making money. . . . The letter is
> read by every inhabitant of the village and perhaps passed on
> to other neighboring hamlets. Others are induced to emigrate,
> selling their belongings, mortgaging their property, almost
> enslaving themselves in order to procure the amount of passage
> money.[19]

Ease of transportation and cheapness of steerage encouraged emigration. In 1901 the rate from Naples to New York was
$28.[20] From 40 to 50 percent of the immigrants who arrived
in America had their passage prepaid by relatives or friends.
From 10 to 25 percent bought tickets with money sent from
the USA. Shipping companies poured energy into the encouragement of emigration. In 1895 there were 34 agents and 1,769
sub-agents whose sole purpose was to facilitate emigration to
America.[21] The "padroni" as well cooperated with shipping
companies, often financing transportation, in recruiting their
work gangs. Edward Corsi wrote:

> We saw strangers proudly wearing heavy gold chains and
> we knew they came from the New World. Stories of the ease
> with which money could be earned in America flew through
> the peninsula and thousands of people from grandfathers to
> small boys came to center their new interest in America. My
> own cousin returned from New York and spoke of nothing but
> the wonders of America while at the same time berating what
> he termed those "stupid" people who remained to suffer in
> Italy.[22]

While Nebraska did not feel the immediate impact of the
increasing numbers of Italians entering the United States, the
Italian settlement in Omaha progressed towards permanence

and stability. Rising to prominence at about the turn of the century were Samuel Mancuso and Lousi J. Piatti. Mancuso worked untiringly to assist newcomers in getting jobs and adjusting themselves to the new environment. "Il Calabrese," as Mancuso was called, worked with Piatti, an attorney, to encourage Italians to take an active role in politics. Mancuso, a Republican, and Piatti, a Democrat, held up to Italians the objective of exercising group political influence.

Piatti was selected as an Omaha delegate to the Democratic state convention of 1896 and in 1900 as a Nebraska delegate to the Democratic national convention. Mancuso founded the Omaha Italian Club, organized primarily as a mutual benefit society but channeling its energy to the furtherance of Republican candidates in the 1900 election. Mancuso became president of this organization and became known as "King of Little Italy," with a "somewhat indefinite domain extending over the Calabrese colony and other scattered Italian groups."[23]

The arrival of an overwhelming number of Sicilian immigrants eventually resulted in the loss of power by Mancuso, however he and Piatti and other leaders of recognized stature in Omaha not only stimulated Americanization ambitions among the newcomers, but also modified the general attitude of Omahans towards the Italian population lumped together in slang designations as "dagos," "guineas," and "wops."[24]

At the time the Sicilians came in large numbers to Nebraska, the demand for unskilled labor was unprecedented. The railroad, packing plants, stockyards, and smelting plants were expanding and adding maintenance crews and shop workers. General construction was booming. "Omaha had become an open shop town in which there were no barriers between new immigrants and the jobs they sought."[25]

The information on the next page gives a breakdown of the Italians coming to, and leaving, Nebraska from 1900 to 1920.[26]

ITALIAN IMMIGRATION TO NEBRASKA

Year	Arrivals		Departures	
	North Italians	*South Italians*	*North Italians*	*South Italians*
1900-01	11	43		
1901-02	13	13		
1902-03	28	46		
1903-04	50	100		
1904-05	35	68		
1905-06	44	264		
1906-07	41	573		
1907-08	27	259		
1908-09	39	504	21	91
1909-10	45	578	18	74
1910-11	48	575	24	148
1911-12	39	248	14	260
1912-13	70	891	13	134
1913-14	93	875	25	99
1914-15	85	13	8	145
1915-16	51	26	12	244
1916-17	18	21	4	32
1917-18	0	35	1	21
1918-19	0	23	1	15
1919-20	51	226	15	208

Joseph Salerno[27] came to Omaha in 1895 from Carlentini, eastern Sicily, in response to an invitation from his brother-in-law, who wrote of business opportunities. Salerno opened a shoe repair shop at 6th and Pierce Streets, a district into which Italians were moving. Sebastiano, Joseph's brother, followed in 1897 and opened a shoe shop and second-hand clothing store at 10th and Pierce. At the same time, Joseph added a small grocery store to his own shoe shop.

In 1904, Sebastiano Salerno, who was prospering in his

business, received an appointment as a steamship company
agent and went back to Carlentini to encourage more people to
emigrate. He persuaded many of his friends to buy tickets and
even lent them money when financing was needed. On Sebastiano's return, the brothers established a group of boarding
houses in the vicinity of 6th and Pierce Streets:

> . . . This ready-made community, presided over by the friendly
> Salernos—with its cheap housing, prospects for immediate
> jobs, a store where American clothes could be bought on
> credit, a grocery store selling foodstuffs familiar to the new
> arrivals—eased somewhat the transplantation of the immi-
> grants from a warm climate into a radically altered environ-
> ment.[28]

As the immigrants prospered with the aid of the Salernos,
the Salernos prospered in turn through the success of the
Sicilians. The Salernos inspired so much confidence that they
were sought out to safeguard the treasured dollars the Italians
were able to save. Eventually the brothers set up a private bank
in 1908, the Bank of Sicily (Banca di Sicilia), of which Sebastiano was president. Many of the new arrivals also had a
passionate desire to own their own houses; with a bank loan
(from Banca di Sicilia) and a $100 down payment, one could
buy a five-room house for $2,000.[29]
An unhappy footnote to the story of the Salernos was the
failure of the Bank of Sicily in 1920. At that point the bank
held about $100,000 for some 500 depositers. Sebastiano
invested heavily in the Florida land boom and when much of
the land was declared useless swamp, he lost practically everything. He was bitterly resented by his friends and compatriots
and found life in Omaha impossible; he scratched enough
money together to move to San Pedro, California. From what
he could salvage from his wretched enterprises, he opened a
small clothing store. An embittered depositer from Omaha, a
dishwasher who lost his life's savings in the bank, followed
Salerno, tracked him down seven years after the demise of the
Bank of Italy, and shot him to death.

There were others besides the Salernos who who directed their energy in and investments towards the needs of the new immigrants. Angelo Charles Rosso was a prosperous fruit dealer who ran the "Palazzo Rosso" with manager Agostino Minardi. The "Palazzo Rosso"—at 14th and Leavenworth Streets—was a rooming house and business center for Italians. On the first floor were a bakery, saloon, personal loan agency, barber shop, labor agency and restaurant. The "Palazzo Rosso" was apparently widely known, so that immigrants who had ideas of traveling west when they landed in New York were told of it before they left the East Coast.[30]

Through the activities of these and many other Italians, the state welcomed immigrants from Italy and the Italian population in Nebraska continued to increase. In 1908 the government established a Royal Italian Consular Agency in Omaha and Antonio Venuto was appointed Royal Italian Consular Agent.[31] Venuto, who had come to Omaha as a wandering musician, was the first Italian in Nebraska to be made Cavalier of the Order of the Crown by the King of Italy, largely for his work in recruiting over 2,000 soldiers for the Italian army during World War I.

In 1910, the demographic picture of Italians in the Midwest region was:[32]

Minnesota	9,669
Iowa	5,846
North Dakota	1,262
South Dakota	1,158
Missouri	12,984
Kansas	3,520
Nebraska	3,799

**The Southern Italian Social Background:
Sources of Conflict in America**

The Italian immigrants left behind their homes, their shops, their farms, and their families; they brought with them particular ways of looking at life, certain patterns of behavior, emotional responses, codes and ideals. They also brought over almost intact the mores that governed their behavior. The conflicts between American mores and the southern Italian way of life surfaced immediately. The family provides a good example of the cultural conflict.

The family in Italy was an inclusive social world which embraced all blood and in-law relations.[33] A "contadino" community would usually consist of several family groups, and sometimes one family unit included the entire population of a village, in which case, every inhabitant was related by blood or marriage. The absolute code of this life was family solidarity and exclusion of outsiders: defiance was tantamount to cardinal sin. A statement made by the Italian Inchiesta Parlamentare (Italian Parliamentary Inquest of 1896) and quoted by Foerster reads: "Life in the South exalts the family. It has been said of Sicily that the family sentiment is perhaps the only deeply rooted altruistic sentiment that prevails."[34] Covello comments that the "significance of this dictum is not whether this sentiment is altruistic, but that the family sentiment was practically the only sentiment with a social content."[35] Even a slight disobedience by a child was regarded not only as a concern to the parents, but to the entire greater family. The family solidarity was manifested by uniformity of behavior, adherence to the family tradition and harmony of economic interests. A marriage was partially an economic concern of all family members; the direction of a child's education might be decided by a family council; a loan, a dowry, a funeral or even a fight was a family affair. Family solidarity was strengthened by the sentiment of "onore della famiglia"—family honor, which increased exclusivity, and complemented all social behavior.[36]

Language habits reflect the strength and pervasiveness of the family. The word "forestiere" (stranger) referred to anyone not a member of the family group. In other words, a "contadino" could be intimately associated with someone, perhaps through daily business dealings, and yet refer to that person as "forestiere." Covello says:

It is probably no exaggeration to say that "la famiglia" was the only social concept, and that any other term such as "paese" or "villaggio" . . . had no other than a purely spatial connotation. It would be hard to find in southern Italy a synonym for the English word "community" . . .[37]

The term "comunita" in Italian stands not for national or public mindedness, but for the community that exists in the monastery.

The unquestioned head of the family was one male member, usually the father, although the system was not strictly patriarchal. Age priority was not an absolute determinant of power or prestige. A leader remained in power as long as he was the main provider and was healthy in mind and body. Most importantly, his status as a married male was a mandatory requirement to head a family. Thus a widower would be replaced by a married son, not necessarily the oldest, but the first married. Often, economic and marital status being equal, there was intense rivalry between brothers for supreme authority. This "capo di famiglia" assumed responsibility for the behavior of all family members and was the keystone of the family organization; bad conduct by anyone, even a child, was attributed ultimately to a weak "capo." Although there was no question that the father dominated, the family was somewhat "mother centered." Not only were females accorded scrupulous, if only superficial, respect the potential power of the father was often seriously lessened by the emotional and social leadership of the mother. The mother's role figured in the private life of the family; the father's role was public.

There were no acceptable allegiances outside the family. Even the church was subordinate. Acts of charity, church attendance, hospitality were all matters of individual or family conscience, not moral virtues in themselves. Covello relates the experiences of a former organizer of Cooperative Farmers' Society in Sicily:

I was sent out (by government) into a district near Trapani. . . . I was given instructions as to the best method to

bring the farmers together. One of the instructions was to pro-
ceed from town to town making contact with people in these
towns who were in some way related to each other. . . . In one
instance I brought together a group from four villages compris-
ing about fifty members. Actually it consisted of the grown up
men from thirteen or fourteen families who, though in different places, were related to each other.

This cooperative society did not last long, but I must
say, it outlived all the others whose members were not related
to each other. They usually disintegrated from the first meeting. The one above lasted two months.[38]

Even friendship did not carry mutual confidence. The
word "amico" was used among those who might have common
interests, a co-worker, a "paesano" was a townsman. The closest
friends outside the family are "compari" and "commari," words
which actually mean "godfather" and "godmother"—co-father,
co-mother. These people who may have been "best man" at a
wedding or actual godfather at baptism, were thus brought into
the family orbit.

Most activities, thought and social patterns were based on
traditional customs, so that little room was left for individualism or initiative. There was a good deal of stability, but it was
of a static character, brought about by the insistence on a rigid
social order and preserved by cultural isolation. An Italian
proverb goes: "Che lascia la via vecchia per la nuova, sa quel che
perde e non sa quel che trova" (He who forsakes the old road
for the new, knows what he is losing, but does not know what
he will find).[39]

Michael Novak describes the moral self-righteousness inherent in the dream of a perfect community where there would be
perfect individualism and full-self expression. This model runs
counter to the ideal of the Italian-American immigrant family,
in which "loyalty and virtue and obedience bind each member
to seek each other's holiness, usefulness and happiness."[40] The
intellectual dream is symbolized by Huck Finn's response when
he is about to be taken into the bosom of the Sawyer family: "I
reckon I got to light out for the territory ahead of the rest,

because Aunt Sally she's going to adopt me and civilise me, and I can't stand it. I been there before." Novak submits:

> The intellectual appears to be in reaction against the family. Almost every cause he espouses destroys the tissue of the family. Almost every idea he imagines renders life more inhospitable to the family. Almost every thought of his atomizes American society, separates persons from others, encourages the notion that each individual is and ought to be solitary, self-directed, self-watchful.[41]

Thus the southern European was further alienated by an American prejudice against the unenlightened and uneducated. Everything about America and becoming Americanized ran contrary to the southern Italian sanctum of family solidarity. Public education, neighborhood, work, even church, represented a threat to family values and standards and adjustment was a difficult process. In the midst of a strange and often hostile environment, the natural tendency for Italians (as other groups) was to cluster into cultural and geographic shells in ethnic ghettos. Howard Chudacoff's neighborhood studies of Omaha demonstrate the felt presence of ethnic neighborhoods.

> Omaha did have a "little Italy," a Jewish section, a Bohemia town. The identification of these involves two components. . . . First, the labeling of an area was obviously associated with the kinds of people who lived there. . . .
> In Omaha no single nationality group ever comprised a majority in any area as large as half a mile square. However particular ethnic groups did form pluralities even if they accounted for at most only a third of a district's population. Thus one could identify a certain district with a certain group because more of that group lived there than anyone else.[42]

The following chart shows indexes of dissimilarity, that is the degree to which an ethnic group tended to cluster in segregated neighborhoods. (Each value listed gauges the degree of segregation from the native white population; thus an index of 100 would denote complete residential segregation—all of a particular group living in one area with no one else. A value of zero indicated even residential distribution and therefore greater residential intermixture.)

INDEXES OF DISSIMILARITY[43]
Omaha, 1910 and 1920

Country of Birth	1910	1920
Austria	60.6	45.7
Canada	14.4	16.4
Czechoslovakia	–	59.4
Denmark	12.8	12.2
England	9.3	16.4
Germany	21.3	11.0
Hungary	39.2	–
Ireland	9.7	12.1
Italy	69.4	53.1
Poland	–	55.8
Russia	34.4	44.3
Sweden	15.1	15.5

Sources: U.S. Bureau of the Census, *Thirteenth Census of the United States Taken in the Year 1910, Population,* III, 71; and U.S. Bureau of the Census, *Fourteenth Census of the United States Taken in the Year 1920, Population,* III, 609.

The tendencies for ethnic neighborhoods to persist was partially attributable to the amount of other ethnics living there, but also to the degree of permanent institutions (churches, stores, etc.) in the vicinity.

> . . . the location of that group's business, social and religious institutions was . . . conspicuous to those who lived both nearby and farther away. That is, the churches and clubs, plus the bakeries, groceries, butcher shops, shoemakers, tailors, saloons, and restaurants, which directed their services to a special clientele and were operated by members of a specific ethnic group helped markedly to define a neighborhood's character.[44]

There was among the Italians a tendency to colonize but also a tendency to shift. The shifting has to do usually with outside forces: floods, intrusion from heavy industry which forced people out of their homes, rampant commercial growth. Families tended to move away from areas in which there might be danger to their children from one of these forces or the threat to morality posed by urban vice. Howard Chudacoff's chart listing names, addresses and occupations on 6th Street and Pierce gives an example:[45]

	1912	1916	1920
1101	Linninger Implements	Linninger Implements	Vacant
1102	Lewis Nelson, saloon	Vacant	Vacant
1104	Willow Springs Hotel	Willow Springs Hotel	Jacob Pepto
1106	Gaetano Caniglia	Sebastian Hernandez	Vacant
	Anton Sorrentino		Myers-Freeman, brooms
1108	Paul Maligazzio	Vacant	Joseph Longo
	Frank Piccolo		
	Samuel Pinis		
	Pirri Santo, cigars		
	Giuseppi Incerra, tailor		
1110	A.H. Brtez	Tony Colamino	Joseph Richie
	Joseph Kowski	G.N. Hirsch	Alfio Randazzo
	Paul Nelson	Gio Bellarmeno	Joseph Bellarmeno
	Della Straight	C.S. Hutton	
	Marion Swope	Lawrence Peterson	
1112	Henry Frosh	Joseph Bellarmeno	Joseph Fiala
			Anthony Greco
1113	Peter Turkelson, saloon	Peter Turkelson	Peter Turkelson
1114	Peter Cosentino	Joseph Caniglia	Joseph Caniglia
1116	Dominic Scarpello	John Parnicello	James Lawson
	James Story	Anthony Pernicelli	
1117	Joseph Mangano, pool	Tony Vacirca	Tony Vacirca
	Gaetano Nocita, barber		John Benno
1118	Ross Caniglia	Vito Caniglia	Dominic Sofia
	Dominick Sofia	Dominick Sofia	
1119	Luigi Pardini	Nuncio Constantina, shoemaker	Cirino La Fato, shoemaker
	Salerno and Garroto, grocers		
	Frank Sorrentino, shoemaker		
1121	Forest Hall	Salerno & Garroto, grocers	Caniglia Bros., hardware
	Joseph Rusica		

	1912	**1916**	**1920**
1123	Pietro Cosentino, pool	Pietro Cosentino, billiards	Vacanti Bros., soft drinks
1201	James Kohout, saloon	James Kohout, saloon	A.S. Caniglia, soft drinks
1203	G.A. Baumann, barber	W.H. Born, barber	Seb Manamelli, barber
1205	Jody Pspisil, pool		Thomas, Dopita, pool
1206	Joseph Ferro Sam Morello Sireno Orto	Vacant	Vacant
1207	Max Moskowitz, grocer	Vacant	Alfonso Canella, dry goods
1212	P.J. Vachal	Pietro Cosentino	Pietro Cosentino
1213	Carmelo Partivino	Fred Mangamello	Joseph Camore, grocer
1214	Mary Kennedy	Howard Kennedy	Vacant
1217		Humphrey Clark (c)	
1219	Samuel Amato	Luciano Sacco Frank Genna	Alfio DeMaro, shoemaker

NUMBER OF MOVES MADE BY PERCENT OF PEOPLE [46] REMAINING IN OMAHA FOR FOURTEEN YEARS BY NATIVITY

Nativity Group	Number of Moves					Number in Sample
	0	1	2	3	4 or More	
Native 1880	12.1	20.3	22.5	22.0	23.1	182
Native 1900	13.4	31.1	20.1	17.1	17.7	164
Foreign 1880	18.5	27.3	18.5	16.9	18.9	195
old	17.8	27.4	17.8	17.8	19.4	175
new	25.0	25.0	25.0	10.0	15.0	20
Foreign 1900	20.9	34.7	24.6	10.5	9.7	124
old	27.5	35.0	20.0	8.8	8.8	80
new	9.1	34.1	31.8	13.6	11.4	44

Chudacoff's findings (see chart on previous page) indicate similar mobility rates for foreigners and natives: permanence was low for both groups. Only one-seventh of the American-born group occupies the same residence for eight years; one-fifth of the foreign-born did the same thing. Until 1920, Chudacoff concludes that "while they may have retained their social, economic and religious communities, their incidence of movement out of old neighborhoods and around the city made residential coherence a very temporary experience."[47]

In moving, smaller families tended to seek out more established ones. The Sicilians tended to move towards lower Pierce Street. The nucleus of the Little Italy formed by the padrone activities of the Salerno brothers, and the continental Italians moved towards the Calabrese colony in the north around 20th and Poppleton Avenue. A 1941 Work Projects Administration report on Italians in Omaha described these two colonies as follows:[48]

. . . Omaha's Little Italy lies in Ward 5 and the segments of Wards 4, 9 and 8.

Little Italy is defined on the east by the Missouri River, on the north by Marcy Street extending westward to Twentieth, then north to Leavenworth and westward to Twenty-seventh Street. From Twenty-seventh Street, the limits run south to Hickory and then east to the intersecting railroad lines. Across the tracks, the limits beginning with Twentieth Street run south to Bancroft and then directly east to the river. Thus Little Italy sprawls over an area which has characteristics of nearly all sections of Omaha, the unpretentious residential sections, the heavily industrialized sections, sections in which there are through traffic lanes with heavy passenger and industrial traffic day and night, sections having small industries and a congestion of small shops and taverns.

The eastern part of Little Italy, the intense Sicilian settlement, is more definitely set off from the rest of the city by natural lines of demarcation, with the entrance to Pierce Street, the main artery, at Tenth. Beginning at the limits of the city on the bottom lands of the Missouri River with unpainted shacks patched with strips of tin and cardboard, the colony assumes a progressive aspect as it reaches beyond the bare-faced clay bluffs to the west. To the northeast is the Union Pacific bridge over which the trains rumble to and from Iowa. A brewery is at Second and Hickory Streets and a soap factory is at First and Hickory. On the northern limits of the colony are the Burlington and Union Pacific passenger stations and the Burlington mail terminal. Pierce Street presents a mixture of small shops and dwellings indiscriminately mated, and Sixth Street at Pierce is the heart of Little Italy. Santa Lucia Hall, with its garish sign showing crossed American and Italian flags, once was a city fire barn.

What used to be mainly "Calabresi" eventually became a mixture of north, central and south Italians:[49]

> The area is nondescript and presents the anomaly of a residential district trying to flourish in the shadow of industry and only half succeeding. On the eastern and southern fringe are railroad right-of-ways and heavy industries and the district is close-in to all of Omaha's heavy industries with the exception of the packing houses in South Omaha. A large brewery fronts on Sixteenth Street as does a flour mill and elevators. The Union Pacific shops are easily accessible over the Nicholas Street viaduct. Skirting the southern edges of the colony are machine shops, garages, oil and gas storage companies, a large creamery and cold storage company, the city dog pound, lumber companies and coal yards. Within the colony, the Italians have numerous small business establishmens—grocery stores, shoe shops, tailor shops, barber shops and saloons. Some sections of the colony are mottled with scrap iron heaps from dismantled automobiles and these are generally on the back yards of the owners or on adjacent vacant lots. There are several small used car lots angling for the ten to a hundred dollar buyers. The district is generally shoddy and many of the houses, having long since seen their best day, still provide shelter for many families. The houses are very close together with, sometimes, only a few feet separating them, and numerous houses fronting the street have smaller, generally dilapidated, houses in the rear. There is barely yard space and children must of necessity dodge traffic in the streets in order

to play at their games. These homes more closely abutting the industrial streets are in a state of disrepair and their appearance is grimy, scarred and blotched with the siding badly in need of paint. As the homes reach toward the north and west, away from the industrial streets, the substantial, well-kept appearance of the house reflects the economic status of the dwellers. . . .

Holy Family Church, with its school and auditorium at Eighteenth and Izard Streets, is the center of religious and social life of the colony. Saint Alfio Hall, another religious-social center, is at Seventeenth and Clark Streets.

Earning a living in America was the first thought in the immigrant Italian's mind . . . whether or not he intended to settle permanently. Like most immigrants, the Italians came with little money. Alphonse T. Fiore investigated heads of Italian families in Omaha and found that 80 percent brought only $8-$13 with them.[50] There was no lack of employment in Omaha's booming economy, but 90 percent of the work was at the lowest economic scale, the pick and shovel, crowbar and wheelbarrow jobs. Immigrants arriving after 1880 went into the shops, construction crews and maintenance gangs of the railroad. The 1890 census lists 522 wage-earning Italians and placed them in the following categories: agriculture, 35; professional service, 26; trade and transportation, 186; manufacturing and mechanical industries, 31; domestic and personal service, 244. (The domestic and personal service included laborers, cooks, barbers, clerks, etc.) Nine years later, 45 percent of the Italians were unclassified laborers: peddlers, fruit merchants, musicians, barbers, carpenters, cooks, tailors, printers, clerks, stone-cutters, stenographers, etc.[51] By the early 1900's, immigrant Italians had to be placed in jobs by the scores instead of as individuals; the result was that the number of Italians in unskilled jobs comprised three-fourths of all the wage earners in Omaha. While, as before, most of the jobs were in railroad and general construction, there were those who now worked in packing plants, smelters, iron foundries, and in the creamery and grain milling industry. The average wage of the Italian immigrant in the period from 1900-1914 was $1.75 a day.[52]

World War I temporarily halted the flow of immigrants into the United States. Many men returned to Italy when the Italian government called home army reservists, and others felt impelled to volunteer. This in itself increased the earning power for the Italians, since there were fewer immigrant laborers flooding the market at a time when there was increased industrial demand. With less competition and increased opportunity many unskilled laborers moved into semi-skilled jobs. Little Italy prospered and many Italians were able to shift from low-paying jobs into small businesses or crafts. The 1916 directory lists Italian barbers, shoe repairmen, bakers, macaroni makers, candy makers, tailors, butchers, carpenters, bricklayers, stonemasons, and cooks. Still more than one-third of the employed males were working for the Union Pacific, mostly in the shops, where hundreds of them had found employment replacing men who had walked out in the shop strike of 1911.[53]

In the next ten years, there were several events affecting the earning power of the Italians: the Union Pacific shop strike of 1922, the rise of the bootlegging industry, and the collapse of two Italian banks. The shop strike reflects a philosophical change among the workers who for the most part began to side with American labor unions; in 1922 the Italians made up a large percentage of the shop men who walked out in protest against low wages and long hours.[54] Failure of the strike left hundreds of Italians unemployed. Having lost their jobs, many turned anxiously to the whiskey making business.

Little Italy became notorious for flaunting the liquor laws. In Omaha and elsewhere newspapers portrayed "the mob" and its alleged involvements in circumventing Prohibition. While many Italians were embarrassed at the ethnic characterizations which flowed from this publicity, others scoffed at the violations. Crime among Italians in Nebraska before 1920 had been no greater than among other foreign-born groups.[55] By 1935, however, of the 112 persons arrested for operating illegal stills, 34 were of Italian ancestry.[56] Outside of bootlegging, criminal activity was negligible among the Italian immigrant community.

As recently as 1976, the United States Attorney for the District of Nebraska remarked that there does not appear to be a large-scale, complex Italian Mafia syndicate which controls illicit activities throughout the state. "There certainly is organized crime, but we don't think there is a 'capo di famiglia' running the entire show."[57] Nevertheless, with the written and cinematic portrayals of the Mafia in the past forty years, Nebraska Italians, as others across the country, have been tainted by the image of the slick mobster. A current spokesman for the Italians in Omaha, Anthony Troia, Grand Venerable of the Sons of Italy, bemoans this unfortunate defamation. Much of the ethnic activity among today's Italian community, he says, is directed toward changing this image, restoring a strong ethnic pride which has atrophied over the years, and asserting a united role in the political marketplace in competition with the other "minority" groups in Omaha such as the Irish, Jews and blacks.[58]

Conclusion

There was a perpetual conflict between the old world values of the first generation Italian "contadini" and the demands of an immigrant society. Cultural fusion between Italians and Americans was highly unlikely and the evolution of a strong ethnic community was an equally unfamiliar social expectation. The communities that did arise, the Little Italys and "Dago Hills," were more a clustering of discrete families, each with their private hierarchies, than any kind of cooperative settlement.

Gallo's polls of first, second and third generation Italians bring out some of the feelings of frustration. A majority of first generation and second generation Italians sensed a disturbing lack of power in the affairs of the polity. They saw a government "run by the powerful," complicated and unrelated to daily life.

> . . . The ethnic American is sick of being stereotyped. . . . He pays the bill for every major governmental program and gets

nothing or little in return . . . he himself is the victim of class prejudice. . . . He has worked hard all his life to become a 'good American' . . . (but) in many instances he is treated like the machine he operates.[59]

Among third generation immigrants, Gallo notes, the feeling of powerlessness was usually somewhat diminished owing to increased affluence, education, higher occupation categories, and a general feeling of acceptance. Yet along with the confidence accorded these American-born Italian children came the inevitable deterioration of the stronghold of the family. Loyalties outside the household impinged upon the traditional roles of the family.

The family had neither the means nor the living space to provide recreation to replace the labor previously expected by the adolescent. New conflicts also appeared in the parent-child relationship as the teenager attempted to transmit his newly acquired American expectations of life into the weakened family structure.[60]

Covello's analysis of school adjustment among Italian immigrant children lists the following as chief elements of conflict:

1. The assimilative process of the southern Italian immigrants in America has been characterized by a lag in acculturation brought about by their communal isolation and the consequent lack of contacts with the American culture, and their attempts to adjust to a transplanted, but changed, Italian environment rather than to the alien American environment.
2. The retention of Italian family mores and patterns led to attempts to impose these patterns upon the American scene. Since the education of children in southern Italy was carried on mainly in the home, within the inclusive environment of the traditional *contadino* family organization, compulsory school attendance in America led to antagonism and conflict between the *contadino* family and the school.
3. The sources of the conflict were both economic and

cultural. Italian parents must now support their children during a prolonged period of social infancy. Their children, who in Italy would have begun at an early age to work toward the support of the family, must now be supported through elementary school, and up to "working-paper" age. The loss of their children as economic assets, and all the disorganization of the economic family pattern which resulted, served to motivate their antagonism toward the school. They also feared the indoctrination of their children with alien concepts of the duty of children toward the family and their parents, which would endanger the life and welfare of the traditional family organization.

4. While the *contadino* parents became, outwardly at least, adjusted to elementary education for their children, latent antagonism remained. They delayed their plans for financial assistance from their children until their children might legally work. An antagonistic attitude toward high school education then developed with much the same intensity as the earlier antagonism toward the elementary school. The rejection of high school education is based upon old-world concepts of higher education, as well as upon economic factors. The Italian parent in America can see no moral or economic value in an expansion of the schooling period beyond the elementary school level. Contrarily, he considers the high school a place where time is spent in play or idleness.[61]

While the authority of the family weakened over the years, the tremendous sense of family identity persisted. Mark Zborowoski interviewed male patients in a veterans' hospital in 1969 and relates the following:

Well, if anybody ever asks me my nationality, I'm always proud to say I'm Italian instead of—like so many people say— they're Americans. I don't see myself superior to anyone— don't get me wrong. But I think deep down inside that Italian is the best. Why? Maybe it's something inside of me which I can't identify just yet. My parents were Italian, all my friends—my real close friends. Before I got hurt I would say 90 percent of my friends were Italian. We still at home listen to an Italian opera, and if I don't know what it means, I can

always ask my father and he can always explain it to me. And
if my father doesn't know, maybe my mother knows or maybe
my brother knows. The relatives were always around. We had a
lot of Italian friends we visited too.[62]

Given the cultural dissimilarities among the various immigrant groups and the persistent identification with family and
homeland, even among later-generation immigrants, Michael
Novak proposes a new kind of politics based on cultural
pluralism.

If I were to propose a political program for the future,
particularly for the poor and the lower-middle class, I would
center its social focus on family and neighborhood. Its cri-
terion would be: what helps family and neighborhood is good;
what injures them is bad. The family is the center of the social
universe. It is so, in any case, for the poor, if not so for wealth-
ier classes. . . . Groups whose members are alienated from their
families are doomed to seeking ersatz, transient, and ultimately anomic relations elsewhere. . . .

I propose . . . an Ethnic Democratic Party. The EPD
would be, at the very least, a caucus within the Democratic
party. Its goal would be genuine cultural variety; strong
communities of value, identity, and conscience; and strong
families and neighborhoods. It would aim to convert the
mechanical, functional image of society to an organic, living
human image: closer to primordial preceptions and primordial
strengths.[63]

It has been suggested that the compelling mores of the
family prevented easy acculturation for the Italian immigrant.
Perhaps it is also this value—intimate human association—that
becomes the Italian legacy for modern community builders.
Richard Sennett sketches the failure of the modern nuclear
family and points to the traditional concepts of family life as
a model.

There is a groundswell of communalism in this country
among the young, and not just among the minority who are

radicals; there is a widespread yearning to find some kind of intimate human association which will put behind the sense of privateness and fixed role embodied in the small, isolated family. There is a yearning for human contacts which will approximate the richness of extended family life in the past. . . .

I believe this revolt against the narrow confines of the middle class home is not a fashion of the youth culture that will disappear. History is too much on the side of the young; in some ways the communalism we see now appearing is a conservative reaction, in that it is trying to recapture threads of human association cut during the rise of the industrial order. Rather than a healthy, adaptive form, the small and private family seems to have been a historical fluke that destroys itself under conditions of economic stability and affluence. . . .[64]

This change in values comes too late for the Italian immigrant in Nebraska. The countless misunderstandings between old and young, between old world and modern ways have deeply saddened the lives of all ethnic families. Yet, even though some have predicted the demise of family, its conception can be changed, altered and expanded. Novak argues, "Age-old ethnic views of family and neighborhood, given a new flexibility and governmental support, can ground a new form of political and social organization."[65] And Nebraska Italians have a rich base upon which a modern ethnic/family-oriented community can be refashioned.

FOOTNOTES

1.   *The Italians of Omaha,* written and compiled by workers of The Writers' Program, Work Projects Administration (Omaha, Nebraska: Independent Printing Company, 1941), p. 13.

2.   *Ibid.,* p. 15.

3.   *Ibid.,* for a fuller accounting of these first Omaha settlers, see pp. 13-32.

4.   *Ibid.,* p. 22.

5.   Robert McMorris, "The People Who Make Up Omaha," in *Omaha World Herald* (October 15, 1961), p. B5.

6.   Alphonse T. Fiore, "History of Italian Immigration in Nebraska" (unpublished thesis, University of Nebraska, Lincoln, 1938), p. 29.

7.   *Ibid.*

8.   *Annual Report of the Commissioner of Immigration* (Washington, D.C., June, 1903), indicated 83.97 percent of Italian immigration came from the South; 16.03 percent came from North/Central.

9.   Patrick J. Gallo, *Ethnic Alienation in the Italian-Americans* (Cranbury, New Jersey: Associated University Presses, Inc., 1974), p. 76.

10.   Oscar Handlin, *The Uprooted* (Boston: Little, Brown and Company, 1951), p. 64.

11.   Andrew F. Rolle, *The American Italians: Their History and Culture* (Belmont, California: Wadsworth Publishing Company, Inc., 1972), p. 55.

12.   *Ibid.,* p. 58.

13.   *Ibid.,* p. 59.

14.   *Ibid.,* pp. 58, 59.

15.   Fiore, *op. cit.,* p. 4.

16.   Rolle, *op. cit.,* p. 2.

17.   Fiore, *op. cit.,* p. 24.

18.   Pascal D'Angelo, *Pascal D'Angelo, Son of Italy* (New York: Macmillan, 1924), p. 55.

19.   Fiore, *op. cit.,* p. 19.

20.   *Ibid.,* p. 20.

21.   *Ibid.,* pp. 18-19.

22.   Edward Corsi, *In the Shadow of Liberty* (New York: Macmillan, 1935), p. 20.

23.   Rolle, *op. cit.,* p. 28.

24. *Ibid.,* p. 25.

25. *Ibid.,* p. 28.

26. *Ibid.,* p. 30.

27. This account of the Salerno brothers was condensed from *The Italians of Omaha,* pp. 26-28 and Robert McMorris, "People Who Make Up Omaha," p. B1.

28. *The Italians of Omaha,* p. 28.

29. McMorris, *op. cit.,* p. B5.

30. *The Italians of Omaha,* p. 29.

31. *Ibid.,* p. 29.

32. Abstract of the Thirteenth Census of the United States, Washington, D.C., 1914, pp. 204-07.

33. The source for most of this discussion is Leonard Covello, *The Social Background of the Italo-American School Child* (Leiden, Netherlands: E.J. Brill, 1967).

34. Robert L. Foerster, *The Italian Emigration of Our Times* (Cambridge: Harvard University Press, 1919), p. 95.

35. Covello, *op. cit.,* p. 95.

36. *Ibid.,* p. 152.

37. *Ibid.*

38. *Ibid.,* pp. 175-76.

39. *Ibid.,* p. 176.

40. Michael Novak, *The Rise of the Unmeltable Ethnics* (New York: Macmillan, 1971), p. 143.

41. *Ibid.*

42. Howard P. Chudacoff, "A New Look at Ethnic Neighborhoods: Residential Dispersion and the Concept of Visibility in a Medium-Sized City," *The Journal of American History,* Vol. LX, No. 1 (June, 1973), pp. 81-82.

43. *Ibid.,* p. 78.

44. *Ibid.,* p. 89.

45. *Ibid.,* p. 90.

46. *Ibid.,* p. 84.

47. *Ibid.,* p. 91.

48. *The Italians of Omaha,* p. 36.

49. *Ibid.,* p. 35.

50. Fiore, *op. cit.,* p. 20.

51. *The Italians of Omaha,* p. 53.

52. *Ibid.,* p. 55.

53. *Ibid.,* p. 57.

54. *Ibid.*, p. 58.

55. Earl T. Sullenger, "Study of Crime in Nebraska, 1920," quoted in *The Italians of Omaha,* p. 45.

56. *Ibid.*

57. Telephone conversation with Daniel Wherry, U.S. Attorney for the District of Nebraska, March 29, 1976.

58. Anthony Troia, interview, March, 1976.

59. Gallo, *op. cit.,* p. 207.

60. *Ibid.*, p. 83.

61. Covello, *op. cit.,* p. 328.

62. Mark Zborowoski, *People in Pain* (San Francisco, California: Jossey-Bass, Inc., 1969), p. 183.

63. Novek, *op. cit.,* p. 279.

64. Richard Sennett, "Break Up the Family," *New York Times,* July 19, 1971.

65. Novak, *op. cit.,* p. 276.

CATALOGUE

ORGANIZATIONS—THE BEST SOURCE
TO FIND OUT MORE ABOUT NEBRASKA ITALIANS

The largest community of Italian-Americans in the state is in Omaha, where the population numbers around 10,000. The following is a list of Italian-American organizations in Omaha, Lincoln, and around the state.

Order Sons of Italy in America—The Nebraska Grand Lodge is an affiliate of the National Order Sons of Italy in America and is the largest Italian-American organization in the United States today. The Sons of Italy work together for Liberty, Fraternity and Equality of the Italian people and stresses brotherhood and achievement in education, public offices, job opportunities, etc. Every state has the right to form their own Charter and affiliate themselves with the National Order. The date as to when Nebraska became a part of the National Order is uncertain, but it was probably about 1920 in Omaha.

In 1954, the Grand Lodge became very active in national and local problems. In the early 1960's, the Nebraska Grand Lodge incorporated as a non-profit corporation and is still incorporated today. The Nebraska Grand Lodge consists of three filial lodges that are subordinate to the Grand Lodge. Each individual lodge consists of a Venerable (President) and assistants, all under the jurisdiction of the Grand Lodge, whose head is the Grand Venerable. There are approximately 1,200 men and women in Omaha who belong to the Order Sons of Italy. The men's lodge is called Christopher Columbo, and the two women's lodges are called Santa Lucia and Regina Elena. The lodges all have individual functions, but are subordinate to the Grand Lodge for approval of many of their functions. The largest function is the annual Columbus Day Banquet held in October of every year and there is a spaghetti dinner held in the spring of each year. Both of these activities are coordinated through the Grand Lodge.

The Order has many other charitable functions to help finance the betterment of the Italian people as well as other underprivileged who live in the community. The Sons of Italy sponsors Italian language classes, youth groups, sporting activities and many other social functions during the year.

The second largest Italian-American organization in Omaha is the **Santa Lucia Festival Committee,** made up of about 150 men responsible for coordinating and putting on the Santa Lucia Carnival which takes place on the last weekend of July each year. Approximately 90 percent of the festival committee are members of the Sons of Italy. The President of the Santa Lucia Festival Committee is Russell J. Monaco, and he is also an officer in the Order Sons of Italy.

In 1923, Gaetano Caniglia started the Santa Lucia Festival Committee to honor Saint Lucy, the patron saint of the Italian people in Omaha. Several Italian men went to Italy to obtain the statue of Saint Lucy and brought it back to Omaha. After that, a festival was planned that lasted for weeks, but today only four days are set aside because many of the people have moved out of the area between 6th and 10th and Pierce Streets where the Carnival is set up.

The Resveglio Society is made up of a group of men and women with the average age of about 75 years. They no longer have functions, and their only reason for participating is the fact that most of them have a death benefit plan. Vincent Emmanuel heads that group and negotiations are now under way to absorb this membership into the Sons of Italy.

There is a group of seven Italian men composing the **Columbus Day Observance, Inc.**, which is incorporated to work with the downtown businesses in putting on a Columbus Day Parade. Vincent Emmanuel is the head of this group, and they are seeking funds to build ships or replicas of the Nina, Pinta and Santa Maria. The Columbus Day Observance sponsors a banquet the day after the Sons of Italy banquet.

In Lincoln, there is a group of Italians that have a **Christopher Columbus Lodge**. There are some Italians in Bellevue, Nebraska, and most of them are in the Order Sons of Italy. Grand Island has a few Italians but no organization.

Newspaper

The American Citizen is an Italian language newspaper published semi-monthly in Omaha. In it are items of news interest to the Italian-American communities in Nebraska and Iowa, editorials, advertisements and social announcements. The paper has been in existence since 1923.

Language Classes and Italian Culture Seminars

The modern language department at the University of Nebraska in Lincoln offers Italian language and civilization courses. Walter Centuori, professor of Italian, frequently offers seminars in Italian culture and literature.

The Irish: The Heritage of Charles Stuart Parnell

By James McShane and Nadine Murphy

ACKNOWLEDGMENTS

It would be impossible to list all those of our families, clans, and compatriots from whom we learned who we are and how we live.

> *Many times man lives and dies*
> *Between his two eternities*
> *That of race and that of soul*
> *And ancient Ireland knew it all. (Yeats)*

So we single out but one. In acknowledging with gratitude the contribution of that fine son of Ireland whom we quote most extensively, Mr. Joe O'Brien of Plattsmouth, we gratefully remember the rest:

> *Ireland's history in their lineaments trace*
> *Think where man's glory most begins and ends,*
> *And say my glory was I had such friends. (Yeats)*

Author Murphy, a university art student, has done the graphics for this essay. The first is based on the elaborate, intricate illuminations found in the ancient *Book of Kells,* a masterpiece of typical Irish art. The rest are cartoons, based on the simple, shallow stereotypes the Irish had to deal with as typical representations of themselves.

Paddy was a clever rogue with
a gift of gab and lots of flair.
It was Blarney and every Irishman
was born with it.
Blarney could get him out of
trouble and out of work; which
naturally headed him into politics.

Paddy was depicted as always having
a pig and loving a good fight. This
throws up the picture of our Hero,
walking down the street with his ever
present pig, probably on a leash. In
a fight, to keep said pig safe, it is
tied to any handy light post or such.
the fight is joined; won or lost, the
pig is collected and off they go
looking for the next bout. In
Irish neighbahoods there were always
pigs tied to lamposts.

It's called 'the Irishmans disease'
If he was sober it was a miracle.
He loved his 'wee dhrop'.

What
was a good conversation with friends
with out the jug to loosen the tongue
and limber the knees. Of course everyone
knows the drinkers ended drunk, the
jig ended in a brawl and they were
all taken to the jug in the Paddy wagon.

IX

The Irish: The Heritage of Charles Stuart Parnell

By James McShane and Nadine Murphy

Ireland's *"sons and daughters are scattered throughout the world, and they give this small island a family of millions upon millions who are scattered all over the globe, who have been among the best and most loyal citizens of the countries that they have gone to, but have also kept a special place in their memories, in many cases their ancestral memories, of this green and misty island. . . ."* [1]

President John Kennedy
Reply to President DeValera's Welcome to Ireland, June, 1963

The Nebraska contingent of this scattered Irish family has roots reaching back to the very beginnings of extended European activity in the area. They came slowly at first; then they came, as did so many other ethnic groups, in greater numbers in the second half of the 19th century. They came from two sources: some came from Ireland directly; others, and the greater number, came in a second wave of immigration from the cities and industrial towns of eastern United States. To understand either group it is essential to know about the Ireland from which they came. And to understand the relatively small numbers of Irish-Americans in Nebraska, it is essential more generally to know of Irish-American communities of which they are a part.

Background

Early 19th century Ireland was one large "depressed area." For a hundred years English authority had suppressed any Irish agricultural or industrial progress which might threaten any area of English economic supremacy. Furthermore, the population was divided in two or three parts. At the top was the "Protestant Ascendency," holding virtually all the land, all political power and offices, and practical control of capital and business. Below them were the tenants and laborers, mostly Catholic, but some Presbyterians—especially in the north. The latter lived in conditions a little better than their Catholic compatriots and their efforts to protect that little accounts for the rivalry then and still existing between the two.

(What follows deals largely with the Catholic Irish contingent, because that is what the term "Irish-American" usually refers to. This is in part because, especially since the 1830's and 40's, Irish immigration has shown the same or greater disproportion of Catholics over protestants as does the population distribution in Ireland as a whole. It is in part true also because protestants, especially Presbyterians, have elected once in this country to distinguish themselves as "Scotch-Irish"—a distinction which does not appear to have been usual in Ireland. Needless to say, this historical essay would have been different had it dealt with the Scotch-Irish as well. Their reception was different, so were their areas of concentration and their political and social contributions.)

The Catholics were legally non-persons throughout the 18th century in Ireland. They had only recently been permitted to receive any education, to practice their religion, to own land, and to enter some professions. Until 1829 they were to remain without power to vote or hold public office and were subject to the most degrading landlordism.

This locked-out class was politically apathetic until Daniel O'Connell, by his magnetic appeal and his organizational skills, welded them into a potent political force. On contributions of a penny a month from very poor people, he established an enormous war chest. With the force of mobilized peasantry, he won Catholic Emancipation—that is, rights for propertied Catholics to vote in elections and serve in political and professional offices. Ten years later, seeing that Emancipation brought little of the expected benefit to Ireland, O'Connell tried to use the same tactics to bring to Ireland its own legislature and control of its own domestic affairs. This effort, executed in ways which involved millions in mass public protests, was a great tactical success. But it failed to achieve its strategic goals because English public opinion was not moved. Shortly after this disappointment there followed the "Great Hunger," the disastrous famine of 1845-48.[2]

In 1850, then, Ireland was in a state of acute economic and social collapse, and of acute political frustration. The collapse can be quickly gauged from the fact that the population of that "misty island" declined from a peak of eight to ten million in 1845 to a nadir of three to four million in 1860. This decline came from a terrifying death rate and from emigration. (From 1845 to 1855, 200,000 people emigrated each year.) These horrors were accompanied by an even greater depopulation of the countryside. Many peasants moved to the towns and cities in Ireland as landlords dispossessed tenants wholesale in an effort to make farming profitable again. The purpose of these evictions was to enlarge the tiny holdings so as to allow more profitable farming. Specifically, since demands of the English market now required it, they shifted from tillage to pasturage, from a dense labor to a sparse labor economy. The frustration can be gauged from the fact that this unparalleled disaster came fifteen years after "Emancipation" and within two years of the most massive political demonstrations the country had seen. Political action, even successfully organized peaceful agitation, had proven futile: the grip of the destructive landlord system remained tight and political decision-making remained in a distant unresponsive London.[3]

Nevertheless, post-famine Irish held on to two bequests from O'Connell. First, they had risen from their 18th century political apathy and would never again completely succumb to it. Second, they had learned effectively to organize themselves even in the face of grinding poverty, to band together to help themselves, to establish viable institutions for self-help, and to turn available political processes to their own advantage.[4] At home and abroad these lessons learned in failure provided a basis on which future successes could be built. They provided successive generations of Irishmen with the seeds of a pride which had yet been experienced by precious few but which Yeats was later to claim as the due inheritance of all.

> I declare They shall inherit my pride,
> The pride of people that were
> Bound neither to Cause nor to State,
> Neither to slaves that were spat on,
> Nor to the tyrants that spat . . .
> Pride, like that of the morn,
> When the headlong light is loose . . . ("The Tower")[5]

But the road to achievement in Ireland, even truncated achievement, was long and bitter. Not until the Easter Rising of 1916 did the birth pangs of the Irish Free State begin—convulsions which included violent repression and civil war before the State was fully established in 1923. Between 1850 and 1916, the Irish bore that "Too long a sacrifice/ (which) Can make a stone of the heart."[6] The price exacted by that sacrifice was fearful—as can be clearly seen in the figure and fiction of James Joyce. Joyce's family was one in which forefathers survived famine and hard times by moving from country to city. Joyce himself continued the pattern followed by so many Irishmen: he emigrated in 1904, at age 22, and established successive residences in Italy, Switzerland and France. Joyce was but one of millions who paid the price of emigration, a hemorrhage of talent that has not yet been stanched. Joyce's fictional world, a sensitive viewer's perspective on Ireland in the period before the Easter Rising, shows another price of the protracted struggle. In their frustration, many Irishmen suffered a loss of self esteem, a crisis of self image. Joyce portrays a nation and a people beset with moral paralysis, unable to do or achieve anything. At its worst, this paralysis seemed spasmodically to dash its heroes down, and then to replace them with grim parodies.

The ruining of Charles Stewart Parnell, the parliamentary genius who was repudiated on the eve of apparent success in the campaign for Home Rule and land reform, was for Joyce the prime example of this perversity. He repeatedly portrays Parnell as a martyr, a Christ crucified for an ungrateful nation. A major Joyce character sums up this frustrated view, saying, "Ireland is the old sow that eats her farrow."[7]

Exile a Recurring Irish Phenomenon

Exile for political and economic causes has been a central Irish experience since the dawn of modern times. Starting with the Flight of the Earls in 1607, Ireland's native leadership was faced with the choice of emigration or suppression. By 1800 the ancient aristocracy had virtually disappeared at home, and was only visible over the waters. The major Catholic courts of Europe had continuing lines of Irish courtiers and soldiers. In fact, the first significant impact made by Irish in mid-America was made by a member of one of these expatriate families. Alexander O'Reilly, a Spanish aristocrat of Irish descent, was the colonial governor of the Louisiana Territory. He led the effort to put down the rebellion which broke out after France ceded the Territory to Spain late in the 18th century. Manuel de Lisa, an explorer, who in the first decade of the 19th century traced the Missouri up to the Yellowstone region and who established Fort Lisa near Council Bluffs, was married to an Irish wife—probably the first European woman to live in Nebraska.[8]

By the 19th century, exile was appealing to Irishmen of other classes as an alternative to intolerable conditions at home. This option was taken in sizable numbers by people from Ulster, mostly protestants, in the late 18th and early 19th century. U.S. government records indicate that Ireland was the native land of the largest number of immigrants in each census period from 1790 to 1840—that is, even before the famine. By 1840, people from all over Ireland were swelling the tide.[9] Long before that their impact was being felt even as far west as

Nebraska. In 1810 the agent at Fort Atkinson, the first center
of white man's activity in the state established sixteen miles
north of Omaha, was Benjamin O'Fallon. He was succeeded by
John Dougherty, and there seems to have been a considerable
number of Irishmen working the fur trade out of the fort during
the 1820's. Dougherty was an enlightened person, who as a fur
trader considered the well-being of the Indians as of central
interest to his trade since he recognized the Indian excellence
as guides and trappers. He applied to be Superintendent of
Indian Affairs, but unfortunately for the cause of Indians and
of civil rights, was not appointed.[10]

After the Nebraska territory was opened for settlement in
1854, the Irish were among the first to seize the opportunity.
The following year, for example, a wagon train of Irish people
settled what is now Dakota County, south of Sioux City. This
group appears to have been one which pushed westward immediately after their arrival from Ireland. Their settlement was
largely successful and permanent. It served as a source of support and as a way-station for later waves of Irish immigration
into the state. It also served, as one might expect, as a focal
point for state Democratic Party politics. The names of those
original settlers are still on the mailboxes of Dakota County
farms, farms held in the same family for each successive generation.[11]

The later Irish settlers came by various ways and in groups
of various sizes. Irish surnames can be found in county rosters
across the state by 1870. One way they came, of course, is on
the railroad, since railroad building was one job which an Irishman could get when signs were up in many establishments saying "Irish need not apply." Railroad work was hard, the pay
poor, and the shelter meagre. But conditions were not all bad,
and might even be said to be better than those they left behind.
One man wrote home to Ireland that he had eaten meat three
days in a week when, in fact, it was every day. He explained
that no one at home would believe the truth.[12] As the railroads moved west, many of those who built them settled along
the route. While it is true that most of these laborers settled in

large towns such as Chicago and St. Louis, Omaha received a sizable share and many smaller Nebraska towns did, too. By the end of the Civil War, Omaha's Irishmen were sufficiently well established for that city to be another receiving base for their later arriving fellow countrymen.

Irish Experience on Farms

The Irish success in agriculture in Nebaska, as in the rest of the United States, is very limited: less than 10 percent of Irish-Americans remain on farms. The high rate of failure of Nebraska Irish farms can be partly accounted for by the factors which rendered high plains farming so grueling—soil conditions, drought and other weather hazards, water shortages, locusts, etc. Contemporary descriptions of the damage wrought by "Rocky Mountain Locusts" in Holt County in the 1880's are remarkably similar to that wrought by potato blight in Ireland in the 1840's: green fields blackened overnight![13] To many Irishmen this catastrophe must have seemed the recurrence of a nightmare, and enough to frighten them from the land again.

But the fact is that the majority of Irish immigrants into Nebraska were ill equipped for farming even if indigenous factors had been less severe. Social and economic conditions in Ireland had created an explosive agricultural situation. The landlord's search for the highest profit encouraged tillage, which was labor intensive, and severe rack-renting. This led the peasant to come to depend on the potato for its sustenance and other qualities (land reclaiming and pig fattening). With regular milk and cheese from a cow and occasional bacon and pork from pigs, the potato formed the sustenance which was cheapest in cost and land usage. It was so cheap, in fact, that it supported disastrous overpopulation. One man could plant enough potatoes to feed forty; it required no cultivation, and could be harvested at mealtime. On tiny farms (25 percent five acres or less, another 40 percent between five and fifteen acres, and 135,000 holdings of less than one acre) potatoes fed the family and maybe a pig while other crops were sold for rent money. There was no security for most beyond the year's lease, that is, until the annual rent auction; there was no claim for any improvements a tenant might make on the land. These conditions produced the poorest peasantry in Europe and gave them no incentive for betterment.[14]

Consequently, the Irish were little equipped by their experience to handle enormous American holdings, to ride out bad years which regularly recurred on the prairies, or to endure the loneliness. Furthermore, many of the Irish who came west were at least a generation away from the countryside. Many had come to America financed only by poor relief funds which supplied them no more than passage money in the cheapest and most over-crowded vessels. "Coffin ships" they were called. They thus lacked not only suitable agricultural skills and culture, they frequently lacked the health and the means to get away from the place where they docked; they certainly lacked the means to invest in land or implements. So they squatted, many of them, in the teeming cities or grim coal fields of the East, hanging onto as much of their past as they could while they learned new ways. They stayed near the coast, not because they were better qualified for such a life, but because they couldn't go elsewhere, and here at least they could sell their one asset—muscles. Most remained in the East, moving west in sizable numbers only with the railroads in the '60's and '70's, or with colonization parties after '75.

Experience in places like Boston and New York had a radical effect on the American future of the Irish. Although conditions were better than those they had left beyond the Atlantic, the Irish still found themselves segregated and economically depressed. This situation promoted severe social debilitation: insanity abounded, moral degradation increased, drink became a worse problem than it had been at home. Family structures suffered in situations where too frequently only women could get steady work, as they could in domestic service. But nevertheless, the Irish had in reserve the legacy of O'Connell, which gave them the tools to improve their lot in the cities. They banded together to form political organizations unlike any previously seen in America. They financed these "political machines" as the Emancipation struggle had been financed, on the pennies contributed by impoverished thousands. They established mutual self-help societies, self-contained quasi-legal systems, separate Catholic schools (which they had unsuccessfully sought at home), etc. As it became clear that they were not to share Yankee success, these institutions became more firmly established and they forged new ones. They formed labor organizations to protect themselves and to improve their lot as America's first white working class. The result of these activities was mixed: they allowed survival but they contributed to the permanency of separate, unequal communities.[15]

"Nativist" Americanism arose which encouraged such "segregation" for religious and economic reasons. These exclusivist notions found support and respectability in fashionable English plays and novels. This literature was not only a justification of British imperialism in Ireland, it specifically fed the popular English response to Catholic Emancipation and to agitation for Poor Law reform. The Irish in this context were depicted as clever rogues or social climbers, or as dumb, drunken, good-for-nothings whose economic contribution to society was to depress wages and whose contribution to the transportation industry was the "paddy-wagon." [Author Murphy, a university art student, has provided a set of cartoons for this essay, reproducing some of these stereotypes.] This picture held sway in popular English culture throughout the 19th century. Indeed, as so often happens, the victims of the caricature had to adopt it if they were to be heard: the stage Irishman can be found even in the works of Boucicault, an Irish playwright popular in England and America at the end of the last century.[15]

In time Yankee and Irish learned to co-exist, but not without occasional revivals in the new world of the darker aspects of political and social agitation remembered from the old. Demagoguery was not unknown, nor was the terrorism of secret societies (e.g., Molly Maguires) and instigators both Irish and nativist promoted civil disturbances, convent burnings, draft riots, labor agitation, and the like. These clashes at times grew so violent that paving blocks came to be known in some places as "Irish confetti."[17]

Irish Settlements in Nebraska

Good times succeeded bad ones, and bad times came again. The Civil War produced relatively good times: jobs were plentiful and Irishmen clearly bore their share in the struggle for the Union. But they bore a heavier burden of the post-war hard times. Relief seemed available through greater mobility, and the lure of inexpensive land in the West. Once again the Irish organized for self-improvement. One result was The Irish Catholic Colonization Association, fathered by Bishop James O'Connor, a Philadelphian who was appointed to serve the Nebraska Catholic Church in 1876. The goal of the association was to establish specifically Irish towns in the Midwest as an economic and ethical refuge for Irishmen caught in the cities of the seaboard or in the mine fields of the Bishop's native Pennsylvania and neighboring Ohio. It was founded on $100,000 capital and designed as a self-renewing business venture. A town was to be established in Greeley County in central Nebraska, where land was cheap; settlers would be assisted to move into it and they would later be assessed $100 for their lots. This money was to finance establishment of Catholic institutions, the finding of a priest, and the assisting of other settlers; it was also to help in the cause of Irish freedom. The association was founded in 1879, and by 1883, over two hundred families had settled in the colony which came to be known as O'Connor, Nebraska. The association was hampered by a remote central authority which tried to administer the colony from Omaha and Chicago; these bureaucratic clamps further complicated the usual problems faced by Irish settlers in local farming conditions. By 1887, the association had begun to close down. The O'Connor colony eventually failed as a town and most of the settlers did not remain successfully on the land. But Greeley County remained a strong Irish Catholic area for some time, and is heavily Catholic to this day.[18]

O'Connor was not an isolated experiment. O'Neill, Nebraska was another, founded by General John O'Neill, a captain of the U.S. Army. He later became commanding general of the army of the Irish Republican Brotherhood. (The IRB was a secret society, known as the Fenians, which organized both in Ireland and America to achieve Irish nationhood; the abortive Irish rebellion of 1867 was the work of this group.)[19] O'Neill was a veteran of three unsuccessful attempts to seize and hold Canada to force the English to pay the ransom of Irish freedom. He turned from that futile exercise to Irish community building in Nebraska. Folklore that he intended his settlement as an arsenal for a new Canadian invasion is apparently groundless.[20] Rather his Irish nationalism was taking a new form. In a letter to Bishop O'Connor on December 27, 1867, he wrote, "We could build up a young Ireland on the virgin plains and prairies of Nebraska. . . ."[21] To understand his plan, one must remember that "Young Ireland" was the name of an idealistic nation-building movement in Ireland in the 1840's. It emphasized a revitalized Irish culture, self-help, self-determination, land reform, and ultimately, if necessary, the use of arms to achieve an independent Ireland. It even fielded an abortive rebellion in 1848 which sent many of its leaders into American exile. (One, Thomas Meagher, called "Meagher of the Sword" for a famous speech in which he opposed O'Connell's pacifism, became a Union general of a Massachusetts Irish regiment in the Civil War, and later died on his way to take the post of territorial governor of Montana.) When O'Neill speaks of "a young Ireland," he is depicting his colony as a bootstrap exercise which would revitalize the Irish in America and ultimately, like the O'Connor settlement, serve to support the Irish freedom movement in the mother country. To that end he led four successive groups of settlers from the East, and died recruiting more.[22]

Many of these second-tier migrants to O'Neill, O'Connor and other communities spent only a relatively short and insecure period on the land. They set up their soddies and dugouts. A few tried to run a small bar or dry goods store on the

side to support the homestead. But when hard times came,
many Nebraska Irish (like the Joyces in Ireland) followed what
had become an ethnic pattern. They left the countryside for
the towns and cities where they had learned to cope, indeed
became "savvy." With their highly developed skill in ward
politics and their instinct for communal self-support, they
found their way into town councils, county commissions,
legislatures, and into the executive branch of government. They
then were appointed to the other government agencies, the Civil
Service, police and fire departments, and the postal service.
Indeed every major political movement, event, or agency in the
state has felt the presence of Irish politicians.

Irish Politicians and Influential Men

The first prominent Irish politician in Nebraska was Sam
Daily, who ran against J. Sterling Morton during the first congressional election in the state. Daily had but a few years of
education and was a rough and tumble fellow with a limited
vocabulary—his speeches contained no "highfalutin' " phrases,
but plain words delivered with an Irish brogue. Morton was
well educated, a man of great wealth, given to the fine
oratorical style which he polished during his college years.
Morton would make fun of Daily's brogue and ridicule his
rough style. Daily, on the other hand, would remind his audience of his own struggle for education and position, and call to
mind Morton's silver spoon. By playing on the common-man
sympathies of his audience, he won the election of 1860 as the
territorial representative. In 1862 he retained his seat, defeat-
ing Judge Kinney. Daily was the first of a long line of rough
Irish Nebraska politicians having roots in poverty and rough
labor.[23]

A few early Irish urban Nebraskans achieved traditional
American success, even affluence. Ed Creighton was born in
Ohio in 1820. He made his fortune constructing telegraph
lines, particularly telegraph lines from St. Louis to Omaha, for
which he received a large amount of telegraph stock. His ambi-

tion was to extend the line from coast to coast. Creighton made at least two lasting contributions to Nebraska. The first derived from his telegraph construction. For purposes of efficiency he drove livestock with him while working on the lines, oxen for hauling purposes and cattle for food. One winter he left the cattle in western Nebraska, figuring to gather them in spring if they survived and to lose but little if they perished in the winter. When he returned to the lines the following year, he found his cattle had survived. He thus demonstrated for the first time the fact that ranching might be viable in the Sandhills region—a fact on which a major Nebraska industry is now based. Creighton did not pursue his intention of stringing lines to the Far West, but settled eventually in Omaha as a banker. He founded the First National Bank in Omaha and the First National Bank in Denver. His second lasting contribution came upon his death in 1874; he left a bequest to start a college in Nebraska. His widow and brother carried out this project which led to the foundation of Creighton University in Omaha. The institution was designed to keep the sons and daughters of Nebraska in this state, and to give them an education second to none.[24]

Many Irish railroad laborers left the work gangs, bought a wagon and team, and became independent freighters and suppliers for the companies they left. When the railroads were completed, many of the leading railroad contractors were Irishmen; and some of these became affluent. John Fitzgerald of Lincoln, Richard Cushing, the O'Keefes, the Callahans, the McShane brothers, the Sullivans of Omaha—all of them began as workers on the Union Pacific and branch railroads. John McShane of the McShane brothers came originally from Ohio and established himself as a cattleman. He founded and was president of the Union Stockyards and of a packing center in Omaha. In 1865-66, on land which belonged mainly to other Irish, he built the three packing plants which developed specifically into the Armour-Cudahy Company and generally into the huge Omaha stockyard and meat packing industry.[25]

Relation of Nebraska Irish to Ireland

The Irish nationalism imbedded in the plans of O'Connor and O'Neill was visible in other ways in Nebraska, as it was across the nation. The local Irish kept in touch with events in their mother country and indeed contributed to them. The major thrust of events in Ireland in the 1870's and 80's was toward land reform and Home Rule. These movements went forward on a triple impetus: an Irish grassroots organization called the Land League, supporting funds from an American counterpart, and the dynamic leadership of an Irish parliamentary leader—Charles Stewart Parnell. The League in Ireland was suppressed by the British in 1880; Parnell was briefly jailed and the League's treasurer, Patrick Egan, fled to America and settled in Lincoln, Nebraska. In 1884, at a convention in Boston, Egan was elected president of the American branch of the Irish National League (successor to the outlawed Irish Land League) and he moved its headquarters to Lincoln. In 1886, another Lincolnite, John Fitzgerald, succeeded Egan—who had resigned because his church-going habits (or rather lack of them) upset the rest of the leadership. In 1886, too, Parnell succeeded in earning for his Irish party the balance of power in the English Parliament; he used it to convince the British Liberal Party to endorse Home Rule for Ireland—a measure that they could not carry in Commons. Thereafter, Parnell came under increasing conservative attack. Most devastating was the attempt begun in 1887 by the *Times* of London to implicate him in murder plots, specifically the murder in Phoenix Park in 1881 of the two chief English civil servants in Ireland. The campaign climaxed with an investigation into the charges by a committee of the House of Commons, a committee packed against Parnell. But the committee had to exonerate Parnell, largely because Egan from Lincoln provided evidence which proved that certain incriminating letters—the main prop of the prosecution case—were in fact forgeries. This left Parnell at the pinnacle of his career. But he was almost immediately cast down by his constituents in the wake of a scandalous divorce case.[26] Curiously, the leadership of the Irish politician was cut down on moral grounds, just as had that of his Nebraska supporter, Egan.

Weakening Ties to Ireland and Developing as Americans

Irish politics, both in Ireland and America, suffered severe internal stresses after Parnell's fall; and English politics, firmly in control of the Conservative-Union party allowed little influence to the Irish in Parliament. So political dynamism was replaced by factionalism and relative dormancy. Parnell himself died in the fall of 1890—mourned on the same stage in Nebraska by Egan, Fitzgerald, and another popular Midwest leader, William Jennings Bryan. Between 1890 and the First World War, Irish energies were turned in other directions: bettering living conditions, building schools and churches, cultural enrichment, and increasing their voice in the political, social, and economic institutions which surrounded their lives. In Ireland this was the time of renaissance, a renewed effort to build a national culture which might replace the lost Gaelic one. The Gaelic League tried to reestablish the national language which by 1900 was the primary tongue of only 10 percent of the population, a calamitous fall from the 90 percent in 1800. The Gaelic Athletic Association was revitalizing national sports, while the Sinn Fein worked on the capacity for self government and self help. Yeat's Irish Theatre was trying to establish an Irish cultural movement in English, with outstanding success.[27] But in American-Irish these ethnocentric forces were diluted by the concomitant try to establish a place for themselves in mainstream America. They had no culture to revive, and could hardly afford to vitalize Gaelic, or popularize curling in America. Further, they had no need to establish para-political institutions since they had real access to politics already. There were "green-power" activities designed "to give people of Irish birth or descent" substantial reason for 'pride of race,' and to provide the confrontation of the efforts of any who would "ignore or belittle the part taken by men and women of Irish birth or

blood in promoting the spread of religion, civilization, education, culture and freedom. . . ."28 Since these cultural and
political activities in both countries differed so widely from
each other, vital ties between the two groups weakened.

The direct influence of Nebraska Irish lessened in Ireland
during this period. They did, however, along with their cousins
across the United States, continue to provide financial support
for Irish independence, and to encourage an American foreign
policy which would mitigate British repression in Ireland and
enhance Irish freedom.

The best source of information about the Irish in this
period is still probably oral history. One surviving son of Nebraska Irish rural settlers, Joe O'Brien of Plattsmouth, recalls
his family history as follows:

> My family came in 1891 to the Cortland area first.
> This fellow named Oliver Cooper had a farm near there for
> rent. We lived there fourteen years; then the farm got sold,
> and the new owner wanted to raise the rent. So we moved.
> The new farm was near Manley. We lived in town for
> some three months while a house was being built on the farm.
> At the time, in Manley, they wouldn't rent out to anybody
> but Catholics; that's how we got it. Well, at this time, while
> we were in town, the fellow doing the plastering at the farm
> told my dad he knew another O'Brien named Shemus. There
> were words carried back and forth, and my dad finally said he
> didn't know of any O'Brien named Shemus but he bet the
> man's right name was Henry. He invited Shemus out and sure
> enough, his name was Henry. My father's father and his fath-
> er's father were brothers. Henry left home at age 14 and
> nobody had heard from him since.
> When he came up the first thing he asked was, "Is my
> poor mother and dad living?" "No," my dad said, "your
> mother is dead." "Oh—God bless her," Henry said. Then
> Henry made a trip back to Illinois to visit his father.
> His name was Henry but everyone called him Shemus.
> There's a history somewhere of Manley that says he was an
> implement dealer but he never was as long as I knew him. He
> bought old iron and metal and such and shipped it off. I guess

that made him a junk dealer. He was good to kids—Shemus was.

One day three boys came around with one of these little old stoves. One came into Shemus and said, "Shemus, I got an old stove out here, what'll you give for it?" "Oh, a dime," says ·Shemus, "and put it out back." About an hour later another boy came in with an old stove and Shemus gave him a dime and told him to put it out back. Still later a third boy comes in. "Shemus, you want to buy a stove?" he asked. "Oh sure, here's your dime, but put it in the same place the first boy put it will you." I guess that got them because they didn't bring that old stove back a fourth time.

Now the O'Briens are related to the Murphys down around Manley. The Murphy farm down there celebrated its centennial a year after Nebraska did. It's been in the same family, the ones that homesteaded it, that long. The first man there, he had seven boys. During the war (WWI), they were called up to serve. When the father died, Joseph bought the farm from his brothers and he had seven boys, too, I think. Well, some of them served the next war, and now one of his sons lives there and his boys fought in Vietnam. So there's about fifteen Murphy boys born and raised on that one farm that have served their country in time of war.

I didn't get to go fight in WWI. I had flat feet. When I went home and told them that all my neighbors took off their boots and started walking in the puddles joshing each other, declaring their feet were flat too. It was quite a sight. One of my cousins' wife and his mother went to the draft board and got him out of it. He was furious. He told them to mind their own business and what good was a farm like they had if he couldn't go and defend it.[29]

These remarks contain much that is typical of the Irish-Americans, especially their humor, cohesiveness, and mobility. The ambivalence about World War I that is visible in Mr. O'Brien is also fairly typical Irish sentiment about that issue and many other American issues. Irish-Americans who fought that war did so for patriotic American and Irish reasons. Irish on both sides of the ocean took heart when President Wilson proclaimed, as America entered, that it was "a war for freedom and justice and self-government amongst all the nations of the world." But there were also American and Irish reasons for not fighting it: why should American boys be inveighed into fighting a foreign war for someone else's mercantile interests? This was especially problematic for those Americans, and there were many, who were convinced that British commercial interests and those of the United States were coming into increasing conflict, a conflict which might well lead to an Anglo-American war.[30] Why should America's Irish boys defend England's imperialism?

Besides these internal stresses, the Irish, like German immigrant people, felt the added wartime burden of being suspect Americans in the eyes of some of their more righteous fellow citizens. Their patriotism was questioned and great demands were placed on them to demonstrate it. These pressures were particularly felt during World War I, but they had earlier roots and continued later. Consistently they found their patriotism impugned when they sought to view or influence American policy in ways which seemed to reflect the experience or perspective of their country of origin. Although it may be natural to rely on one's inherited wisdom, and although expressing such wisdom may contribute a fuller range to the discussion of public issues, it has nevertheless been a right reserved to Americans of few nationalities to do so with impunity. Some Irish-Americans responded to such special challenges by adopting the kind of super-patriotism which seemed required. Others, in reaction, adopted a super-Catholicism, and some tried to combine the two. Few could avoid feeling some defensiveness about the alleged impossibility of being both Irish and American. Even President Kennedy's remarks quoted at the beginning of this chapter reveal this strain. It is almost embarrassing that in a largely ceremonial speech in Ireland about how fondly her expatriate children recall the land of their fathers, the President of the United States feels the necessity to reiterate their loyalty, and by implication his own, to their own country.

Americans of Irish origin also felt ambivalently about Prohibition, about racial matters and about the League of Nations.

The Irish temperance movement had a long effective history both in Ireland and America; yet Prohibition was frequently described as a way of saving the stereotyped drunken Irish. For the Irish, as for other ethnics, racial justice was a noble goal in theory; it has been forwarded by very prominent Irish politicians. But it seemed to many that in practice its cost too frequently weighed heaviest on themselves and the other white ethnics. It was they who felt the wage lowering and displacement effects of more equitable job competition, and the economic and social impact of housing and schooling improvements based on the concern for civil rights.

At the same time the Irish-Americans were working through these strains, the Irish situation "at home" was changing dramatically. Clear identification with the "cause" was becoming much more difficult, for the cause was no longer so distinctly defined. "Freedom" was coming to Ireland, but only to part of it. Irish and Irish-American goals began to diverge, both because of different needs and of different perceptions of strategy. Of the million dollars for the "Irish Victory Fund" collected in America in 1920, three quarters went to the campaign to block the League of Nations. American-Irish felt satisfied to spend these monies in this fashion since they felt it served to prevent entangling America in British webs—and so kept alive the chance that America might intervene to aid Irish freedom. But in Ireland national leaders did not oppose the League if a free Ireland had a place in it; and besides, having a war to fight at home (the Anglo-Irish War of 1919-21) they had better uses for the money. Other divergences became evident when Eamon DeValera, the American-born rebel chief and "President of the Irish Republic," came to America in 1920 and proved to be a difficult person. He became entangled in Irish-American factional disputes. He embarrassed his hosts by trying in person to influence the national conventions of both political parties in ways opposed by leaders of the American-Irish community. He set up a rival fund-raising program. The Americans won in the political arena, but "Dev" won the money. Further clouding Irish-American sympathies, in 1922-

1923 Ireland endured a Civil War over the question of partition and other conditions attached by Britain to "independence." Undoubted patriots fought on both sides, DeValera leading the "Republican" minority into the field against those who had formed a government based on the settlement. "Right" was unclear.[31]

After its Civil War the isle cooled. Righteous fervor declined, and retrospective glances (see O'Casey's plays)[32] cast a light on recent history which rendered nationalistic idealism untenable in the face of the horrors it had caused. The demands of practical politics and actual administration brought new issues to the fore in Ireland. These issues were barely comprehensible to Americans far removed from the scene and were hardly suitable to "rally round." Depression brought hard times and a consequent renewed emphasis on survival problems for the American-Irish as for everyone else. The antecedants of World War II created some of the same ambivalence in Irish-Americans as had World War I. But after Pearl Harbor, the official and popular response in America differed completely from that of the neutral stand taken by Ireland under the guidance of DeValera, now Prime Minister.[33] All these factors, as well as the pressure continuously felt from Americanists who looked down on folk unable or unwilling to shed pre-immigration ties, served to distance American-Irish from the land of their ancestors. "Green power" tales were not enough to keep an accurate vital image alive: even in Ireland such tales did not provide much sustenance. It was one of Joyce's characters who noted the frustration of hailing a "land of saints and scholars" when Ireland had produced neither saint nor scholar for "a thousand years."[34] So their view of Ireland was becoming romanticized. For many, as for President Kennedy, Ireland increasingly was seen as largely "green" and rather "misty."

This romanticized vision supports less fund raising and Ireland-related political activity. Irish-Americans can go for years without hearing an appeal. In March, 1976, the Irish Prime Minister told the U.S. Congress that most of what appeals there were were misguided efforts to support blind terror-

ism. Politically, Senator Ted Kennedy has been notably unsuccessful in his effort to get a Senate investigation of current
conditions in Ulster, although there was precedent for it in the
time of the 1919-21 "Troubles" in Ireland. Rather, contemporary Irish-Americanism has its chief outlet in celebrations,
particularly St. Patrick's Day festivities. Even these seem to be
passing, as the commercial interests which promote them draw
back from the dissociated rowdyism which they seem to
encourage. It's hardly a loss that O'Neill, Nebraska, cut back
its Irish festival, since it turned out to be merely an excuse for
all sorts to participate in the revival of a vicious stereotype—that
of an Irish drunk.

Less harmful, perhaps, are other expressions of cultural
festivity or identity. It is at least curious to note how similar
the intentionally stereotypical cartoons accompanying this
essay are to the pictures on the usual St. Patrick's Day cards
exchanged by Irish-Americans. The similarity suggests that the
Irish have adopted as their own images those which were originally developed by others to accomplish and justify oppression of previous generations of Irish people. This may be
another example of people accepting their popular image as an
unavoidable necessity. Or it may suggest that such oppression
is no longer felt, so its instruments can be laughed at. But however it may be explained, it is clear that the American Irishman's most frequent ethnic self images rather lack vitality and
substance.

Current Situation of America's Irish

But in America and in Nebraska there remains a vital force
which can be identified as emanating from the American-Irish.
They showed a special pride when John Kennedy was elected
President of the United States. Given the extent to which Irish
have given themselves to American politics, the extent to which
they have shaped it, this election of one of their own (and such
a fine broth of a boy he seemed, too!) to be the most powerful
man on earth was a crowning achievement. It was an achieve-

ment which both he and they regularly spoke of with ebullient good humor. The source of this humor lies, of course, not in the melting of the Irish into the great pot, but in their capacity to win without shedding that common identity which allowed them to survive even while it caused them pain and difficulty.

President Kennedy's election, then, had great symbolic value. He was the most evident figure, although in some ways an anomalous one, of Irish achievement in America. He was an anomalous figure because he was not fully representative. To many in America he was acceptable because his schooling had been "in no way parochial." To others he was acceptable because he was not "really Irish," not an urban worker or the product of machine politics.

Perhaps a better indication of real success of the Irish in America can be seen in the institutions they fostered. It can be seen in the relative affluence of laboring men and women which springs from the power of the labor movement. This power is evident in the number of working people of Irish extraction who have emerged as union leaders and as influential figures in the President's cabinet and other national councils. Success can also be seen in the American Catholic Church, its schools, colleges, and other benevolent enterprises—institutions like Nebraska's Creighton University, St. Mary's College and Father Flanagan's Boys Town. Irish political potency remains vital across the political spectrum; Irish politicians are prominent in the Unicameral and in congressional elections in Nebraska. The force of the pragmatic "ward politics" continues to be felt in many American cities, including Omaha. Even the major cities where the ward politician's day has passed, there is no overwhelming evidence that idealists who have replaced him (and the real abuses his system was given to) have proven capable of providing government which is as responsive to rank and file voters, or as functional, as efficient, or even as just. Many Irish-Americans have made an emminent place for themselves in business, finance, and the professions, profiting from an ancient Irish emphasis on learning and an equally characteristic insistence on renewed effort.

Perhaps the most significant, at least the most lasting, identifiable contribution of a community comes from its artists. The American-Irish community has produced a goodly number of these, and their work and their place in history reveals much about the community from which they come. The list of the nationally and internationally known Irish-American writers is substantial: Eugene O'Neill and Philip Barry as dramatists; James T. Farrell, F. Scott Fitzgerald, John O'Hara, and Flannery O'Connor as writers of prose fiction. One thing notable about those writers is how many of them produced works which are dissociated from mainstream Irish-American traditions and particularly from the Catholic Church. It is not that they are critical of those traditions; much in modern Irish culture (i.e., the work of Joyce, O'Casey, O'Connor, O'Faolain, Kavanaugh, Behan, etc.) renders such criticism normal. Rather it is their apparent effort to achieve artistic and popular success by denying their background and associations, as if their place depended on it. Of course, there is some evidence that it may, for their work is generally studied (except where the subject does not allow it) without any focus on the community which nurtured them, and it. Another notable aspect of their literary output is its recurrent concern with class distinctions, whether through sympathetic portrayals of the very poor or an absorbing outsider's concern with the rather rich. These materials suggest facets of the American-Irish experience which may well prove to be characteristic qualities. They suggest an experience responding both to an internal need and to an external pressure to be identified as real, unhyphenated Americans, and to achieve the typical American success, socio-economic improvement, moving toward affluence.

If this is a true interpretation of the aspirations of Irish-Americans, then they have been remarkably successful indeed. There are indications that, after the Jews, Irish Catholics have a higher average income and educational level than any other identifiable ethnic or religious group in the country.[35] What that means in terms of their future as an identifiable community can only be a matter for speculation. It would seem, if this

were a predictable and a sensible world, that the days of that
community are numbered. The history of the real decay in the
vital substantial images of Ireland and of Irish-Americanism
would be grounds to predict its quiet end. Surely, in a sensible
world, nativist American pressures to maintain socio-economic
barriers on the basis of race or religion would wither. But, of
course, history has a way of undercutting both prophecy and
good sense. There may yet be a generation arise to heed in
America Yeats' final advice to Irish poets and by implication to
makers and doers of all sorts:

> Irish poets, learn your trade
> Sing whatever is well made,
> Scorn the sort now growing up
> All out of shape from toe to top,
> Their unremembering hearts and heads. . . .
> Cast your mind on other days
> That we in coming days may be
> Still the undomitable Irishry. ("Under Ben Bulben")[36]

Sources

This essay is an effort at interpretive history, developed by
relatively inexperienced, though interested, amateurs. It is based
on many formal and informal sources, but the research necessary to do an adequate job has only begun. We are indebted to
many others for information and correction; our errors we
claim as fully our own.

Most of the Nebraska research on which this paper is based
was done by Nadine Murphy who appends the following note:

> If I have concentrated too heavily on eastern Nebraska
> it is because this is where I live and I knew where to get con-
> tact with the people, especially the grandparents whose mem-
> ories are so valuable. Please view my work with a kind eye to
> its deficiencies, and if you have yourself possible sources of
> information which I lacked for want of time and knowledge,
> please write. Consider this small chapter a possible beginning

to an Irish history of Nebraska and not an end in itself. Share your memories and your heritage. I can't promise to use everything I might receive or even that a book might be written from it. I do promise my ongoing interest in Nebraska's Irish and their story.

Nadine Murphy/
James McShane
c/o Department of English
University of Nebraska - Lincoln
Lincoln, Nebraska 68588

FOOTNOTES

1. Maurice N. Hennessy, *"I'll Come Back in the Springtime":* *John F. Kennedy and the Irish* (New York: Ives Washburn, Inc., 1966), p. 50.

2. Sean O'Faolain, *King of Beggars, Life of Daniel O'Connell, The Irish Liberator, in A Study of the Rise of the Modern Irish Democracy (1775-1847)* (New York: The Viking Press, 1938), *passim.*

3. F.S.L. Lyons, *Ireland Since the Famine: 1850 to the Present* (New York: Charles Scribner's Sons, 1971), Part I; Lawrence J. McCaffrey, *The Irish Question 1800/1922* (Lexington: University of Kentucky Press, 1968), Chapters 1-3; and O'Faolain, *Ibid.*

4. O'Faolain, *op. cit.*

5. William Butler Yeats, *Selected Poems and Two Plays,* ed. by M.L. Rosenthal (New York: Macmillan Publishing Co., Inc., 1962), p. 100.

6. *Ibid.,* "Easter 1916," p. 86.

7. James Joyce, *Portrait of the Artist as a Young Man* (1916); *Dubliners* (1914), *passim.* The quote is from *Portrait,* V.

8. A.E. Sheldon, *Nebraska: The Land and the People* (Chicago: The Lewis Publishing Co., 1931), Chapters VII-IX.

9. Lyons, *loc. cit.*

10. *Nebraska History,* magazine of the Nebraska State Historical Society (July and September, 1936) and John B. Duff, *The Irish in the United States* (Belmont, Calif.: Wadsworth Publishing Co., 1971).

11. Interview by James McShane with Professor Thomas Kuhlman, English, Creighton University. (Professor Kuhlman has lectured in the area, and spoke briefly with Mr. McShane before he became involved in this project.)

12. Sheldon, *op. cit.*

13. Burns E. McCulloh, *A Piece of Emerald* (Centennial History of O'Neill, Nebraska) (O'Neill, Nebraska: Miles Publishing Co., 1974), p. 13 and Cecil Woodham-Smith, *The Great Hunger, Ireland 1845-1849* (New York: Harper & Row, 1962), pp. 91-92.

14. Lyons, *loc. cit.,* and Woodham-Smith, *op. cit.*

15. Oscar Handlin, *Boston's Immigrants, 1790-1880* (New York: Atheneum, 1971), *passim.*

16. For these materials see Sister Mary Edith Kelley, *The Irishman in the English Novel of the Nineteenth Century* (Washington, D.C.: The Catholic University Press, 1939), and G.C. Duggin, *The Stage Irishman* (New York: B. Blom, 1969), *passim.* Particular examples can be found in

in the novels of Charles Lever, Samuel Lover, William Meginn, and William Hamilton Maxwell.

17. Interview by James McShane with Professor Clay McShane, History and Urban Development, Carnegie Mellon University.

18. Gerald J. Burback, "An Irish Colony in Nebraska" (unpublished master's dissertation, Saint Paul Seminary, 1960).

19. Lyons, *op. cit.*

20. Interview by James McShane with Steve Ross, who interviewed several Holt County Irish, particularly John J. Harrington and P.C. Donahoe.

21. Burbach, *op. cit.*

22. McCulloh, *op. cit.*

23. *Nebraska History, op. cit.*

24. *Ibid.*

25. *Ibid.*

26. Lyons, *op. cit.*, Part II, Chapter 3.

27. *Ibid.*, Part II, Chapters 4-6.

28. Joseph Dunn and P.J. Lennox, *The Glories of Ireland* (Washington, D.C.: Phoenix Ltd., 1914), v.

29. Interview by Nadine Murphy with Joseph O'Brien.

30. Lyons, *op. cit.*, p. 384.

31. *Ibid.*, p. 404 ff.

32. Sean O'Casey, *The Shadow of a Gunman; Juno and the Paycock; The Plough and the Stars* (New York: St. Martin's Press, 1966).

33. Lyons, *op. cit.*

34. Joyce, *op. cit.*

35. Rev. Andrew M. Greeley, *That Most Distressful Nation: The Taming of the American Irish* (Chicago: Quadrangle Books, 1972), p. 122.

36. Yeats, *op. cit.*, p. 192.

X

The Dutch: A World of Calvin and Cream

By Corine Simon

X

The Dutch: A World of Calvin and Cream

By Corine Simon

When the first Dutch pioneers crossed the Mississippi River and looked for a place to settle down and make their fortunes, it was the rolling, well-drained and fertile area of Lancaster County which seemed most appealing to them. Prior to coming to Nebraska, many Dutch had settled further east, in Michigan, Wisconsin and Illinois. Also, in Iowa a large Dutch community had been thriving since 1847.

During the period between 1840-1850 an almost epidemic urge for emigration was taking place in The Netherlands. Every day the Dutch newspapers had "Emigration to North America" in the headlines. People discussed it in the streets and in present day terms one could call it a "mass psychosis." Exactly what the origin of this great migration was has been debated extensively. Some historians emphasize the economic factor. The failure of the potato crop in 1845 caused a major disaster for the Dutch population. There were food riots, and unemployment was high. Others mention spiritual causes in the people's urge to emigrate. In those days there was a great deal of unrest in the Dutch Reformed Church. The name of the State Church was changed, in Dutch terminology, from "de gereformeerde Kerk" to the "Hervormde Kerk." "Hervormde" meant "re-organized" in the minds of the critics, which was translated as: to suit the wishes of the king.[1] The state interference resulted in the so-called Secession of 1834. Different religious

groups under the leadership of ministers seceded from the State
Church. Persecution took place, fines were imposed on the leaders of the groups, and failure of payment often resulted in
imprisonment. A combination of both economic and religious
causes, culminating in a general dissatisfaction, seemed to be the
real motive.[2]

Moreover, large groups of other European nations came to
the Dutch ports and embarked from there to North America.
Their example appeared contagious. Although most of the aspiring emigrants were poor farmers and laborers and emigration
seemed the only way out to better their lives, there must have
been also a great deal of adventure involved, especially for single
men.

During the years between 1846-1850 the trip by boat
from Rotterdam to New York was 35 guldens—approximately
$12.[3] One needed another 20 guldens for food during the six to
eight week period on the ocean. Guide books on North America
were available which described in particular the low cost of
government land and the good prices farmers made for their
products. Letters from relatives and friends who had already
left for North America and which praised the "promised Land,"
were perhaps the most convincing. These letters were often
published in newspapers under the heading of: "Voices of
North America."

Important large settlements were established in Holland,
Michigan; Pella, Iowa; and near Milwaukee, Wisconsin in Sheboygan County. Their respective leaders were the secessionist
Reverends van Raalte, Scholte and Pieter Zonne. After the
Homestead Act of 1862, and following the admission of Nebraska into the Union in 1869, immigration from the eastern
states increased rapidly.

In the spring of 1868, Henry Brethouwer left Sheboygan
County, Wisconsin with his father-in-law to search for a new
homeland. Dissatisfied with his property of thickly forested
land, its swampy grounds reminded him too much of his native
country, he sold all of his belongings and travelled west into the
southeast part of Nebraska.[4] He staked his claim in the Panama

Precinct and a "dug-out" was constructed for shelter. A year later his brother, Chris Brethouwer, came to visit him and decided to return with his family. A few other families joined him and they made the trip by train from Wisconsin to the east bank of the Missouri River opposite Nebraska City.[5] After a difficult crossing, their meager funds were expended for a team of oxen and a wagon with which they completed the journey. These were the first Dutch immigrants to enter Nebraska. Soon other families from Wisconsin followed to augment the original settlement. According to the United States Census, there were: 180 foreign-born Dutch in Nebraska in 1870, 753 in 1880, and 1143 in 1890. After that year the Dutch population declined to a low of 174 in 1970.[6]

It is interesting to mention that the Dutch in Lancaster County often had great difficulties understanding one another as they came from different provinces in The Netherlands, Gelderland and Zeeland, where different dialects were spoken. Most Dutch pioneers came with little or no money but were determined to rise above the rigid system of social classes they had known in their native country.[7]

It hardly needs mentioning how primitive their living conditions were. Dug-outs served as homes. When new families arrived, the dug-outs were shared until new living conditions were made. Only the most necessary belongings were taken, such as clothes, the Bible, pots and pans, and a coffee mill.

Baking break involved the following procedure: The dough was put in an iron kettle or pan. This was covered with hot ashes and left in this way in a fireplace—usually a hole in the ground on one side of the dug-out—until the bread was baked. Often the bread was so hard that it could not be eaten. It was then ground up in a coffee mill and used as coffee.[8] The diet consisted mostly of potatoes, buttermilk pap, dark bread and wild game which was found in abundance. Prairie chickens were raised for their eggs and meat. A favorite dish in those days was "boerenkool,"—a green garden plant (kale) mixed up with mashed potatoes. It is still a favorite dish in The Netherlands, especially in winter time when the first frost has come over the kale. It is usually eaten with knockwurst. Also buttermilk pap is still used in The Netherlands as a dessert. The recipe goes: bring buttermilk to a boil, add some salt and buckwheat flour. The trick is not to let it curdle. When the consistency is thick, it is eaten with syrup.[9] "Balkenbrij" is a dish which is still known among the older generation of Firth and Holland today. It is a concoction of beef and/or pork scraps. After this is cooked, the juice is strained and mixed with buckwheat and flour. One adds the meat and spices to taste. When cold and stiff, slices are cut which are then fried in oil or butter.

In the early pioneer days "het koffie drinken" was almost a religious ceremony. Besides the three meals, coffee was served at 9 a.m. and 4 p.m.—and if a guest wasn't served his "kopje koffie," then the host could be assured of having acquired a bad reputation. It was the expected entertainment when a guest came over.[10]

The nearest store was in Nebraska City. Shopping was usually done for the entire community by one person who possessed a couple of oxen and a wagon. The first store in the settlement was opened by Chris Brethouwer and was taken over by William Walvoord in 1873. With the establishment of this store, the place was given the name Holland (after Holland, Wisconsin). For many years this store was known as the "Walvoord and Lubbers Co.," and became the meeting place for the old pioneers with their long pipes and wooden shoes. They exchanged reminiscences there and the owner kept a cigar box well filled with tobacco, free to those who cared to smoke.[11]

There were two established families who were very helpful to the Dutch. They were the Billie Morrison and Henry Hickman families. They owned timberland, which was rare in Lancaster County, and they provided the Hollanders with poles and logs for the construction of their dug-outs. No trees were to be found in that area until the last part of the 70's. A Dutch pioneer's wife and her eldest son planted a grove of about one hundred trees north of their home. She remarked: "One day I will entertain my grandchildren in the shade of these trees."[12]

She lived to see her prophesy come true.

Gradually their living conditions improved. Sod houses were built and the more well-to-do built frame houses. A successful crop was often threatened by prairie fires, hailstorms, droughts and invasion of grasshoppers. In 1871, three Dutch children were burned to death in a sudden prairie fire while their parents were attending a church service. Only perseverance and faith kept these early settlers alive through such phenomena of nature. For the wives of the early pioneers, the visits of groups of Indians, the howling of coyotes at night and sickness were most frightful experiences. They are described as strong women who helped with all the farm work and were indispensible in planting of the crops, the harvesting of grain and in haying.[13] On top of that, they had big families—often with seven or eight children—to care for. One pioneer woman gave birth to sixteen children. In childbirth the only assistance was a midwife whose knowledge and technique was gained only from practical experiences. However, few babies died in childbirth. One ascribes this to the simple diet and sturdy outdoor living of the Dutch pioneer mother, rather than to the efficiency of the midwife.[14]

Throughout the history of the Lancaster County settlement, the Dutch Reformed Church played a pivotal role. Dissatisfaction with the Americanization of the religious customs in Wisconsin had been an important reason for the westward migration, and upon arrival steps were taken at once to preserve the character of the settlers' religious heritage. The first Dutch group started religious meetings in the different dug-outs. Printed sermons from Wisconsin were used, and the singing of psalms was the main element of the religious gathering. In 1870 the Reverend Dunnewald from Wisconsin came to the Dutch settlement, and soon a congregation was formed which counted 51 members by the end of the year. Need for a permanent minister and a place to worship was greatly felt. Two ladies of New York made a donation of $3,000 for the building of a church and the employment of a minister. Dominee (the Dutch name for reverend) te Winkel became the first minister, and a barn-like building was erected as the first church. Its architecture was very reminiscent of Holland, preserving the Dutch custom of separating men and women by means of a large partition dividing the interior of the structure. With more money from the East and an increasing number of church members, a second church was built several years later. The first structure was used to stable the horses of the church members during the services. In 1876 Dominee Huizinga from Virginia came to Nebraska and remained the minister for 15 years. He played an important role in the Dutch settlement, as did his followers. A total of 12 ministers served the Dutch Reformed Church of Holland over a hundred year period. In 1935 the congregation had 400 members; today this number is 339. There are a total of 1,500 members in the five Dutch Reformed Churches in Omaha, Lincoln, Holland, Firth, and the Pella Church towards Adams.[15]

The Dutch pioneers believed strongly that God directed their lives. He brought them material fortune, but also interfered with their prosperity, bringing droughts, grasshopper plagues and hail to destroy their crops. This was done, they believed, to prevent their self trust.[16] The Dutch language was used in church services until 1910, by which time most of the homes had become Americanized. Until 1935 two services were held, one in the Dutch, and one in the English language. Since that time the services have been conducted only in English.

As of today, Holland and the small neighboring communities of Firth, Hickman and Pella—which originated around the same time—are thriving agricultural centers. Over the years the Dutch scepticism toward innovations in agriculture, which was very strong toward the end of the previous century, has disappeared. During the 1930's the Dutch showed more interest in state and federal research. They made more intensified use of the Farm Bureau, State Fair and the United States Department of Agriculture. They joined the Lancaster County Milk Association, with an office located in Lincoln. The object of this organization was to secure better prices through cooperation.[17] Still in existence in these small communities is the strong sense of religion which was so predominent in the early years of the settlement.

The church at Holland was destroyed by a fire in 1955. The present church has a handsome appearance with an educational wing attached. The separation of men and women was abolished in 1903. According to the present minister, Reverend Gordon Damsteegt (from Wisconsin) 98 percent of the members attend church every Sunday and participate in the social activities organized by the church.

I talked with a few ladies from Firth whose parents came to Nebraska as teenagers. They remember that the reason for their parents coming at that time was evasion of the draft. One lady, Mrs. Gerty ten Hulzen, still uses her Dutch Bible. She thinks—and Mrs. Glenn Lefferdinck agrees with her—that the Dutch language used in the Bible is more melodious. The latter receives letters from an elderly lady in The Netherlands whom she met three years ago on a trip to the Old Country. From the letter it is quite obvious that it is the religion which has a strong common denominator. She said she was strongly moved in seeing with her own eyes where her parents had worshipped in the Old Country.

Although Mrs. Lefferdinck, whose name dates back to the first group of Dutch immigrants in Nebraska, admits that very little Dutch tradition remains in their communities, all are strongly aware of their Dutch ancestry. These women still remember the "boerenkool, karnemelk and boeren rijstpap"— and one lady, Mrs. Martha Docter, whose maiden name is Wieskamp, still makes "balkenbrij" from time to time. The munching of peppermint during the church service is a custom that has survived from the early days.

In 1973 an upheaval of Dutch tradition was seen in the Holland community when eight civil patrol cadets from The Netherlands came for a visit. After an agricultural tour, the Dutch young men were treated to a street festival followed by a parade. The entire Holland population was dressed up in traditional Dutch costumes, including wooden shoes chartered from Holland, Michigan, for the occasion. For the older generation it was a day full of reminiscences of the Old Country. Dutch names still prevail in the area, but today's youth are hardly conscious of their Dutch ancestry.

In contrast to Nebraska, Dutch immigration to Michigan, Illinois, Iowa and Wisconsin continued in large numbers since the early years of 1850. According to the decennial reports of the United States Bureau of the Census,[18] the following distribution of foreign-born Dutch immigrants was seen in these states:

	1850	1880	1920	1970
Michigan	2.542	17.177	33.499	15.095
Illinois	220	5.012	14.344	5.825
Iowa	1.108	4.743	12.471	3.087
Wisconsin	1.157	5.698	7.473	2.730

The Dutch Immigrant Society in Michigan (1239 East Fulton, Grand Rapids, Michigan 49503), founded in 1959, is the center of Dutch culture in the United States. The Society has a quarterly publication, the *D.I.S. Magazine*, with a total of 18,000 subscribers in Canada, the United States and The Netherlands. Written in English and Dutch, this magazine contains a calendar of cultural events and activities held in the Dutch communities of Grand Rapids, Holland, Detroit, Kalamazoo and Muskegon, Michigan and has very interesting articles concerning the Dutch in this country. The Society keeps a very close link with its native country and its benefits today include charter flights to The Netherlands and other organized cruises to different countries. The most recent publication of *D.I.S. Magazine* is a bicentennial project. Professor Chris Stoffel Overvoorde, a native of Rotterdam, The Netherlands, who came to the United States in 1957 and is presently an Associate Professor of art at Calvin College, Grand Rapids, was in charge of a Dutch art exhibition. Sixty-two works of Dutch masters (38 paintings, 20 etchings and four drawings), compiled from private collections and public institutions, were shown. The exhibition was closed March 19, 1976.

By far the best known recent intellectual in this area who identified with the religious and cultural traditions of the Dutch people was Professor O.K. Bouwsma. A Frisian from Michigan, professor of philosophy at the University of Nebraska, and a world authority in modern philosophy, Bouwsma spoke the language of his province, attended the Dutch Reformed Church in Lincoln, raised flowers, and made whimsy the way any Dutchman might be expected to do. At the same time, he developed his understanding of religion beginning with Calvin and moving on to Kierkegaard and Socrates. His students, Robert Herbert and Martin Heinken, wrote some of the first and best articles and books on Kierkegaard as a religious thinker. While looking at religion, Bouwsma pursued his own skeptical ways with respect to what men can know and do, also perhaps an interest which grew out of his Calvinism. His critique of G.E. Moore's "common sense" philosophy made him internationally celebrated; he became the second American to receive the distinguished Locke lectureship at Oxford; and in his later period at the University of Nebraska he was Ludwig Wittgenstein's close friend and associate in philosophical investigation with respect to the limits and uses of language. When Wittgenstein was dying of cancer, he wrote to a friend to the effect that he was no good as a philosopher anymore. All he could do was go to Bouwsma's house (in England that year), eat Mrs. Bouwsma's cooking, and listen to a real philosopher talk. Bouwsma's students include nearly a dozen philosophers of world reputation. Now full of years and wisdom (well over 70), Mr. Bouwsma, who was recently given an honorary doctorate by the University of Nebraska, teaches at the University of Texas and continues to ponder, pursue the meaning of religion and of men's wonderfully weird ways with words.

FOOTNOTES

1.   Gerald F. deJong, *The Dutch in America* (Boston: Twayne Publishers, 1975), p. 129.

2.   Bertus Henry Wabeke, *Dutch Emigration to North America 1824-1860* (New York City: The Netherlands Information Bureau, 1944), p. 89.

3.   *Ibid.*

4.   Gustav Adolph Bade, "A History of the Dutch Settlement in Lancaster County, Nebraska" (unpublished master's thesis, University of Nebraska, Lincoln, 1938), p. 32.

5.   *Ibid.*, p. 34.

6.   deJong, *op. cit.*

7.   Wabeke, *op. cit.*, p. 94.

8.   Bade, *op. cit.*, p. 51.

9.   Recipes from Mrs. Adriana v.d. Grindt and Mrs. Martha Docter residents of Firth, Nebraska.

10.   Bade, *op. cit.*, p. 59.

11.   *Ibid.*, p. 65.

12.   *Ibid.*, p. 47.

13.   *Ibid.*, p. 58.

14.   *Ibid.*, p. 75.

15.   Information obtained from Reverend Gordon Damsteegt, The Dutch Reformed Church, Holland, Nebraska.

16.   Bade, *op. cit.*, p. 104.

17.   *Ibid.*, p. 144.

18.   deJong, *op. cit.*, pp. 264, 266.

XI

The Japanese: Buddha and Christ

By Domingo H. Cabacungan

XI

The Japanese: Buddha and Christ

By Domingo H. Cabacungan

Nebraska has, throughout its history, become home to a wide range of peoples of various national origins. During the first 30 to 35 years of Nebraska's statehood, the population essentially consisted of immigrants of European descent and, of course, the Native American Indians. It was only in the census of 1890 that the population included two women of Japanese descent, making them the second group of migrants from the Orient (the first being the Chinese who apparently settled in Nebraska in a much earlier time.)

In 1900, there were three Japanese men, two residing in Lincoln and one in Dawes County. By 1910, the Japanese population suddenly increased to 590 individuals. Ten years later, the population saw another increase, so that by 1920 there were 804 persons of Japanese descent in Nebraska. This was the largest population size until about 40 years later, when in 1960 there were 905 Nebraskans of Japanese descent. In the 1970 Census there were 1,314 Japanese-Americans reported.[1]

The migration from Japan to the United States in the late 1800's was mainly composed of laboring class males. Almost all of them were eager to make quick money and return to Japan, but with the passing of years their hopes of getting rich quickly and returning home were abandoned. Each year of life here made adjustments easier. The early eagerness to get back to Japan became less urgent. In reporting his findings about the

early Japanese settlement in America, sociologist Sotaro Miyamoto relates that these migrants had thought of America as a
land of opportunity, and they came willing to work at anything
which would permit them to save. They worked as railroad
section hands, as sawmill hands, or as domestic servants—for
they dreamed of eventual prestige and comfort in their homeland.[2]

It was indeed by good chance, Miyamoto explains, that
the Japanese came to America about that time when the West
was progressing rapidly toward industrial and commercial expansion. The construction of the railroad tracks from the West
Coast to the Midwest in the late 1800's and early 1900's, for
example, provided work for hundreds of Japanese migrants. The
Japanese had done a great deal of work laying track, building
bridges, and constructing coal chutes and ice houses. A few of
the workers who became proficient in English were hired as
interpreters to communicate with those workers who still did
not understand English. It was the railroad work for various
companies that brought almost all of the first group of Japanese
immigrants (or Isseis) to Nebraska. The completion of the railroad work in the Midwest in 1904 temporarily rendered
hundreds of Japanese workers, along with many others, jobless.
Many Japanese went back to the West Coast to find other
jobs. Some, however, remained to settle permanently in the
Midwest—in Colorado, Wyoming and Nebraska—where they
initially worked either as farm laborers or factory workers. At
the time, the new sugar beet industry in the "panhandle" area
of Nebraska attracted most of the Japanese who remained.
Between 1904 and 1910, the Great Western Sugar Company
employed about 300 Japanese. Most of them worked as farm
hands in the company's 120,000 acres of sugar beet fields.
Others were employed in the factory itself where beets were
processed into sugar. Eventually, some Japanese who worked
for the company were promoted to tenant farmers, some of
them to farm owners.[3]

Another set of circumstances brought a new group of
Japanese into Nebraska, but this time into the Omaha area. In

1905, while there were widespread labor disputes in the meat packing industry, employers brought in nearly 200 Japanese who were recruited from the West Coast to work as strike-breakers. Although they faced some hostility because of their role as strike-breakers, the group—mainly men—settled down to stay for a while. Most of the men looking for a place to stay ended up boarding in a building the neighbors called the "Japanese Camp." The "Camp" was a large frame building the Japanese had rented and remodelled into a boarding house designed to make the Japanese feel at home—to the point of including a community-style bathtub. Eventually, many of the workers moved to other jobs, so that by the beginning of World War I there were only about 100 Japanese still working in the packing plants.[4]

Other immigrants found occupations in various places in Nebraska. For example, several popular restaurants (the Togo Restaurant in Lincoln, Palace Cafe in Grand Island, Eagle Cafe in Scottsbluff, etc.) were founded and run by Japanese immigrants. Other business-minded Japanese opened photography studios in Omaha, as well as import businesses.

As the Japanese settled in Nebraska, they sometimes established small Japanese "communities." The Japanese-born generation, the Isseis, formed ties with others from their homeland and taught Japanese traditions to their American-born children, the Niseis. Weekly newspapers written in Japanese and published in Scottsbluff in 1917 by the late Kokin Yamanaka showed evidence of early attempts to preserve close ties within the Japanese community. This concept of community was necessitated to bridge the gap between their native heritage and the American environment for the settling Japanese immigrants. Promoted as a community effort was the Americanization program in the 1920's, which proved to be successful in realizing the Isseis' desire to be 100 percent Americans.[5]

Religious Life: Buddhism and Christianity

Almost all of the first Japanese who came to Nebraska

were originally Buddhists. However, in part because of the shortage of Buddhist religious leaders in Nebraska, Buddhism failed to maintain a large following. The only existing Buddhist Church close to Nebraska was in Denver, Colorado, so that participation by Isseis from Nebraska had been restricted mainly because of difficulties with travel. Only occasional visits by ministers from Denver had helped maintain the existence of Buddhism in this state. In fact, it was only in 1927 that regular Buddhist meetings started to be held, and these were held mostly in the homes of the members.

On March 13, 1949, in a meeting attended by 36 Niseis, the Scottsbluff *Kyudokai* (a laymen's organization—the first and only one in Nebraska) was organized. The first set of officers included: Ichisaburo Yokomize, president; Tatsukichi Aratani, vice president; Yoshiemon Ito, treasurer; Goro Morimoto, auditor; and Ghotaro Kishiyama, secretary. The size of the *Kyudokai* since that time has remained about the same even today. A few other known Buddhists lived in North Platte and Omaha.[6]

The conversion to Christianity by most of the Isseis in Nebraska in the late 1920's had been largely the result of the many years of missionary work by the late Bishop George Allen Beecher of the Episcopal Church. Bishop Beecher was responsible for the establishment of the two Japanese Christian Missions in the panhandle area—St. Mary's Church in Mitchell and St. George's Church in North Platte. In 1925, Bishop Beecher sought the assistance of a Japanese, Mr. Hiram Kano, who initially served as a lay worker and later on became an ordained priest in charge of the Japanese missions in that area.

Fr. Hiram Kano: A Leader in Assimilation

Rev. Fr. Hiram Kano has been a prominent figure in the history of the Japanese-American community in Nebraska—not only because of his role as a priest, but also as a farm consultant, English teacher, interpreter, and most recently as a well-known resource person on the early history of the Japanese community in Nebraska. His career in Nebraska actually started in the city of Lincoln in 1916 when he arrived from Japan to begin his graduate work in agricultural economics at the University of Nebraska. In 1918, shortly after he received his master's degree, he moved to Litchfield, Nebraska, where he worked as a farmer for about six years.

In 1920 an Anti-Japanese Land Bill, patterned after the California Land Law, was presented to the Nebraska legislature. The bill was designed to deprive all Japanese-born residents in Nebraska of any right to hold title to property or to be legal guardian for the property of a native-born minor, if the property could not be held legally by the alien himself. The bill, of course, alarmed the Japanese community because of its obvious discriminatory sentiments. It was through his role in organizing a strong opposition to the bill that Mr. Kano became known to other Japanese in the state. Recalling the implications of the bill, Fr. Kano wrote:

> There were about 150 Japanese farmers in Nebraska at the time. Learning about the introduction of this bill to the state legislature through the newspapers had made the Japanese really frightened. It was the darkest moment for them, because they were fond of rural life and had no hope of making a living in town. Representatives from Mitchell, Scottsbluff, and North Platte areas came to Lincoln and discussed the matter and studied the situation and chose Hiram Kano, who was a farmer near Litchfield, as their delegate and representative. They asked him to go to the state capital to discourage the passage of the bill. Late Bishop Beecher, the late Rev. Thomas Osborne, and some other leading citizens of the state thought this bill was truly discriminatory, unjust and 'un-American.' They were present at the hearings and spoke their views against the bill. Finally the original bill was killed. Since this time, there has been no similarly strong anti-Japanese movement in Nebraska.[7]

In the process of generating successful opposition to the bill, a strong friendship developed and grew between Mr. Kano and Bishop Beecher. Awareness of the difficulties among the

Isseis in achieving full acceptance into the mainstream of society led to the establishment of the Japanese-Americanization Society of Nebraska. Mr. Kano served as president and Bishop Beecher as the counselor and advisor of the Society until it disbanded—like all other Japanese organizations in the United States—at the break of World War II in 1940. The Society set the teaching of American thinking, American living, democratic process, and Christian doctrine as its goals.

Mr. Kano, his wife and family became Episcopalians in 1924. The following year, he left farming to become a lay worker of the Episcopal Church among the Japanese in the North Platte Valley and served more than 30 years in the active ministry. Through these years, he was ordained as a deacon of the church, and on February 2, 1936, became the first Japanese to be an ordained priest in Nebraska.

On the day of the attack of Pearl Harbor by the Japanese on December 7, 1941, known Japanese leaders across the country were taken into custody by federal authorities. In Nebraska, Fr. Kano was singled out as a leader, so that he too was among those who were sent to various internment camps in the country. In the five years of forced absence from his family and friends in Nebraska, he was moved from one internment camp to another until he was finally transferred to Wisconsin in 1943. Through Bishop Beecher's appeals, he was finally allowed to attend an Episcopal seminary in Wisconsin to pursue further theological studies.

When the war ended in 1946, Fr. Kano returned to Nebraska and continued his active ministry among the Japanese. He also resumed leadership in various civic projects. For example, when the United States Naturalization Act was passed in 1952, he and his wife, Mayitana Kano, took active part in helping their fellow Isseis to become naturalized citizens. Citizenship schools in various places in Nebraska were organized and the family, among others, served as instructors. Almost all of the Isseis in Nebraska at the time eventually became citizens, and Nebraska had one of the most successful records in the country. In 1953, the Kano family themselves were among the first Japanese who became citizens under the new naturilization law.

On his retirement on January 30, 1957, Fr. Kano was honored in a reception which also formally marked the merger of the predominantly Japanese congregation of St. Mary's Church and the predominaltly Caucasian congregation of Holy Apostles' Church in Mitchell, Nebraska. The same type of merger also took place in North Platte between St. George's Church and the Church of Our Savior. The title of Rector Emeritus was conferred to Fr. Kano by the vestry of the Holy Apostles' Church.[8]

To be close to their daughter, the Kanos chose to move their residence to Ft. Collins, Colorado for their retirement years. Fr. Kano has recently completed a book which is both a biographical and historical sketch of Nebraskans of Japanese descent. The book, written in Japanese, is pending publication by a book company in Japan.

In 1968, in connection with the celebration of the 100th anniversary of Japanese immigration to the United States, Fr. Kano received a medal, The Fourth Order of the Sacred Treasure, from the Emperor of Japan in recognition of his outstanding contributions to his fellow Japanese-Americans. He also received a medal from an agricultural association in Japan for his leadership among the Japanese, most of whom were farmers in Nebraska.[9]

Japanese-Americans in Farming and Business

Unlike Fr. Kano, significant contributions by other Japanese-Americans in Nebraska have been directed toward various fields of endeavor. Most notable of these is the contribution of the Japanese to the farming industry. Despite their initial low-paying jobs as farm laborers or factory workers and difficulties with the English language, the Isseis have shown surprising mobility over a relatively short period of time. Fr. Kano wrote that around 1925 there were already about 150 Issei-owned farms scatted in communities along the Platte River between Omaha and Henry, Nebraska. These farms, with an average size of about 160 acres, were invariably operated to raise sugar beets, potatoes, corn, etc. By 1959, nearly all these Isseis have died or retired and there came to be about 45 Nisei farmers as their successors. Near Morrill, Nebraska, a 3000-acre cooperative farm owned by Harry Sato and his sons is noted by Fr. Kano as an outstanding example of the Niseis' successful farming. Besides farming, some farmers also raised cattle and hogs, while others owned and operated dairy farms. Kano mentioned in particular the Matsutani dairy farm and George Kuroki's potato hybridation farm among the many successful ones.[10]

In a 1962 newspaper article, Robert McMorris wrote about some of Omaha's Japanese-born businessmen who established themselves in several non-farm occupations. "The businessmen included Joe Watanabe, who operated two downtown area restaurants; society photographers Shoji Osato, Harry Matsou and James Ishii; and importers Chuichi Taso, S.K. Yoden and Harry Watanabe."[11]

Because of the encouragement of the first generation Japanese and through the avenues of formal education, succeeding generations (the Niseis and the Sanseis) have branched out into various professions at a high rate. Fr. Kano wrote that the Isseis, realizing their handicap, ". . . made a tremendous effort to educate their children."[12] Consequently, Fr. Kano estimated that almost all Niseis have finished high school, and 35 percent of these have advanced to college or university.

(Kano mentioned, as examples, Dr. Tokuji Okamoto, a chemist who graduated from the University of Nebraska; Lt. Col. Perhing Nakada of the United States Army, also a graduate of the University; Dr. Harry Matsuyama, a dentist in Scottsbluff; Dr. Kenneth Sato, a medical practitioner in Pullman, Washington; and Mr. Ed Miyahara of Morrill, a high school teacher. Interestingly enough, occupational achievements by some Niseis happened during World War II when many served the country as soldiers and nurses. Among these were Harley

Tanaka of Haig, Frank Sato of Mitchell, Margaret Ugai, a nurse from North Platte, and Ben Kuroki of Hershey.[13] After the war, among those decorated for their outstanding military services was Ben Kuroki whose biography written by Ralph G. Martin has brought national attention to the achievements of the Japanese-American regiments during the war. To Bill Mauldin, *Boy From Nebraska: The Story of Ben Kuroki,* is the story of a man "who went through war, made his buddies proud to wear the same uniform he did, and who will make you proud to be his countryman."[15])

Throughout their presence in Nebraska, the Japanese immigrants and succeeding generations made Nebraska their home in every respect. The Isseis' enthusiastic participation in the Americanization program in the 1920's and their assimilation into the Christian church and the later generations' achievements in the farming, business and academic fields are evidence of early efforts to establish and maintain a just share of their claim to Nebraska as home. To be sure, the Isseis, most of whom initially worked in the railroad construction, left behind them literally miles of tracks across the state that are a monumental contribution in itself to Nebraska's economy and early history.

FOOTNOTES

1.   United States Bureau of the Census, *Thirteenth Census of the United States Taken in the Year 1910: Abstract of the Census with Supplement for Nebraska* (Washington, D.C.: U.S. Government Printing Office, 1931), p. 595; U.S. Bureau of the Census, *Census of the Population, Vol. I, Characteristics of the Population, Part 29, Nebraska* (Washington, D.C.: U.S. Government Printing Office, 1973), p. 33.

2.   Shotaro Frank Miyamoto, "Social Solidarity Among the Japanese in Seattle," *University of Washington Publications in Social Sciences* (Seattle, Washington: University of Washington, 1939), p. 65.

3.   Rev. Hiram H. Kano, "Japanese-Americans in Nebraska," (unpublished paper, Scottsbluff, Nebraska, about 1958), pp. 1-2.

4.   Robert McMorris, "The People Who Make Up Omaha: Boys Town Brought Second Wave of Japanese," *Sunday World-Herald* (Omaha, Nebraska: January 7, 1962), pp. 1B-2B.

5.   Kano, *op. cit.,* p. 1.

6.   Matajero Watada, *A History of Fifty Years of the Tri-State Buddhist Church 1916-1966* (Denver, Colorado: The Tri-State Buddhist Church, 1968), pp. 258-59.

7.   Kano, *op. cit.,* p. 5.

8.   Rev. W.J. Barnds, "Missionary Work Among a Minority Group in Scotts Bluff County," *Gering Courier* (Gering, Nebraska: July 17, 1975), p. 8; James Denney, "Ed Miyahara Likes What He Sees," *Sunday World-Herald Magazine of the Midlands* (Omaha, Nebraska: November 9, 1975), pp. 7-8; Domingo H. Cabacungan, personal interview with Rev. Hiram Kano (Ft. Collins, Colorado, February 17, 1976).

9.   Cabacungan, *Ibid.*

10.   Kano, *op. cit.,* p. 2.

11.   McMorris, *op. cit.,* p. 1B.

12.   Kano, *op. cit.,* pp. 2-3.

13.   *Ibid.,* p. 3.

14.   Ralph G. Martin, *Boy From Nebraska: The Story of Ben Kuroki* (New York: Harper & Brothers, 1946).

15.   Bill Mauldin, "Introduction," in Ralph G. Martin, *Boy From Nebraska: The Story of Ben Kuroki,* p. XII.

BIBLIOGRAPHY

BY ETHNIC GROUP

INDIANS

Alexander, Hartley Burr. *The World's Rim.* Lincoln: University of Nebraska Press, 1953. [A brief overview of American Indian philosophy.]

American Horse, Leo and Joseph, eds. *Lakota Stories.* Pine Ridge, South Dakota: Red Cloud Indian School, Inc., 1970. [A collection of Sioux stories, ranging from the creation account to trickster tales. Most of the stories are from J.R. Walker.]

Brown, Dee. *Bury My Heart at Wounded Knee.* New York: Bantam Books, 1972. [A detailed look at the history of white-Indian relations from an Indian perspective. This book dispells many of the myths about America's pioneering days and exposes America's genocidal tendencies.]

Brown, J. Epes, ed. *The Sacred Pipe.* Baltimore: Penguin Books, 1971. [A rather detailed look at the Sioux's seven sacred ceremonies. Black Elk's accounts.]

Burnette, Robert. *The Tortured Americans.* Englewood Cliffs, New Jersey: Prentice-Hall, 1971. [One man's view of the Indian's political situation.]

Chapman, Abraham, ed. *Literature of the American Indians: Views and Interpretations.* New York: New American Library, 1975. [An anthology and critical review.]

Danker, Kathleen. "The Hollows of Echoes." Unpublished master's thesis, University of Nebraska, Lincoln, 1974. [A collection of rewritten Winnebago tales, told to her by Mr. Felix White.]

_____ . *Winnebago Clothing Styles.* Macy, Nebraska: Nebraska Indian Press, 1973.

Deloria, Ella. *Dakota Texts.* Washington: American Ethnological Society Publications, 1932. [Sixty-four Teton Dakota tales with the Lakota texts, their transliteration and translation. Deloria's footnotes add valuable cultural and linguistic information.]

Deloria, Vine, Jr. *Behind the Trail of Broken Treaties.* New York: Dell Publishing, 1974. [Deloria subtitles this "An Indian Declaration of Independence."]

_____ . *Custer Died For Your Sins.* New York: Macmillan, 1969. [A somewhat dated manifesto for Indian rights.]

_____ . *God is Red.* New York: Dell Publishing, 1973. [A comparison of traditional Indian religion with Christianity (a term he uses to describe western civilization) and a look at what the differences mean to traditional Indian culture.]

_____ . *We Talk, You Listen*. New York: Macmillan, 1970. [An update of *Custer Died For Your Sins.*]

Dorsey, James Owen. *Omaha and Ponka Letters*. Washington: Government Printing Office, 1891.

Dyck, Paul. *Brule, the Sioux People of the Rosebud*. Flagstaff: Northland Press, 1971.

Evers, Larry, Alice Fletcher, and Francis LaFlesche. *The Omaha Tribe*. 2 volumes. Lincoln: University of Nebraska Press, 1972. (Originally published as *27th Annual Report of the Bureau of American Ethnology*, Smithsonian Institution, Washington, D.C., 1905-06. Bison Book is a reprint.) [This is the definitive study on the Omaha people. It is especially helpful in the areas of social custom, religion, and political divisions.]

Goldsmith, Edwin, *et. al. Blueprint for Survival*. Boston: Houghton Mifflin Company, 1972.

Hamilton, Henry W. and Jean Tyree. *The Sioux of the Rosebud: A History in Pictures*. Norman: University of Oklahoma Press, 1971.

Harris, Ramon I., ed. *Oyate Iyechinka Woglakapi. An Oral History Collection*. Vols. I, II, III. Vermillion: American Indian Research Project, University of South Dakota, 1970-71. [A series of Sioux manuscripts.]

Hassrick, Royal. *The Sioux*. Norman: University of Oklahoma Press, 1964. [A descriptive analysis of pre-reservation Teton Sioux culture.]

Henry, Jeanette, ed. *The American Indian Reader*. 5 volumes. San Francisco: Indian Historian Press, Inc., 1973. [A series of five anthologies, each on a separate subject dealing with American Indians. The subjects covered are: Anthropology, Education, Literature, History, and Current Events.]

_____ . *Index to Literature on the American Indian*. San Francisco: Indian Historian Press, Inc., 1972-1974. [A yearly bibliography complete for the years 1970-1972. A good list of Indian periodicals is included.]

Hodge, William. *A Bibliography of Contemporary North American Indians*. New York: Interland Publishing Company, 1976. [A partially annotated bibliography. Besides the usual listings, this bibliography includes sections on Canadian Government Documents, United States Publications, Arts, Crafts and Supplies, Museums and Maps.]

Jackson, Helen Hunt. *A Century of Dishonor*. New York: Harper and Row, 1965. (Original edition, Harper and Brothers, 1881.)

Jung, Carl. *Man and His Symbols*. New York: Dell Publishing Co., Inc., 1964. (Copyright 1964, Aldus Books, London – first Dell printing 1968.) [Includes a discussion of the Winnebago trickster cycle.]

LaFlesche, Francis. *The Middle Five: Indian Schoolboys of the Omaha Tribe*. Madison: University of Wisconsin Press, 1963. [An autobiographical account of Indian school experiences in the early part of the 20th century.]

Lame Deer, John (Fire) and Richard Erdoes. *Lame Deer Seeker of Visions*. New York: Simon and Schuster, 1972. [An autobiography, in which Lame Deer discusses both the spiritual and the profane sides of Lakota life.]

LaPointe, Frank. *The Sioux Today*. New York: Macmillan Books, 1972.

Libhart, Myles and Arthur Anniotte, eds. *Photographs and Poems by Sioux Children*. Rapid City: Indian Arts and Crafts Board and Tipi Shop, Inc., 1971.

Meyer, Roy W. *History of the Santee Sioux*. Lincoln: University of Nebraska Press, 1967. [The definitive history of the Santee Sioux.]

Mooney, James. *The Ghost Dance Religion*. Chicago: University of Chicago Press, 1892. [Classic scholarly study of the Ghost Dance religion.]

Native Voices: The Native American Today. San Francisco: Indian Historian Press, 1974. [A record of the second convocation of American Indian Scholars held in 1971 at Aspen, Colorado.]

Neihardt, John G. *Black Elk Speaks*. Lincoln: University of Nebraska Press, 1961. [Neihardt's account of the life and visionary experiences of Black Elk.]

_____ . *The Twilight of the Sioux*. Lincoln: University of Nebraska Press, 1971. [A poetic account of Sioux history in the late 19th century.]

_____ . *When the Tree Flowered: A Fictional Biography of Eagle Voice, A Sioux Indian*. Lincoln: University of Nebraska Press, 1970.

Nurge, Ethel, ed. *The Modern Sioux: Social Systems and Reservation Culture*. Lincoln: University of Nebraska Press, 1970. [An anthology of scholarly essays on the dynamics of modern reservation culture.]

Radin, Paul. *The Autobiography of a Winnebago Indian*. Berkeley: University of California Press, 1952. [The transcription of Crashing Thunder's life with particular emphasis on his religious experiences both within the traditional Winnebago ceremonial structures and in the Peyote religion. Radin's notes add relevant cultural information.]

_____ . *The Evolution of an American Indian Prose Epic: a Study in Comparative Literature*. Basel: Ethnographical Museum, 1954.

_____ . *The Road of Life and Death, a Ritual Drama of the American*

Indians. New York: Pantheon Books, 1945. [The transcription of the Winnebago Medicine Rite. The rite. indicates the nature of Winnebago attitudes toward life after death and reincarnation.]

_____ . *The Trickster.* New York: Schocken Books, 1956. [The Winnebago trickster cycle with commentaries by Karl Kerenyi and C.G. Jung.]

_____ . *The Winnebago Tribe.* Lincoln: University of Nebraska Press, 1970. (Originally published as *37th Annual Report of the Bureau of American Ethnology,* Smithsonian Institution, Washington, D.C., 1905-06. Bison Book is a reprint.) [The definitive study on the Winnebago people.]

Sanders, Thomas E. and Walter W. Peek. *Literature of the American Indian.* Benziger, Bruce and Glencoe, Inc., 1973. [An anthology. Includes both traditional and modern material.].

Schusky, Ernest L. *The Forgotten Sioux.* Chicago: Nelson Hall Co., 1975. [A history of the lower Brule Sioux extending through 1960.]

Stabler, Eunice W. *How Beautiful the Land of My Forefathers.* 1943.

Standing Bear, Luther. *Land of the Spotted Eagle.* Boston: Houghton Mifflin, 1933.

_____ . *My Indian Boyhood.* Boston: Houghton Mifflin, 1921.

_____ . *My People the Sioux.* Boston: Houghton Mifflin, 1924. [All three of Standing Bear's books are autobiographical accounts of Sioux life in the late 19th and early 20th century.]

Storm, Hyemeyohsts. *Seven Arrows.* New York: Ballantine, 1972. [A retelling of Cheyenne religious stories. These stories are woven into a "novel" which deals with the Cheyenne world view and Cheyenne ceremonial practices.]

Witt, Shirley Hill and Stan Steiner. *The Way: An Anthology of American Indian Literature.* New York: Alfred A. Knopf, 1972. [A collection of both traditional and contemporary pieces.]

CHICANOS

Acuña, Rodolfo. *Occupied America: The Chicano's Struggle Toward Liberation.* San Francisco: Canfield Press, 1972. [Historical study based on the thesis that the Chicanos' experience in the U.S. is in many ways parallel to the experience of Third World peoples who have suffered under the colonialism of developed nations.]

Alford, Harold J. *The Proud Peoples: The Heritage and Culture of Spanish-Speaking Peoples in the United States.* New York: New American Library, 1972. [Concise and comprehensive coverage of the Spanish and Mexican history in the U.S., beginning with "The Explorers"

(1536), through "The Settlers," "The Ranchers," "The Migrants," and "The Militants" of the 1960's and '70's. Good overview.]

Anaya, Rodolfo. *Bless Me, Ultima.* Berkeley: Quinto Sol, 1972. [Novel about a boy's coming of age in New Mexico, descendant of early Spanish-Mexican settlers of the region. With the assistance of Ultima —elderly wise woman (curandera)—the protagonist is able to reconcile seemingly discordant heritages.]

Arajon, Luis Cardoza y. *Mexican Art Today,* trans. Asa Zata. Mexico: Fondo de Cultura Economica, 1966.

Cíaz, Bernal. *The Conquest of New Spain,* trans. J.M. Cohen. Baltimore: Penguin Books, 1963. [Important first-person narrative account of the Conquest of Mexico by one of Hernan Cortez' *conquistadores* who landed in the eastern coast of Mexico in 1519.]

Enciso, Jorge. *Design Motifs of Ancient Mexico.* New York: Dover Publications, Inc., 1953.

Galarza, Ernesto. *Barrio Boy: The Story of a Boy's Acculturation.* Notre Dame: University of Notre Dame Press, 1971. [Autobiography by well-known scholar and writer on Mexican labor in the U.S. Recounts his experience in Mexico during the start of the 1910 Revolution and his family's move to the U.S.]

Gamio, Manuel. *The Mexican Immigrant: His Life Story.* New York: Dover Publications, 1971. (Companion volume to *Mexican Immigration to the United States.)* [Contains actual transcribed interviews with the immigrants.]

Gonzales, Rodolfo. *I Am Joaquin—Yo Soy Joaquin.* New York: Bantam, 1972. [Historical poem on Chicano identity based on recognition and acceptance of a past that begins with the pre-Columbian civilizations of Mexico. Bilingual edition. Includes photographs.]

Kiev, Ari. *Curanderismo: Mexican-American Folk Psychiatry.* New York: The Free Press, 1968.

Leon-Portilla, Miguel. *Aztec Thought and Culture: A Study of the Ancient Nahuatl Mind,* trans. from the Spanish by Jack Emory Davis. Norman: University of Oklahoma Press, 1963. [History of ideas. Using original Aztec documents, the author discusses the philosophy of the Nahuatl wise men: explanation of origin of the universe and of life, conjectures on the mystery of God; the possibility of comprehending things beyond the realm of experience, life after death; the meaning of education, history and art.]

_____ . *Pre-Columbian Literatures of Mexico,* trans. Grace Lobanov. Norman: University of Oklahoma Press, 1969. [Introduction to the literature of the Aztecs, Mayas, Mixtecs, Zapotecs and other peoples. Includes myths, sacred hymns, lyric poetry, drama and various forms of prose.]

Matthiessen, Peter. *Sal Si Puedes: César Chávez and the New American Revolution.* New York: Dell Publishing, 1969. [Biography of César Chávez, leader of 1960's farm workers' movement in California and other parts of the Southwest.]

McWilliams, Carey. *North From Mexico: The Spanish-Speaking People of the United States.* New York: Greenwood Press, 1968. [Published originally in 1950, McWilliams' book continues to be the most authoritative work on the Mexican people's movement north to the U.S. As well as being a historical study, the book includes analysis of influences that have formed Hispanic culture in the United States. Excellent!]

Moquin, Wayne and Charles Van Doren, eds. *A Documentary History of the Mexican Americans.* New York: Praeger Publishers, 1971. [Collection of 65 selections (some of them historical documents, e.g., The Treaty of Guadalupe Hidalgo, which ended the Mexican American War and guaranteed the property, religious, and cultural rights of the Mexican American). Organized chronologically, the selections span the period from 1536-1970, divided into five parts, beginning with The Hispanic-Indian Synthesis, 1536-1809, and concluding with Travails of La Raza, 1940-70, which includes selections on the mid-20th century Chicano Liberation movement.]

Myers, Bernard S. *Mexican Painting in Our Time.* New York: Oxford University Press, 1956.

Nava, Julian, *Mexican Americans: Past, Present, and Future.* New York: American Book Company, 1969. [Generously illustrated, general treatment of the subject.]

Orozco, José Clemente. *An Autobiography,* trans. Robert C. Stephenson. Austin: University of Texas Press, 1962. [Autobiography of one of greatest painters the Americas have produced. Orozco spent several years in the U.S. and much of the *Autobiography* is devoted to the painting he did in the U.S. 1927-1934. The Pomona frescoes, those of the New School for Social Research, and those of Dartmouth College.]

Parades, Americo. *With His Pistol in His Hand: A Border Ballad and Its Hero.* Austin: University of Texas Press, 1971. [Folkloric study of Gregorio Cortez, legendary folk hero and *corridos* (Mexican folk ballads) dedicated to him in the Texas, Rio Grande Valley.]

Peterson, Frederick. *Ancient Mexico: An Introduction to the Pre-Hispanic Cultures.* New York: Capricorn Books, 1959.

Popol Vuh: The Sacred Book of the Ancient Quiche Maya. English version, Delia Goetz and Sylvanus G. Morley. Norman: University of Oklahoma Press, 1950. [Generally regarded as America's oldest book, the *Popol Vuh,* in fact, corresponds to our Christian Bible, and it is, moreover, the most important of the five pieces of the great library treasures of the Maya that survived the Spanish Conquest.]

Posada's Popular Mexican Prints: 273 Cuts by Jose Guadalupe Posada. Text by Roberto Berdecio and Stanley Appelbaum. New York: Dover Publications, 1972. [Some of the work of Mexico's most important printmaker, José Guadalupe Posada (1852-1913). Profound influence on Diego Rivera, Orozco and other 20th century Mexican painters, as well as on the contemporary Chicano painters.]

Quirarte, Jacinto. *Mexican American Artists.* Austin: University of Texas Press, 1973. [Illustrated with black and white, and color plates, describes and defines the work of living Mexican American artists. Includes discussion of antecedents for the art and architecture of the Southwest, and discussion of work in the United States of Mexican muralists, Jose Clemente Orozco and Rufino Tamayo.]

Rendon, Armando B. *Chicano Manifesto: The History and Aspirations of the Second Largest Minority in America.* New York: Collier Books, 1971. [Treatment of the origins and the militancy of the Chicano social movement that began in the mid-1960's.]

Rivera, Feliciano. *A Mexican American Source Book.* Menlo Park, California: Educational Consulting Associates, 1970. [A guide to the history of the Mexican American people in the U.S. Includes chronology, bibliographies—books, newspapers, journals—listings of films, filmstrips, and other audio-visual materials. Includes drawings of outstanding Mexican Americans and beautiful photographs of Spanish missions in California.]

Rivera, Tomás. *". . . y no se lo tragó la tierra"--". . . And the Earth Did Not Part."* Berkeley, California: Quinto Sol, 1971. [Prize-winning work of fiction based on migrant farmworkers' experience. Short stories, sketches and anecdotes unified thematically by protagonist's search and recovery of part of his past that he has lost. Bilingual edition.]

Rufino Tamayo. Text by Emily Genauer. New York: Harry N. Abrams, Inc. Publishers. [Black and white and color plates.]

Sejourne, Laurette. *Burning Water: Thought and Religion in Ancient Mexico.* New York: The Vanguard Press, 1956. [Excellent study of Aztec religion as it was influenced by Toltec civilization. Includes detailed analysis of Nahuatl iconography. Amply illustrated with drawings and photographs.]

Shular, Antonia Castañeda, *et al.,* eds. *Chicano Literature: Text and Context.* Englewood Cliffs, N.J.: Prentice-Hall, Inc., 1972. [One of the better Chicano literature anthologies available, though including much that is not conventionally regarded as literature: songs, political proclamations, and history. Places Chicano literature in Pre-Columbian, Mexican and Mexican American cultural and historical context; and within the literary traditions of Latin America.]

Siqueiros. Text by Mario de Micheli. New York: Harry N. Abrams, Inc. Publishers, 1968. [Black and white and color prints by David Alfaro Siqueiros, one of the famous Mexican muralists who has influenced Chicano painting.]

Wolf, Eric. *Sons of the Shaking Earth.* Chicago: University of Chicago Press, 1959. [This, and Frederick Peterson's work above are good general introductions to the extremely complex civilizations existing in the central valley of Mexico prior to the Spanish arrival in 1519.]

BLACKS

Alberts, Frances J. *Sod House Memories,* Vols. I, II, and III. Hastings, Nebraska: Sod House Society, 1972.

Bennett, Lerone Jr. *The Shaping of Black America.* Chicago: Johnson Publishing Co., Inc., 1975.

Breitman, George. *The Last Year of Malcolm X.* New York: Merit Publishers, 1967.

Chase, Judith Wragg. *Afro-American Art and Craft.* Cincinnati, Ohio: Van Nostrand Reinhold Co., 1971.

Cox, George C. *African Empires and Civilizations.* African Heritage Studies, 1974.

Davies, Mary Emily and Genevieve Marsh. "A Study of the Negro in Lincoln." (Unpublished master's thesis, University of Nebraska, Lincoln, 1904.)

Decker, Beryl. "The Lost Pioneers: Negro Homesteaders in Nebraska," *Negro Digest,* Vol. 12, No. 7 (May, 1963), pp. 63-66.

Durham, Philip and Everett L. Jones. *The Negro Cowboys.* New York: Dodd, Mead, 1965.

Franklin, John Hope. *Black Americans.* New York: Time Life Books, 1970.

_____ . *From Slavery To Freedom.* Westminster: Vintage Books Edition, 1969.

Herskovits, Melville J. *The Myth of the Negro Past.* New York, London: Harper & Bros., 1941.

Hughes, Langston and Milton Meltzer. *A Pictorial History of the Negro in America.* New York: Crown Publishing, Inc., 1970.

Jacques, Amy, ed. *Marcus Garvey, Philosophy and Opinions.* New York:

The Universal Publishing House, 1923.
Katz, William Loren. *The Black West*. New York: Anchor Press, 1973.
Lewis, Meriwether. *History of the Expeditions of Captain Lewis and Clark*. Chicago: A.C. McClurg & Co., 1902 (reprinted from the 1814 edition, with introduction and index by James K. Hosmer.)
Malcolm X. *Malcolm X Talks to Young People*. New York: Merit Publishers, 1968.
Nebraska Writer's Project. "Negroes of Nebraska" (WPA Pamphlet, 1940).
Olson, James C. *History of Nebraska*. Lincoln: University of Nebraska Press, 1966.
Wiener, Leo. *Africa and the Discovery of America*. Vols. I and II. Philadelphia: Innes & Sons, 1920.
Wilmore, Gayrand S. *Black Religion and Black Radicalism*. Garden City, N.Y.: Merit Publishers, 1973.

CZECHS

History of Bohemia; Czechoslovakia

Čapek, Thomas, ed. *Bohemia Under Hapsburg Misrule*. New York, Chicago: Fleming H. Revell Co., 1915.
Kerner, Robert J. *Czechoslovakia, Twenty Years of Independence*. Berkeley and Los Angeles: University of California Press, 1940.
Masaryk, Thomas G. *The Making of Czech History*. Edited and with an introduction by René Wellek, trans. Peter Kussi. Chapel Hill: The University of North Carolina Press, 1974.
Monroe, Will S. *Bohemia and the Czechs. The History, People, Institutions, and the Geography*. Boston: L.C. Page and Company, 1910.
Rodnick, David. *The Strangled Democracy; Czechoslovakia 1948-69*. Lubbock, Texas: Caprock Press, 1970.
Seton-Watson, Robert W. *A History of the Czechs and Slovaks*. Hamden, Conn.: Archon Books, 1965.

History of Czechs in the United States

Čapek, Thomas. *The Czechs in America. A Study of Their National, Cultural, Political, Social, Economic, and Religious Life*. Boston and New York: Houghton Mifflin Co., 1920.
Miller, Kenneth D. *The Czecho-Slovaks in America*. New York: George H. Doran Company, 1922.
PANORAMA. A Historical Review of Czechs and Slovaks in the United States of America. Cicero, Ill.: Czechoslovak National Council of America, 1970.

Pranter, E.F. *These Help Build America.* Chicago: The Czechoslovak Re-
view, 1922.
Roucek, Joseph S. *The Czechs and Slovaks in America.* Minneapolis:
Lerner Publications Co., 1967.

History of Czechs in Nebraska

Hrbková, Šárka B. *Bohemians in Nebraska.* Lincoln, Nebraska: Publications of the Nebraska State Historical Society, Vol. XIX, pp. 140-
158, 1919.
Jensen, Alfred R. "The European Background Influences on Education in
the Milligan School." Unpublished master's thesis, University of Ne-
braska, 1952.
Kleinschmidt, John R. "The Political Behavior of the Bohemian and
Swedish Ethnic Groups in Nebraska, 1884-1900." Unpublished
master's thesis, University of Nebraska, 1968.
Kubicek, Clarence John. "The Czechs of Butler County." Unpublished
master's thesis, University of Nebraska, 1958.
Kučera, Vladimir and Alfred Novaček, eds. *Czechs and Nebraska.* Ord,
Nebraska: Quiz Graphic Arts, Inc., 1967.
Kutak, Robert I. *The Story of a Bohemian-American Village. A Study of
Social Persistance and Change.* Louisville, Kentucky: The Standard
Printing Co., Inc., 1933.
Rosicky, Rose. *A History of Czechs (Bohemians) in Nebraska.* Omaha:
Czech Historical Society of Nebraska, 1929.
Van Hoff, Joseph John. "A History of the Czechs of Knox County, Ne-
braska." Unpublished master's thesis, University of Nebraska, 1938.

GERMAN-RUSSIANS

Work Papers

Some of the most useful work on Germans from Russia is to be found in
the work papers published by the American Historical Society of Germans
from Russia with bibliography of work papers by Nancy Bernhardt
Holland. A list of the work papers can be obtained from the Society. The
content of some of the work papers is as follows: No. 5, 1968 interviews
with Volga residents, important German-Russian dates, 1762-1970; No. 6-
10, accounts of various colonies in Russia and the United States; No. 13,
effects of Soviet policy on the Germans from Russia; No. 14, Kansas
Mennonites; No. 16, plains communities; No. 17, history in Nebraska and
Colorado; No. 18, music and dulcimers; No. 19, human geography and
folk medicine. Society address: 615 D St., Lincoln, Ne. 68502.

Periodicals
(Also from Nancy Bernhardt Holland)

Volk auf dem Weg contains notices of new books, lists of names of persons being sought by separated relatives, poems, stories and articles by German-Russians now residing in Germany. Available: Landsmann-schaft der Deutschen aus Russland, 7 Stuttgart 1, Stafflenbergstrasse 66, West Germany.

Heimatbücher contains original research materials concerning German-Russian history and traditions: scholarly articles, personal memoirs, maps and pictures. Available: Landsmannschaft der Deutschen aus Russland, 7 Stuttgart 1, Stafflenbergstrasse 66, West Germany.

Neues Leben, a weekly German newspaper published in Moscow at *Pravda* for German-speaking citizens of the Soviet Union, focuses on activities and accomplishments of Soviet Germans. Special children's section in easy German and short stories and poems. Letters to the editor are always published, and the final page always consists of jokes and stories in the dialect German of "unser leute." Available: Victor Kamkin Bookstore, Inc., 12224 Parklawn Drive, Rockville, Maryland 20852.

Heritage Review, a semi-annual publication of the North Dakota Historical Society of Germans from Russia. Available: LeRoy A. Obberlander, Box 41, Dickinson State College, Dickinson, North Dakota 58601.

Books

The following books from the Nancy Bernhardt Holland list appear to be particularly germane to the study of communities in this area.

Aberle, Msgr. George P. *Anecdotes of the Prairies.* Bismarck, N.D., no Date. [Accounts of experiences among the missionary clergy and their parishioners, the German-Russian settlers of the Dakotas. _____ . *From the Steppes to the Prairie.* Bismarck, N.D., 1964. [History of the German migrations to Russia and the New World; Catholic settlements of North Dakota and western Kansas.]

Baure, Rev. Peter. *Experiences From My Missionary Life in the Dakotas.* [Anecdotes from the life of a Reformed Church pastor who emigrated from Worms, South Russia in 1893 to serve parishes in the Dakotas and Colorado.]

Conquest, Robert. *The Nation Killers: The Soviet Deportation of Nationalities.* New York, 1970. [The most complete study of the deportations and subsequent rehabilitations of all eight ethnic groups. He gives special attention to the Volga Germans, since they (along with the much smaller number of Crimean Tatars and Meskhetians) are the only peoples not to have been restored to full civil rights.]

Giesinger, Adam. *From Catherine to Krushchev: The Story of Russia's Germans.* Battleford, Sask., 1974. [Giesinger's 443-page book is the most complete and authoritative and well-written history of the Germans from Russia to have appeared in English. Final chapter covers emigrants from Russia to the Americas. Available: Dr. Adam Giesinger, 645 Oxford Street, Winnipeg, Manitoba, Canada R3M 3J3.]

Griess, James Rueben. *The German-Russians: Those Who Came to Sutton.* Hastings, Nebraska, 1968. [Recounts the reasons for the immigrations of Germans to Russia and conditions in the Volga and Black Sea Colonies; describes the migration and settlement in the New World concentrating on the role of the railroads in enticing colonists to Sutton, Nebraska. Available: James R. Griess, 2702 Bradfield Drive, Lincoln, Nebraska 68502.]

Gross, Fred W. *The Pastor: The Life of an Immigrant.* Philadelphia, 1973. [The life of the Rev. Gross as a boy growing up in the villages of southern Russia, a pastor to churches in Canada, North Dakota, and California. Account of the pastor's four trips to Russia from 1956 to 1971 to contact relatives who remained in Russia during the tumultous period of world war and revolution.]

Hall, Helen L. *Grandfather's Story.* Centennial/Bi-Centennial Edition, 1974 and 1976. [Contains a translation from the diary of Joseph M. Linenberger who was born in 1838 in Herzog, Russia. This diary includes a short account of life in the Volga Colonies from 1770-1780 when the newly-founded villages were pillaged by raiders of the nomadic Kirghez tribe; it also contains an account of the migration of the Linenbergers to Kansas.]

Hostetler, John A. *Hutterite Life.* Scottsdale, Pa., 1965. [Paperback account of Hutterite communal living. Available: The Herald Press.]

Kaufman, Edna (compiler). *Melting Pot of Mennonite Cookery 1874-1974.* North Newton, Kansas: Mennonite Press, 1974. [Cookbook that contains information concerning food and other elements of Mennonite culture, including religion, lifestyle, and the like.]

Sallet, Richard. *Russian-German Settlements in the United States,* trans. by LaVern Rippley and Armand Brauer. Fargo, N.D., 1974. [Historical background and socio-political study of the Germans from Russia in America. Includes a description of German-Russian architecture, lists of place names, etc. Available: The North Dakota Institute for Regional Studies, North Dakota State University, Fargo, North Dakota 58102.]

Schrag, Martin H. *The European History of the Swiss Mennonites From Volhynia.* North Newton, Kansas: Mennonite Press, 1974. [A 128-page book recounting three and one half centuries of Mennonite history from their origin in Switzerland through Germany, Russia, and to their settlement in Kansas and South Dakota.]

Stumpp, Karl. *Das Schrifttum über das Deutschtum in Russland.* Tübinger, 1970. [Bibliography of books and articles concerning the Germans from Russia, the most complete list available. Lists materials in the language in which they were written. Major portion of the bibliography in German; however, those works in English, and consequently most available in North America, listed in English.]

_____ . *The Emigration from Germany to Russia in the Years 1763 to 1862.* Tubingen, 1972. [Inestimable value to genealogical researchers since it contains alphabetical lists of thousands of names of German immigrants to Russia—many with vital statistics, place of origin in Germany and locality of settlement in Russia.]

Toepfer, Amy Brungardt and Agnes Dreiling. *Conquering the Wind.* Garwood, New Jersey, 1966. [Recounts the experiences of the emigrants from Germany to the Volga and their resettlement one hundred years later on the plains of western Kansas.]

Books Other Than Those Available
From the American Historical Society of Germans from Russia

Kaus, Gina. *Catherine: The Portrait of an Empress,* trans. June Head. New York: The Literary Guild, 1935. [About Catherine the Great, who after all, was the greatest German-Russian of them all.]

Luebke, Frederick C. *Immigrants and Politics: The Germans of Nebraska, 1880-1900.* Lincoln: University of Nebraska Press, 1969. [Demands far more than a brief entry, for it is a very valuable resource toward the understanding of all Germans on the Plains. As is clear from the title, the book does deal primarily with the role of Germans and German newspapers in Nebraska politics nearly 100 years ago, but the book is much more than that, offering a large volume of background about Germans and German migration, dealing in large part with German-Russians. Luebke has used census reports and newspapers to draw a clear picture of the kinds of Germans who came to the Plains, where they settled, how they thought, and how they translated that thought into political action. The bibliography for this book is very extensive and is in itself an important resource for anyone interested in German culture and history in Nebraska.]

Oldenbourg, Zoe. *Catherine the Great.* New York: Pantheon, 1965. [A survey of the life of Catherine the Great—a real literary work. Little

is said about Catherine's Germans on the Volga, but the reader is
given an understanding of the spirit of the times.]

Sykes, H.W. *Second Hoeing.* New York: G.P. Putnam, 1935. [Refers to
the second hoeing of the sugar beet fields, is a fictionalized account
of the German-Russian migrant laborers in the northeastern Colorado fields early in the century.]

Newspapers

The Nebraska State Historical Society has a large collection of documents,
many of which pertain to Germans in the state. There are diaries, journals,
daybooks, and letters by way of manuscripts, many books and articles in
the Society's library and the State Archives, items within the collection,
and of vital importance to anyone interested in any facet of Nebraska
history and culture is the Society's publication, *Nebraska History.* The following are the holdings of the Society's newspaper room in the area of
German-language newspapers: *Die Bloomfield Germania,* Bloomfield,
1908-1914; *Nebraska Biene,* Columbus, 1897-1915; *Platte River Zeitung,*
Fremont, 1895-1917; *Anzeiger und Herold,* Grand Island, 1891-1901; *Der
Herold,* Grand Island, 1886-1887; *Staats-Anzeiger und Herold,* Grand
Island, 1901-1918; *Nebraska Volksfreund,* Hastings, 1895-1899; *Lincoln
Staatsanzeiger,* Lincoln, 1891-1901; *Lincoln Freie Presse,* Lincoln, 1891-
1925; *Welt-Post,* Lincoln, 1916-1969; *Nebraska Staatszeitung,* Nebraska
City, 1907-1912; *Die Welt Post,* Omaha, 1916-1972; *Freie Presse u.
Wochentliche Tribune,* Omaha, 1892-1926; *Katholisches Wochenblatt,*
Omaha, 1950-present; *Volkszeitung-Tribune,* Omaha, 1912-1972; *Nebras-
ka Vorwarts,* Omaha, 1896-1897; and *Nebraska Volksblatt,* West Point,
1879-1916.

The Peter Publications, 4614 Dodge Street, P.O. Box 3785, Omaha, Nebraska 68103, publishes a total of nine German language newspapers
yet today:

Die Welt Post und Der Staats-Anzeiger, every Friday, 8,500 readers,
Lincoln, Nebraska; South Dakota and North Dakota coverage.
Inquiries: 2820 Sumner S.W., Lincoln, Nebraska.

The Volkszeitung-Tribune is the Omaha German-language newspaper,
published every Friday. Inquiries: 4614 Dodge Street, Omaha,
Nebraska.

The *America Herold* and *Sonntagspost* are national weeklies. Inquiries:
4614 Dodge Street, P.O. Box 3785, Omaha, Nebraska 68103.

Maps

Maps of German-Russian settlements in various sections of Russia, the

United States, Canada, Mexico, and South America are also available from the American Historical Society of Germans from Russia, 615 D Street, Lincoln, Nebraska 68502.

Materials for Fieldwork and Research

Baum, Willa K. *Oral History for the Local Historical Society.* 2nd ed. Nashville: American Association for State and Local History, 1971. [This 63-page guide is superb not only for historical societies as the name suggests, but for anyone going into the field with a tape recorder to collect oral history. Available: AASLH, 1400 8th Ave. South, Nashville, Tenn. 37203.]

Collier, John, Jr. *Visual Anthropology: Photography as a Research Method.* New York: Holt, Rinehart, and Winston, 1967. [139 pages. Written as a professional guide, but will be of real use to the serious amateur as well. It is not so much a guide to the camera as it is a guide to how one can use a camera in documenting a culture.]

Guldbeck, Per E. *The Care of Historical Collections: A Conservation Handbook for the Nonspecialist.* Nashville: American Association for State and Local History, 1972. [159 pages. If you or your society are concerned about how one takes care of recordings, photographs, and documents once they are collected, this is the single best handbook you can own.]

Junker, Burford H. *Field Work: An Introduction to the Social Sciences.* Chicago: University of Chicago Press, 1960. [207 pages. This is an advanced analysis of field work and its implications. A sound and necessary book for the professional but may require some preliminary reading and study by the amateur.]

McKee, Harley. *Recording Historic Buildings.* Historic American Buildings Survey, Department of the Interior, National Park Service. [165 pages. Available from the Superintendent of Documents, U.S. Government Printing Office, Washington, D.C. 20402. The best available handbook for anyone interested in documenting buildings. It instructs the reader in the use of the camera, line drawings, records, and documents. Recommended without reservation for the amateur and professional alike.]

Welsch, Roger L. *Interviewing with the Tape Recorder.* Lincoln, Nebraska: American Historical Society for Germans from Russia, no date. [This booklet is a useful guide to tape recording equipment and contains suggestions about how to arrange and handle interviews. Can be obtained from AHSGR, 615 D Street, Lincoln, Nebraska.]

Wigginton, Eliot. *The Foxfire Book.* Garden City, New York: Doubleday, 1972, Vol. 1; 1973, Vol. 2; 1974, Vol. 3. [384 pages. These volumes are collections of folklore collected with a camera and tape recorder and then written up for popular consumption—but they retain all of the information necessary for an accurate and scientific description too. One can recommend them to amateur field workers because these books have been produced by amateur field workers—junior high school students from Rabun Gap, Georgia, and the moral of that is that if they could do it, so can you.]

SCANDINAVIANS

Persons who wish to pursue the specialized topics discussed in the Scandinavian essay and catalogue would do well to consult the specialized works cited in the footnotes to that essay; works on individual men are not cited here.

Alexis, Joseph. "Swedes in Nebraska," *Publications of the Nebraska State Historical Society,* XIX (1919), pp. 78-85.

Ander, O. Fritiof. *The Cultural Heritage of the Swedish Immigrant.* Rock Island: Augustana Book, 1963.

Benson, Adolph. *Swedes in America: 1638-1938.* New Haven: Yale University Press, 1938. [Names and short accounts of leaders and artists.]

General Works

Bergmann, Leola Nelson. *Americans From Norway.* New York: Lippincott, 1950. [A very good account of Norwegian art and culture in the United States emphasizing social-change oriented thought: Pio, Thrane, Veblen, etc.]

Dowie, J.I. and others. *The Swedish Immigrant Community in Transition.* Rock Island: Augustana Book Concern, 1956.

Haugen, Einar. *The Norwegians in America: A Student's Guide to Localized History.* New York: Teachers College, 1967. [Basic guide to Norwegian work.]

Janson, Florence E. *The Background of Swedish Immigration: 1840-1930.* Chicago: University of Chicago Press, 1931.

Kleinschmidt, John. "Political Behavior of Bohemian and Swedish Ethnic Groups in Nebraska." Master's thesis, University of Nebraska, Lincoln, 1968.

Laurin, Carl. *Scandinavian Art.* New York: The American Scandinavian Foundation, 1922.

Manniche, Peter. *Denmark: A Social Laboratory.* Copehhagen: Gad, 1939. [An account of the Grundtvig-cooperative socialist reform movement in Denmark.]

Nelson, Helge. *The Swedes and the Swedish Settlements in North America.* Oxford: Oxford University Press, 1943. [Fairly good accounts of the settlements in Kansas, Nebraska, South Dakota, and western Iowa; traces communities back to specific Swedish provinces.]

Nyholm, Paul. *The Americanization of the Danish Lutheran Churches.* Minneapolis: Augsburg Publishing House, 1963. [Some good treatment of Grundtvigian tradition.]

Olsson, Karl A. *By One Spirit.* Chicago: Covenant Press, 1962. [A strong picture of one kind of Swedish social-religious reform movement— the Covenant Church.]

Paulsson, Thomas. *Scandinavian Architecture.* Newton, Mass.: Charles Branford Company, 1959.

Qualey, Carlton. *Norwegian Settlements in the United States.* New York: Arno Press, 1970.

Skårdal, Dorothy Burton. *The Divided Heart.* Lincoln: University of Nebraska Press, 1974. [A brilliant treatment of literature by Scandinavians who emigrated to America. Bibliography and footnotes include accounts of almost all Scandinavian authors from this area.]

Stephenson, George M. *Religious Aspects of Swedish Immigration.* Minneapolis: University of Minnesota Press, 1932.

Tavuchis, Nicholas. *Pastors and Immigrants: the Role of a Religious Elite in the Absorption of Norwegian Immigrants.* The Hague, Studies in Social Life VIII, 1963.

Wald, Arthur and others. *American-Swedish Handbook.* Rock Island: Augustana Book, 1943. [Includes accounts of lodges, newspapers, museums and a wide variety of socializing institutions not treated in the Scandinavian essay.]

Wefald, Jon. *A Voice of Protest.* Northfield: The Norwegian American Historical Association, 1971. [Traces Norwegian social change hopes.]

Local Histories

Bildt, Ruth. *Pioneer Swedish American Culture in Central Kansas.* Lindsborg: Lindsborg News-Record, 1965. [A good folk picture of the Lindsborg area's culture to 1909. Cf. the same author's *The Smoky Valley in After Years.* Lindsborg: Lindsborg News-Record, 1969. This book gives an account of events after 1909. The various writings of Emory Lindquist on the central Kansas Scandinavians are also of interest here.]

Christensen, Arthur W. *A Story of the Danish Settlement in Dannevirke.* Dannebrog, 1961.

Wilcox, Rolland D. *The Scandinavian Influence on the History of Newman Grove.* Wayne: Wayne State College, 1963.

JEWS

Adamic, Louis. *A Nation of Nations.* New York: Harper and Brothers Publishers, 1944.

Auerbach, Ella Fleishman. "The Jewish Settlement in Nebraska." Unpublished typescript. Lincoln: Nebraska State Historical Society, 1927.

Borowitz, Eugene B. *The Masks Jews Wear.* New York: Simon and Schuster, 1973.

Chudacoff, Howard P. "A Look at Ethnic Neighborhoods: Residential Dispersion and the Concept of Visibility in a Medium-Sized City," *Journal of American History,* Vol. LX, No. 1 (June, 1973).

_____ . *Mobile Americans: Residential and Social Mobility in Omaha 1880-1920.* New York: Oxford University Press, 1972.

Gendler, Carol. "The Jews of Omaha: the First Sixty Years." Unpublished master's thesis, University of Nebraska-Omaha, 1968.

Grayzel, Solomon. *A History of the Contemporary Jews from 1900 to the Present.* New York: Harper and Row Publishers, 1960.

Handlin, Oscar. *Adventure in Freedom.* New York: McGraw-Hill Book Co., 1954.

_____ . *The Uprooted.* Boston: Little, Brown, and Company, 1951.

Hapgood, Hutchins. *The Spirit of the Ghetto.* New York: Funk and Wagnalls Company, 1902.

Kramer, William M., ed. *The Western Journal of Issac Mayer Wise 1877.* Berkeley, California: Western Jewish History Center, Magnes Museum, 1974.

Labeson, Anita. *Jewish Pioneers in America 1492-1848.* New York: Brentano's, 1931.

Mandel, Irving Aaron. "The Attitude of the American Jewish Community Toward East European Immigration as Reflected in the Anglo-Jewish Press," *American Jewish Archives,* Cincinnati, Ohio, Vol. III, No. 1 (June, 1950).

McMorris, Robert. "The People Who Make Up Omaha," *Omaha World Herald,* December 10, 1961.

New Jewish Encyclopedia. David Bridger, ed. New York: Behrman House, Inc., 1962.

New Standard Jewish Encyclopedia. Cecil Roth and Geoffrey Wigoder, eds. Garden City, New York: Doubleday and Company, Inc., 1970.

Olson, James C. *History of Nebraska.* Lincoln: University of Nebraska Press, 1966.

Park, Robert E. and Herbert A. Miller. *Old World Traits Transplanted.* New York: Harper and Brothers Publishers, 1921.

Prostok, Max D. and David Rosenberg. "History of the Jewish People in Adams County and City of Hastings, Nebraska." Unpublished paper. Adams County Historical Society, November 30, 1970.

Roskolenko, Harry. *The Time That Was Then: the Lower East Side 1900-1914, An Intimate Chronicle.* New York: Dial Press, 1971.

Sachar, Howard Morley. *The Course of Modern Jewish History.* New York: Dell Publishing Company, Inc., 1963.

Steiner, Edward A. *The Immigrant Tide: Its Ebb and Flow.* New York: Fleming H. Revell Company, 1909.

_____ . *On the Trail of the Immigrant.* New York: Fleming H. Revell Company, 1906.

Sullenger, T. Earl. *The Immigrant in Omaha.* Omaha: University of Omaha, September, 1932.

"Trail Blazers of the Trans-Mississippi West," *American Jewish Archives,* Cincinnati, Ohio, Vol. VIII, No. 2.

Woldman, Albert. "First Broadcast of Emancipation Proclamation," *The Jewish Digest,* Vol. VIII, No. 5 (February, 1963).

ITALIANS

Adamic, Louis. *A Nation of Nations.* New York: Harper and Brothers Publishers, 1944.

Barzini, Luigi. *The Italians.* New York: Antheneum Publishers, 1964.

Child, Irvin L. *Italian or American: The Second Generation in Conflict.* New Haven: Yale University Press, 1943.

Chudacoff, Howard P. "A New Look at Ethnic Neighborhoods: Residential Dispersion and the Concept of Visibility in a Medium-Sized City," *The Journal of American History,* Vol. LX, No. 1 (June, 1973).

_____ . *Mobile Americans: Residential and Social Mobility in Omaha 1880-1920.* New York: Oxford University Press, 1972.

Cordasco, Francesco and Eugene Bucchioni. *The Italians: Social Backgrounds of an American Group.* Clifton, New Jersey: Augustus M. Kelby Publishers, 1974.

Corsi, Edward. *In the Shadow of Liberty.* New York: Macmillan, 1935.

Covello, Leonard. *The Social Background of the Italo-American School Child.* Leiden, Netherlands: E.J. Brill, 1967.

D'Angelo, Pascal. *Pascal D'Angelo, Son of Italy.* New York: Macmillan, 1924.

Fiore, Alphonse T. "History of Italian Immigration in Nebraska." Unpublished thesis, University of Nebraska-Lincoln, 1938.

Foerster, Robert L. *The Italian Immigration of Our Times.* Cambridge: Harvard University Press, 1919.

Gallo, Patrick J. *Ethnic Alienation: The Italian-Americans.* Cranbury, New Jersey: Associated University Presses, Inc., 1974.

Handlin, Oscar. *The Uprooted.* Boston: Little, Brown and Company, 1951.

Iorizzo, Luciano J. and Salvatore Mondello. *The Italian-American.* New York: Twayne Publishers, Inc., 1971.

The Italians of Omaha. Written and compiled by the workers of the Writers' Program, Work Projects Administration. Omaha, Nebraska: Independent Printing Company, 1941.

McMorris, Robert. "The People Who Make Up Omaha," *Omaha World Herald,* October 15, 1961.

Novak, Michael. *The Rise of the Unmeltable Ethnics.* New York: Macmillan, 1971.

Rolle, Andrew F. *The American-Italians: Their History and Culture.* Belmont, California: Wadsworth Publishing Company, Inc., 1972.

_____ . *The Immigrant Upraised.* Norman: University of Oklahoma Press, 1968.

Sennett, Richard. "Break Up the Family," *New York Times,* July 19, 1971.

Steiner, Edward. *On the Trail of the Immigrant.* New York: Fleming M. Revell Company, 1906.

Sullenger, T. Earl. *The Immigrant in Omaha.* Omaha: University of Omaha, September, 1932.

Tomasi, Silvano M. and Madeline H. Engel. *The Italian Experience in the United States.* Staten Island, New York: Center for Migration Studies, Inc., 1970.

Zborowski, Mark. *People in Pain.* San Francisco: Jossey-Bass, Inc., 1969.

IRISH

Burbach, Gerald J. "An Irish Colony in Nebraska." Unpublished master's dissertation, Saint Paul Seminary, 1960.

Duff, John B. *The Irish in the United States.* Belmont, California: Wadsworth Publishing Co., 1971.

Duggin, G.C. *The Stage Irishman.* New York: Benjamin Blom, 1969.

Dunn, Joseph and P.J. Lennox. *The Glories of Ireland.* Washington, D.C.:

Phoenix Ltd., 1914.

Greeley, Rev. Andrew M. *That Most Distressful Nation: The Taming of the American Irish.* Chicago: Quadrangle Books, 1972.

Handlin, Oscar. *Boston's Immigrants, 1790-1880.* New York: Atheneum, 1971.

Hayes, A.B. and Sam D. Cox. *History of the City of Lincoln, Nebraska.* 1889.

Hennessey, Maurice N. *"I'll Come Back in Springtime": John F. Kennedy and the Irish.* New York: Ives Washburn, 1966.

Joyce, James. *Dubliners.* New York: Viking Press, 1968.

_____ . *Portrait of the Artist as a Young Man.* New York: Viking Press, 1968.

Kelley, Sister Mary Edith. *The Irishman in the English Novel of the Nineteenth Century.* Washington, D.C.: The Catholic University Press, 1939.

Lyons, F.S.L. *Ireland Since the Famine: 1850 to the Present.* New York: Charles Scribner's Sons, 1971.

McCaffrey, Lawrence J. *The Irish Question 1800/1922.* Lexington: University of Kentucky Press, 1968.

McCulloh, Burns E. *A Piece of Emerald.* (Centennial History of O'Neill, Nebraska). O'Neill, Nebraska: Miles Publishing Co., 1974.

Nebraska History, magazine of the Nebraska State Historical Society. July and September, 1936.

O'Casey, Sean. *The Shadow of a Gunman; Juno and the Paycock; The Plough and the Stars.* New York: St. Martin's Press, 1966.

O'Connor, Frank. *A Short History of Irish Literature, A Backward Look.* New York: Capricorn Books, 1968.

O'Faolain, Sean. *King of Beggars, Life of Daniel O'Connell, The Irish Liberator, in a Study of the Rise of the Modern Irish Democracy (1775-1847).* New York: The Viking Press, 1938.

Sheldon, A.E. *Nebraska: The Land and the People.* Chicago: The Lewis Publishing Co., 1931.

Woodham-Smith, Cecil. *The Great Hunger, Ireland 1845-1849.* New York: The Viking Press, 1962.

Yeats, William Butler. *Selected Poems and Two Plays,* ed. by M.L. Rosenthal. New York: Macmillan & Co., 1962.

DUTCH

Bade, Gustav Adolph. "A History of the Dutch Settlement in Lancaster

County, Nebraska." Unpublished master's dissertation, University
of Nebraska-Lincoln, 1938.

De Jong, Gerald Francis. *The Dutch in America 1609-1974.* Boston:
Twayne Publishers.

D.I.S. Magazine. A quarterly publication of the Dutch Immigration
Society. Published at 1239 East Fulton, Grand Rapids, Michigan.

Lucas, Henry Stephen. *Netherlanders in America.* Ann Arbor: University
of Michigan Press, 1955.

Wabeke, Bertus Henry. *Dutch Emigration to North America, 1824-1860.*
New York City: The Netherlands Information Bureau, 1944.